The

Caravan

of

Remembering

For Mark

May Your life Mission

Emerge ongoing

Artfully, Beautifully, Sacred!

& skelly

Daniel Goodenough

The
Caravan
of
Remembering

A Road Map for Experiencing the
Awakening of Your Life's Mission

Daniel Goodenough

Heart's Way Press
Fort Collins, CO

Cover and text design by Bookwrights
Printed in the United States of America

Publisher's Cataloging-in-Publication
(Provided by Quality Books, Inc.)

Goodenough, Daniel, 1952- author.
    The caravan of remembering : a road map for
experiencing the awakening of your life's mission /
Daniel Goodenough.
    pages cm
    LCCN 2016908157
    ISBN 978-1-943222-65-0 (paperback)
    ISBN 978-1-943222-05-6 (hardcover)
    ISBN 978-1-943222-01-8 (ebook)

1. Self-actualization (Psychology)—Fiction.
2. Vocational guidance—Fiction. 3. Fantasy fiction.
4. Psychological fiction.   I. Title.

PS3607.O5632C37 2016   813'.6
                        QBI16-600093

Author's Note:
Inevitably, an author's life experience will influence the stories they write. While events from the author's life created a background of reference, *Caravan*'s story and its characters are fiction, and should not be taken as the author's life story or the story of anyone involved with The Way of the Heart.

 HEART'S WAY PRESS

PO Box 271396
Fort Collins, CO 80527
heartswaypress.com
thecaravanofremembering.com

Contents

v

Preface

THE LONG-AWAITED CARAVAN HAS arrived: a story, a journey, and a call to live a life of authentic purpose. Crafted by Daniel Goodenough, an experienced life-coach and co-founder of The Way of the Heart, *Caravan* looks at the question of life's purpose in a fresh, creative way. Ever since he was aware that he was aware, as he would say, his dedication to helping people discover their true calling has never wavered. Thousands of hours of research and meditation, above and beyond the famous number of 10,000 necessary hours of conscious practice, have gone into articulating this process, which is now available to us as *Caravan*.

One intriguing bit of research suggests that if athletes intensely imagine they are performing their sport, they actually improve. This, mind you, is from a chair in the living room. If, for example, I am an archer, I can concentrate on pulling back the bow, in my mind's eye. I see myself putting into place all the concentration and movements I have been trained to do as I let that arrow fly. This strategy of using the imagination to understand our life mission is the genius of *Caravan*. The great Sufi, Ibn al'Arabi, understands the imagination as a faculty of the soul, which marries the sensory world of form with the formless world of consciousness. For the Sufis, the imagination is an important tool of realization. *Caravan* allows us to enter into this *imaginal* world, bringing together the sounds and shapes of the desert with a new awareness of life mission.

In *Caravan* we enter the mind of a person very much like ourselves, someone with a work life as a graphic artist, who rents a place to live, who will be involved in a budding relationship. He has his favorite haunts: the bookshop, the coffee shop. And somehow a more spacious reality in the figure of Verity intervenes. He's walking in the park; he's in another world, the world of the desert.

It's a great pleasure for us as readers to suddenly find ourselves tagging along for this experience. What would it be like to suddenly find yourself in the desert? Imagine yourself as a part of a caravan with camel bells tinkling and other wanderers gathered around a campfire, guiding you to remember.

In his masterful story, Goodenough introduces us to the features of what it might be like to be called to something greater than yourself and yet something that you yourself are very much a part of. Through the course of the main character's journey, we embark on a pilgrimage to a deeper, richer part of our own knowing. We are invited to think about the kind of story we tell about our lives, and to reflect on other ways of talking about our personal history. If we tell our story differently, is that a way to develop, to broaden and to grow?

The thrill of taking part in *Caravan*, part adventure, part science fiction, part personal growth, is that we are never subjected to pointed personal remarks aimed toward remaking our personality. No, instead we are invited to watch, to witness, and to imagine what it would be like to be a pilgrim searching for our life's purpose. And we are talking here about a modern pilgrim, one who will benefit from Daniel's on-going research into the evolution of many of the important fields in our time: physics, biology, psychology, sociology, visual and performing arts, neuroscience, computers, business and spirituality. Daniel's unique gift is that he is artful in his guidance. He is fond of quoting Rumi, who says, "Let the beauty you love be what you do." And in the nineteen years I have known him, Daniel has held to this. It's what he does, and it's what he helps others to do as well. Love what you do. Do what you love.

The desert appears in the world's great spiritual traditions, including the desert fathers whose spiritual insight Thomas Merton sought out from his monastery in Kentucky. Also the great stories of our time, such as *Laurence of Arabia* and *The English Patient*, bring us to a new understanding of our humanity, which comes to us in the desert. We need the desert to find that part of our being where our longing can be most deeply felt. The desert intrigues us, I think, because we need help in finding our way. The desert is the home of Khidr, in the Sufi tradition, the green man of the desert, who is the ultimate guide.

Here, in *Caravan*, the guiding is done both in community and in individual sessions. And isn't that our own experience? Our child has an insight, the person clerking our groceries offers a pertinent remark, a friend tells us about making to-do lists in which there is an intriguing column: important but not urgent. Then, somehow we resonate in a new way about our lives. Likewise, in *Caravan* we are introduced to figures who are larger than life, including Kairos, whose being invites us to contemplate the way that eternity enters into a moment. All of this allows us to move toward a deeper appreciation of why we are on this planet we love so well.

The Tibetans have a term called "skillful means," used when there's a need to address our natural resistance to moving into a new way of understanding ourselves and our world. Daniel is very knowledgeable here as well, having had years of practice in helping people move safely and surely out of their comfort zone, through unaddressed grief, disconnection to Sprit, doubt and fear, and in short helping us get out of our own way.

The art of Caravan is that it is a full-on exploration of our essential questions: Why are we here? What brings us real happiness? Who can guide us in our lives and towards what? If we imagine our heart as a fertile field, *Caravan* excites that soil, turns it and works it so that we are open in a new way to our life's journey. It is something of a relief as well as a thrill to hand ourselves over to this journey: to see the absolute desert at night, flat, dark, rich and full of promise. To imagine our lives beginning to move in a new way towards a new place that is already deeply familiar.

Daniel Goodenough has written *Caravan* after years of immersing himself in the questions brought to him by thousands of students in the The Way of the Heart program. A thinker, a humanist, and a man of Spirit, Daniel is generous, focused, and alive to this particular need of humanity: to find our life mission. He presents us with a method that is unique in helping us come to grips with our humanity. He deepens our appreciation of our search and ourselves as we travel inwardly to our center and outwardly across our beautiful, luminous planet.

Jeanne Koré Salvato

Jeanne Koré Salvato is the editor of two books about Sufi teachings.

Khan, Hazrat Inayat. *Creating the Person: A Practical Guide to the Development of Self. Revised Edition.* Editor. Jeanne Koré Salvato. New Lebanon: Omega Publications, 2013. Print.

Khan, Hazrat Inayat. *The Soul's Journey.* Editor. Jeanne Koré Salvato. New Lebanon: Omega Publications, 2003. Print.

Acknowledgments

WHEN I FIRST BEGAN to write this book about life mission, it was to be a personal development, non-fiction book. My heart heard *Caravan's* call, and my life mission book became a *Caravan* story.

First to read the early pages were Kimberly Herkert and Eduardo Parra. Their encouragement and enthusiasm for this change of direction meant the world to me, and lovingly safeguarded the early seed stages of *The Caravan of Remembering* story.

In 1988, Kimberly Herkert and I co-founded, then developed and are co-teaching the work of The Way of the Heart together. I owe a great debt of love and gratitude to Kimberly as my dearest friend and professional partner, sharing a vision we both believe in, as well as sharing the joy and the emotional cost of the journey. My profound thanks for her inspiration, guidance, collaboration, generous feedback, and support with *Caravan*, The Way of the Heart, and in life.

From the early years of The Way of the Heart, Kimberly's husband Eduardo Parra has been a blessing and integral part of the work, and friend in my life. I want to express great gratitude for his tireless support, insight, creativity, shared teaching, deep friendship, and his ever-present willingness to help with *Caravan's* birth into the world.

I am especially grateful for the many rounds of revision, advice and editing given by Jeanne Koré Salvato at the many stages and rounds of *Caravan's* development. Thank you for your on going support, generosity and guidance on so many levels.

Posthumous gratitude goes to Cynthia Black of Beyond Words Publishing for her early direction, encouragement, guidance on the road to publication, and her words of faith in my vision for *Caravan*.

I will always be deeply grateful to Dr. Linda Newmark for making space at an already pressing time in her life to help with *Caravan*, at a crossroads moment for both the book and myself. I want to thank her for the editorial help then, and her ever-present guidance as a friend and teacher.

I want to thank Phyllis Stern of Lightwords Editorial Services for an elegant, masterfully-balanced touch with *Caravan*'s copyedit and proofing, and her continued kindness and generosity.

My thanks go to Bookwrights and Mayapriya Long for her patience with my questions and considerations, for her designing excellence, and the perfect attunement of *Caravan*'s layout and cover design.

I want to thank my coach Peter Bowerman for his ongoing wisdom and guidance in navigating the myriad, step-by-step milestones and requirements of the publishing world. I am also grateful to him for his generosity and patience with the host of questions each step of the process brings, and availability when unexpected challenges arise.

I would like to honor and express my profound gratitude for the uncommon generosity and continued support of the team of The Way of the Heart, who make possible the work we do. Thank you for your part in the orchestra. Thank you for asking, caring, and supporting *Caravan*'s development.

My special gratitude also goes to the friends and associates who have read part or all of this book and shared your heart's response.

I want to honor and recognize my great debt of gratitude to my teachers, those living and passed on. I can never express fully enough how much you have meant to me, the blessing, and grace. The echoes of your gifts are present in *Caravan* and in all I do, and I will do my best to "pay it forward."

Last and foremost, eternal gratitude goes to my wife and North Star, Megan, who provided more help and support than I had the right to expect, with endless patience and astounding willingness to drop everything to help. She brought to *Caravan* thoughtful, frank, generous and kind eyes and ears, and at times technical assistance when desperately needed. Truly *Caravan* would not be here without the gift of her tireless love and support, and I am greatly blessed that she is at my side.

₊

Introduction

As a child, I imagined the possibility of a world that honored the importance of everyone's reason for being on earth. I imagined a world where one's individual calling is nurtured, a world that helped each of us to remember, cultivate and unfold this call of the soul throughout our lives. This imagined world has informed my life and inspired the search for an architecture of remembering.

How do we remember our most fundamental *why*, and build a life around what this calls us to do, and who this calls us to become? The story of Caravan is a blueprint and process of this becoming.

This first book of the *Caravan* series begins the personal exploration of what life mission is, while being called to the articulation of the why, what and who of our reason for being here on this planet. It is the beginning of a road map for exploring your unique relationship with life, and the most beautiful way of offering to the world the unique essence of who you are.

The invitation of Caravan is to immerse yourself in the story, moving through both worlds, as the experience of David and your own remembering carry you to the discovery of your own life mission story. Caravan is meant as a shared experience, an example of someone living the process of life mission inquiry. As you move through the story, I invite you to create your own Caravan expedition journal, answering along with David the questions presented, and doing the exercises that he is called to do. You may first read the story through for enjoyment, later returning, as called, to work with the questions and exercises by using the guide in the back of the book.

The process embedded in Caravan's story is meant to develop your skill in articulating your life mission, while also developing skill in unfolding your life mission over time. You can use the questions and exercises as a musician does, daily doing scales to increase the skill with their instrument. In this case, one's own life is the instrument.

Caravan is a place to be revisited as often as needed, with a process that is both a welcome mentor and companion on this journey.

CHAPTER I

My Call

ALL I REMEMBERED WAS the Voice calling from somewhere that didn't at first have a "where," like hearing the voice of someone you know, yet can't place. It was the voice of someone I'd known for eternity and yet forgotten . . . except I remembered. It was the voice of someone I sensed was actually eternal, though I can't tell you how or why I knew this.

It was a moment before I could tell the voice was feminine. I suddenly remembered a woman across from me on a train in Chicago at three in the morning. It was a particularly senseless day I had spent working on a project designed to increase an agency's retainer from a client, a pointless project never meant to see the light of day. Pointless was exactly how I felt about my life, and "why" was the question, especially at three in the morning. With all that I could be excited about, why did it feel like I was at one of the lowest points of my life? Why the impending sense of crossroads, and why did I feel I was on a path I couldn't continue on?

The woman and I had been the only ones on the platform before boarding. She appeared an instant before the train arrived. It was one of those seemingly endless underground platforms, and I was standing in the middle of it. It was midwinter, and watching my breath turn to steam, I could see no one else. Then, in what I would've sworn was a fraction of a second, she moved next to me. I felt space and time ripple, then quiet, and I felt that rushing feeling I get when I know something *real* is going to happen.

Her woolen, earth-colored robe gave the impression of layered silver threads woven with and through ocher, sandalwood, burnt sienna, mahogany, and white that were almost alive with light of their own. We sat across from each other on the train, surrounded by silence, and she simply looked through me. Her eyes also had an impression of silver. I was certain in that moment that she was eternal. Although she didn't speak, I felt my life change in inexplicable ways. I looked down for an instant, and when I looked up, she was gone, the train still moving. I wanted to tell myself it was late and I was overworked, and I was fine with this mystery.

Walking through the park, I couldn't be certain the voice was the woman from the train. She called to me, "Come, wanderer, worshiper, lover of leaving." (Yes, she quoted Rumi, and later she would say, "Though you have broken your vows a thousand times . . . come . . . come . . . come again.") "There is nothing you need to bring," she said. "Leave your things, they will be safe and you will find them exactly as you left them when you return. You have been to the Caravan many times. Now you will be asked to remember when you return.

She smiled and said, "Welcome to the Caravan of Remembering!"

It was only a moment. Really, it was as if I were awakening from a dream. One moment you're deeply enmeshed in the dream and the next you're awake. It felt this way almost exactly. It felt as if my life were the dream and this was my *real life*. As often happens when you wake up too quickly or with a start, it felt surreal.

"Welcome," she said again, bringing me to the caravan's edge. In one direction, her caravan went on as far as the eye could see. In the other direction was an endless, empty horizon. An invitation and a welcome, gesturing at the wonder of it all, and then she was gone. There was that comment about my having been there before. She said I'd been to this caravan many times. And yet, as I looked to the place she'd brought me to, I didn't remember it.

Much later, I would say that was the beginning.

An ocean of sand surrounded me. It was accented by vivid colors adorning people, gear, and camels in the process of preparing for departure. What I felt first was a paradox: activity and teaming life accompanying near silence punctuated by the occasional camel's editorial response. It was an orchestra of life held in the arms of silence, filled with intent. Space itself seemed alive with anticipation.

I felt very much the stranger here, yet this place wasn't completely foreign. Most of the elements reminded me of movie versions of caravans. There were, however, too many races and cultures present to feel completely right. I connected the Chinese banners and East Indian saris with legends of the Silk Road. The long, black, white, and plant-dyed blue robes I'd long associated with the Middle Eastern and African deserts seemed right. Pilgrims with tartan textiles and knot-work jewelry and others with Lady of Guadalupe blankets, however, gave me pause. Other than details like these, this caravan was just what I would imagine, based on my movie versions.

"Is this the key?" I asked myself. "If I had a different image of caravans, would this one look different to me?"

I was surprised to discover I'd actually asked this out loud and in a tone that apparently invited a response. A man emerged, as if magically, from among the camels and walked to my side. In stark contrast to the more colorful pilgrims, nothing in his attire distinguished him from camel or desert. Even his hair and beard blended in.

"Even this world does not entirely accommodate itself to your imagination," he said. "However, what you imagine will have its effect on how you experience it." He was staring in the direction hinted at by the preparation in progress. Random lights danced off eyebrows long and winding over deep-set eyes. "Caravan is its own being and does not wait for your definition," he said. "This Caravan is a gift of the One and has traveled for eternity in service to all. Caravan's work is to bring us home."

He fell silent, and we moved on with our fellow pilgrims. My first night, we traveled quietly, left to simply experience the movement. It wasn't till sometime later that I experienced the stillness of the Caravan at rest. My first travels were always at night.

As we walked with streams of camels moving head to tail in

multiple strings, I thought about this Caravan as a gift. He'd said it was a gift from the One who sent us, created to bring us home. This led me to ask if I was in fact dead and now traveling toward my next life. Then I remembered the Voice saying that my things would be there for me when I returned. So I was to return. What home, then, did my friend with the long eyebrows mean? How long would I be there? Ultimately, I'd realize, this was a question of no relevance in the Caravan.

I was conflicted enough about the life I'd left not to be too attached to it. I wasn't overly relieved to know I'd be going back, and if "going home" wasn't that, then what did it mean? What did remembering in both worlds mean? Why did it matter and why need I care? In spite of a kind of success, I felt lost in one world, now possibly two. The Caravan of Remembering only added to my lost sense of ground. Everything was now in question. I didn't know the rules. I didn't know the reason, and yet in spite of the mystery, the call to the Caravan held some hope for an answer.

My attention returned to the omnipresence of pilgrims in groups with the strings of head-to-tail camels. Bells created a kind of music I would learn more of later. I wondered about the sticks some of the camels had in their noses. Each string of camels had an attendant. Some camels had one hump, others had two. I thought about how life brings us to moments like this, when something that you've never paid attention to suddenly seems important out of proportion to any rational thinking. Sometimes two camels together carried a kind of platform. In other cases, a single camel carried a smaller platform. Some camels were piled high with baggage, whereas others seemed prepared for people only. Saddles and adornment varied greatly. I thought there must be as many ways to pack the camels as pilgrims moving with the Caravan of Remembering.

I traveled in silence, watching and waiting. The Voice had called it the Caravan of Remembering and said I'd be asked to "remember" in both worlds now. So I watched this world, taking in what I could. In what my mind then called the earth world, when someone said you'll be asked to remember, usually there's something they'll ask of you. I had the impression it would be a good idea to pay attention. Then I questioned my relative calm and lack of anxiety. Why me? Why this?

Why everything? Inexplicably, fear seemed optional, and trust, more relevant.

Most of the pilgrims that night traveled in silence. I wondered if this was the normal atmosphere of travel. What seemed universal as I took it all in was the complexity. It appeared to me that all races and ages were present. I also noticed people traveling alone and others in small groups, and I noticed what appeared to be families traveling together. Other groups seemed linked by affiliations of multiple kinds, with loose boundaries morphing as the Caravan of Remembering progressed.

What I began to feel was something moving in me. Inwardly, moving slowly across the desert night, something began to open. The effect of no words created space inside me that reflected my silent environment. Others traveling in the same direction surrounded me, and yet as far as the senses could reach, the landscape was like the surface of a calm ocean, an ocean of sand with an empty horizon. I could find no place to stop my impressions and bounce them back to me. My thoughts simply sped out across this seemingly endless space and did not return.

The effect of this quiet and the openness of the desert stilled my mind and body. A kind of rhythm emerged with which I came to resonate. My breathing slowed and my questions began to fade like the faint, hazy, almost indistinguishable line where desert met sky. I felt the presence of my companions traveling with me. That I had no idea who they were was of no consequence. I stopped caring why I was traveling with this caravan. I stopped caring if or when I'd return to my life in the world I'd known. I stopped trying to figure anything out. I simply stopped everything except the motion of moving with the Caravan of Remembering.

I had no way of telling how long we traveled in this way. How long I'd been in this world and with the Caravan of Remembering had no meaning to me now. What *now* meant was just as far from my thinking. In fact, thinking itself had left me. What I felt was a sense of peace. What I knew was something timeless.

I started to feel as endless as this place with nothing on any of its horizons, enough space within to accept anything. This place had the quality of space itself. We could have been traveling across the space between galaxies, and I'd have felt this same quality of eternity. Light traveling through space at the speed of light may take billions of years to reach the planet where we live. I began to wonder if the Caravan of Remembering was light traveling across the universe of all worlds for billions of years.

Like light traveling between galaxies, we traveled across this desert landscape, a space without borders, adorned by stars unknown, and with no end in sight. Night itself had no boundary that I could discern. As time faded from meaning, the notion of distance also departed and became something my mind would only later remember to care about. When thought returned, I could not register an idea of how long or how far we had traveled. If not for the tracks in the sand behind us, I couldn't find any evidence that we had moved at all.

Why was I not offered a camel to ride? It occurred to me that the walking was perfect. Walking was a kind of grounding. This first experience had a quality of unreality, and walking gave me a sense of really being there. It gave me a sense that I was traveling with the Caravan of Remembering by an act of will on my part. I realized from the start that I could have stayed where I was and watched the caravan move on without me. Though what I would do when it was out of sight made that a crazy option. Still, without consciously making this decision, I had chosen to join the Caravan.

The woman I named the Voice had called me, brought me to the edge of the Caravan, welcomed me, and then vanished. One moment she was pointing to our surroundings, the next, she was gone. Why it didn't occur to me to be afraid in that moment I can only chalk up to her telling me that I'd been to the Caravan of Remembering before and I would return to my world. She'd also told me before we left not to worry about anything. I would be safe.

These are, of course, reasons of the head. They're not really why I felt safe. I felt safe because *I knew I was safe*. I knew this in the same way you sometimes know it will rain when the sky is clear and blue. I knew this in the way you can know your way to a place you've never visited. I knew this in the same way you know you're right about something, even with no evidence.

So I watched and contemplated this world I found myself in. I had no memory of it in spite of her assurance that I'd traveled with this caravan before. Why was she telling me this? Why was it important that I know this? Why didn't she introduce me to the Caravan of Remembering and allow my experience to grow as I traveled? What reason did she have for setting me up in the beginning with the knowledge that it wasn't the beginning?

What eventually became familiar was the experience of being in the middle of something interesting in the Caravan, and then beginning to see a kind of double, then triple, then increasingly, multiple images superimposing themselves on my vision. I felt a sense of moving ever so slightly in a directionless direction. Then the sounds of our world began to call until they anchored me. The wave collapsed, as they say in physics, and I would be back in our world. It was many transitions, however, before I recognized these signs immediately.

The first night the Voice called, I walked out into the night of the Caravan of Remembering and the rhythm carried me to stillness. Back in my world again, I looked around, feeling that stillness, feeling the sand and the rhythm and the presence of the Caravan of Remembering moving eternally home.

She'd said I'd remember the Caravan of Remembering when I returned. It was too soon to fully believe this memory would last. It seemed more like a dream. My first experience of finding myself back in our world, the horizontal world as I came to call it, carried this sense of unreality. Being in the Caravan of Remembering seemed more real.

At the moment of my departure to the Caravan of Remembering, I'd been heading home from another day spent working in a friend's studio. I'd been mindlessly, vacantly, discontentedly making my way through a grassy, tree-filled stretch of the park section of Wicker Park when the Voice called. In truth, I'd been seriously questioning my life in Chicago, my work, my relationships, everything, all that day, and for a long time. Then, in the middle of my walking debate with myself, I'd heard the Voice. Now, returning from the Caravan of Remembering, the only thing in any way different was that I was no longer walking. A triangle refuge of nature angled toward the elevated and six business corners of Daimon, Lincoln, and Milwaukee. As I breathed this in, the rhythm and presence of the Caravan, real and still moving within me, seemed to dance with the park. I've always loved the park in the rain, and that day I was especially grateful I had the park to myself.

For a long time, I simply watched the landscape of our world. It was spring, rain falling, and the air alive with ozone. Everything had that lush, vivid, alive, electric green aura about it. I could still feel the sand and the endless space of the Caravan of Remembering, and I could feel the call of life filling every inch of the park with something growing. My heart was still quiet with the peace of the desert pilgrimage, and now this gentle pattern of one sheet of water following another seemed a melodic counterpoint in the deep place I was breathing from.

It was some time before I felt grounded in our world. Was this real? Was the Voice real? Had I really gone anywhere? Was it a dream? Maybe our world is a dream and the Caravan of Remembering is real. I did feel the ground as solid, and I believed the breath I followed was real, though it was difficult to hold on to what that meant.

I felt compelled to write it all down. If I could write it down, I told myself, I could decide later what it meant. I ran home, found the best blank book I could find, picked up my favorite fountain pen, and began to write . . . "Welcome to the Caravan of Remembering."

Expedition Journal:

I wonder when I bought this expedition journal from National Geographic with the camels on the cover. Blank but for illustrations of 23 people famous for giving their life to pilgrimage, including a guy named Roy Chapman Andrews, known for exploring the Gobi Desert. It has one string of camels in the picture on the cover and seems perfect, even if they are fording what seems like a very wet and wide river.

After describing my night in the Caravan of Remembering, I wrote:

Adjusting to being home, I feel a kind of vigilance. It's the ever-present question of if or when I'll be called back to Caravan. I refer to the Caravan of Remembering as "Caravan" because people there talk about it in that way. "Caravan is a being whose mission is to carry us home," the man said. In my heart Caravan is already a "someone" who could ring me up at any time.

It feels a little like the Christians saying you never know when the Rapture will happen. You could be taken in a moment and you'd never know it was coming. One moment you could be walking down the street and the next moment you wouldn't be there. The experience of Caravan isn't the same thing at all, but it feels like a way of describing it to myself. It's like the Bible's story of the ten brides and the ten lamps, and not knowing when the bridegroom is coming.

It doesn't seem to be a question of being prepared. I will likely go, regardless, ready or not.

After leaving the ensemble of graphic designers/illustrators I'd been working with, I set up a kind of virtual studio with one other partner. We used our collective talents to act as a unified studio. What began as a question of going it alone turned into a partnership design studio without a physical location. To complicate things further, the two of us began negotiating with a third designer/illustrator, which necessitated another new company name and a debate over location. All of this while I questioned what it was I really wanted to do with my life, much less go into business with potential partners.

While this negotiation was in what felt like endless rounds, my current partner and I turned our apartments into studios. My bedroom now had two drafting tables and taborets with shelves for the many kinds and weights of paper and board stock I needed. My living room had cameras and enlargers, an illustration table, an airbrush setup, and more shelves for reference material for inspiration. My coach house apartment overflowed with boxes of files, supplies, tools, and equipment. This left little open space.

What appeared in design/illustration sourcebooks as a studio was really a virtual studio wave that collapsed into a business at any one or more of five or six locations. We might be working in any of several studios we had associations with.

It was a typical day of moving between studios. Heading through the park, taking the El after a quick stop at home, working on a project that was neither exciting nor boring, questioning even more insistently why I did this, I heard the Voice again. As before, it was raining and I was walking with both arms full of portfolios from the project de jour. I heard her calling and set everything down. As I set the last piece on the ground, I felt myself moving without moving, until little by little into view came . . .

My second night in Caravan. The Voice called, and in the proverbial twinkling of an eye, I was again in the midst of pilgrims. I could feel the paradox of cool heat. This was the desert. It was cool evening and Caravan was about to move again. There was no time to decide if I would travel with it. It didn't feel open to debate. Any answers found would be found within Caravan, and I wanted to be there.

We walked for a time out of time. The horizon was as empty and free of shadows as before, the movement as steady, the air as crisp and fresh, space everywhere expanding. The sands of Caravan were endlessly flat in every direction with the color of caramel cream in the night light. My heart slowed, my pulse synching with our pace. My mood was to forget to have a mood. My fellow pilgrims and I breathed together, almost as one.

Then the silence broke. Conversations emerged from somewhere deep inside the silence. These were not conversations to pass the time. Time didn't pass in Caravan. We walked silently and could and might choose to do so for eternity. This stillness was complete, and in it we knew each other.

Like quasars deep in space, conversations bloomed, super novae of silence, poetry in motion. In poetry, the spaces between words carry worlds, and each spoken word can be a bridge between worlds. We can choose which of these worlds to visit, simultaneously, all in the space of a breath that contains the universe itself.

Listening and not listening, present to both, aware of walking and spoken words, we moved through exploding star stories, worlds being born toward the One. Even if I was not always aware of it in our horizontal world, I knew then some part of all of us lives in this Caravan.

"This Caravan carries all of us home," the man had said. "This Caravan holds our place, our infinite full potential possible story, and here I am like every pilgrim."

As I listened to the conversations, there was a kind of grace for me. It may be that it was too soon for me to join them. There may be an unspoken understanding about the freedom to choose, when to jump in, or how long someone has been there or remembers being there. Whatever the reason, I had the space to listen.

Children played softly next to me as I walked. We all moved slowly, and these children silently threaded their ways between us in patterns that felt like a kind of code. For every small group of weaving children, an elder moved with them. It was hard to tell who was leading whom. I felt these groups were distinct unto themselves, though they seemed to overlap in their weaving.

"Do you remember doing this in the horizontal world?" an older man wearing an earth-colored robe asked the children weaving around me. He balanced his questions for the children with a silent look at a young man walking near me. The young man silently responded by following his interaction with the children. Still addressing the children, glancing occasionally at the young man next to me, the older man asked, "Why do you think you do this?"

The children didn't answer him. He didn't seem to expect them to. He asked his questions at intervals as if this were the process. Answering didn't appear to be important. His asking seemed designed to help them tune to something.

"What do you notice now? What is changing? Why?" Still no answer as the children continued to silently weave between us. We moved across the sand in no particular direction.

"What do you notice as you move? How do you know which way to go and who to move toward?"

The young man seemed to understand all of this. In earth-world terms, I guessed him to be in his late teens and South American. Although the questions were not exactly addressed to him, he seemed to move with the process in a different way. As the elder man questioned the children, he also occasionally checked the reaction of the young man. Was the younger man in training? Was he in a different level of the questioning?

As we walked, the weaving of the children had a kind of pull. It felt like they were actually weaving something and I was a thread in their fabric. Soon there were many teens involved with this tapestry-making. Each appeared to be drawn, one by one, by the moving, weaving children and the questions dancing around them.

The elder looked at me. "Do you sense why this weaving is important to you?" His eyes, his hair, and his robe all hinted of silver in the night sky. He felt like someone I'd known all my life, like someone you'd trust to invite into your home on first meeting. Even as an elder, his strong nose with its high bridge and his classic Mediterranean features gave the impression of strength and vitality. "Do you sense intentions carried in the threads of this weave?" he asked. "Do you feel the presence of the souls moving into and out of the thread of your intentions here and in the horizontal world?" The space around us rippled for a moment and everything stopped. Then we all moved again.

His focus was again on the children and the teenagers. Then, back to me: "Why do you think you are you in the horizontal world? Who are you meant to move with? How long are you meant to weave your life together? What is your purpose there?"[1]

As he asked these questions, I wondered about my own life in the great tapestry I might be part of. I imagined myself moving, weaving into and out of and through the fabric of my environment, considering my part in this story and possible interconnections. As I experienced this, teens who had been gathering began to walk with me. A girl, perhaps Polynesian in our world, asked, "You see it then? I sensed you felt something." After a pause, she added, "You seem a little old for this. Why is that? Wouldn't you have done this already?"

"What do you mean by that?" I asked her. She smiled and turned to watch the children. Still, I thought, she had a point. I did seem older than the teens and children. What could this have to do with anything in a world of possible eternals?

"You keep a kind of pace with your horizontal-world self. It keeps the sorting in check." The Mediterranean elder walking next to me answered my unspoken question. "As you begin each time in your world, there is an adjustment here as well. Time is a relationship, and your Caravan self can address the 'in-time' self in less 'time' than you might imagine. There is a great deal of flexibility. We have forever, and yet it wouldn't help much if, when you started over, we had to wait for your horizontal-world self to catch up in one to one units of time.

"The children move through Caravan weaving and following the call of the soul," he continued. "As they move, we ask them questions designed to awaken them to their eternal selves and the movement they agreed to in the horizontal world. The movement helps to open and develop their memory of the connection. As you have felt, you have a connection to these souls. You are part of the fabric of their story."

He pointed to my South American and Polynesian friends. "These two have moved through Caravan in the same way as these young ones. Their horizontal-world counterparts have grown to the point where this dance is leading to the next station of the work in both worlds. Both worlds call them now to choices that will determine the direction of the next major turning point of their journey. They found you in their weaving. It is enough for now."

I couldn't be sure if he said this for me, for them, or both. Either way, they began moving back into Caravan's flow.

Perhaps they had someone else to remember. First I noticed the children moving consistently and at a more relaxed pace. Then I noticed the teens moving even more slowly, and everything in Caravan now moved in a long, slow wave. The children laughed and moved about like children do in our world. They could've been playing games like the ones I know on earth. They were remembering their agreements, he said. Were they also making agreements? As they wove me into their fabric, did they ask and I choose, or was this already established in another place outside of time?

During all of this, the Mediterranean elder walked next me. I felt he might be waiting for something from me. "Were they guided?" I asked. "Are they guided in this weaving? Beyond the questions you ask them, are they steered in the movement they take by Caravan?"

"To some degree, you could say that," he said. "Where you are in the Caravan is determined by your agreements, situation, intention, and the attention you give to your agreements, situation and intention. That you are in this particular position in Caravan is because of this. Even here, the children need to remember to include you. Even here, they must choose to include you. Always this is so."

Gesturing toward the children, he continued. "As you watch now, you are also part of this weaving, though you must agree to it. You could have moved off. Your soul also is reminded by these questions. The teens reminded you that despite your apparent age, you are starting over. You hold this older appearance because it is time to remember. You hold a station that is past the children's beginning awareness of how it all works, and like the teens, you are on the threshold of choice. Sometimes it can help to go back to the beginning.

"These children are a good reminder," he went on. "We know they are as old as Caravan and young to the horizontal world. We know they are growing in ways the appearance of their earth form and apparent age demonstrate. It reminds us they are in the challenge of the horizontal world and we should hold gentle faith for them. It reminds us of how many times we begin. 'Come, come again . . . ' Yes?"

He gave me a kind of tap on the forehead and walked away. I thought there might be a trace of a smile on his face. My teen friends waved and pointed to the expanding and contracting patterns of the children moving among us. Yes, that seems true in the horizontal world as well. We forever move into and out of expanding and contracting circles.

I wondered, watching the children, what they looked like, or would look like in their mature forms. I still didn't know what this meant. What age would they appear to be in our world? What was the nature of these agreements we made in Caravan, and how did they relate to our life on earth? Caravan's work was as yet unclear, and the choices and decisions spoken of seemed foreboding in the absence of any way to understand what might be asked of us. As part of the fabric of their story, were the children now adults in my life on earth? Am I going to appear in their future? Will I be "old" to them there? Going inward with this stream of questions still echoing in the well of my heart, I moved into the wave of Caravan.

I'd settled into a felt sense of the deep wave of the interconnecting weave when I noticed, with barely perceptible and ever so gentle movement, that my vision was beginning to double. I breathed into it this time. As my vision moved to three, then four, then ever increasing multiple simultaneous exposures, I felt the sense of movement more consciously. As the sound of the rain came to me, I anchored in.

As I found myself back in our world, I couldn't help but remember the weaving. Did I echo it here in some way? Did I do this with everyone in my life? I even wondered if my fascination with dance and my thoughts of making it my career when I was young came from remembering this dance of life. I wouldn't look at anyone after that without wondering about the weaving in Caravan.

I found myself in the same place in the park I'd left from. My portfolios were barely wet, as if I'd just put them down. If someone had been watching me, I wondered, would they have seen anything other than my putting them down as if to rearrange them, then picking them up and going on? I smiled a little at that and walked home.

The expedition journal waited.

Sometimes I sat for hours watching the birds fly between trees and overhead wires, listening to the low-end boom of a passing car stereo piercing the relative silence of the yard encasing me, wondering at the paradox of Chicago.

The coach house in which I lived anchored the back of a newly renovated house in Wicker Park. This was a time of transition for Wicker Park. The artists had made it a great place to live. Three flats up and down the streets witnessed various stages of renovation. This meant I could expect the entire spectrum of race, language, occupation, and financial outlook.

My coach house sat far enough from the street to have a yard, but not so far back that I felt left out. This neighborhood was a kind of neutral Switzerland for the gangs that surrounded the area. Here we enjoyed relative calm and safety. The Guardian Angels patrolled the El platform, and gangs flying different colors could almost mingle. At night, if you timed it right, you could join in the drumming and dancing in the street. Wicker Park seemed an island in the landscape of Chicago. I could almost see the colors of every nation of Caravan, all walking together. Caravan and Wicker Park seemed very much alike to me then.

Expedition Journal:

Back home, in what my experience in Caravan has led me to call the horizontal world, I find my things curious. Who is this person and why does he have all of this stuff? In Caravan, the question of possessions is unclear to me, though I suspect owning anything might be unnecessary. Would it just be additional baggage to load and unload? I witnessed pilgrims packing tents and cooking gear as they prepared to leave. They appeared to have everything needed to camp and to travel. Thinking about it, I'm not sure if anyone there has intimate personal possessions. Perhaps they have small items carrying personal symbolic meaning? I will make it a point to look more closely.

I survey this coach house as if it belongs to a stranger.[2] *I see the tools of the trade for a graphic designer/illustrator. I see the remnants of a life as professional musician. I see music, instruments, amplifiers, and books stacked in every direction. I see drafting tables in rows and shelves of paper. I see toolboxes from Sears in fire-engine red, filled with tools and supplies for design and illustration. Half-finished paintings and illustrations lean against the wall. Everywhere it's black and chrome—that most of what I see is directly tied to the professions of my life says something in itself. As with the pilgrims of Caravan, my intimate personal possessions aren't obvious.*

I feel the weight of my things. I feel the weight of my stationary life in the horizontal world. The evidence of my intention, or lack of intention, surrounds me. Some priority is apparent in my home, although it doesn't connect to me yet. I feel a kind of detachment from it. These things are mine and not mine.

Who is this man who has this life and owns these things? What is his life about? As I scan my house, as I walk through it, I feel the children weaving among the pilgrims in Caravan. Each thing has a story and each story has people who shared a moment and movement in the dance. I can imagine the people connected to each piece, people I have and haven't met. I can feel the threads that connect my life to the endless weave in both worlds. I feel a little dizzy imagining these connections sometimes.

Still wondering about the children outside my window, and the children in Caravan waiting for them, I put down the journal. The children of Caravan wait in eternity for a part of themselves to develop enough for Caravan's weave to piece together a life.

As the first days of Caravan entered my life on a conscious level, I thought about what it means to be stationary. Having a home of wood, steel, and concrete and a "permanent" address becomes a kind of identity.[3] What is my identity as I live in this place? What has this to do with life? As this question drifted through my peripheral awareness, I could almost hear Caravan moving through my veins. It was a bit like the old televisions that needed manual adjustment to get the channel to lock in. I could sense both stations. Neither would lock in completely.

As I thought about the questions of identity and place, I remember asking another question. *In accumulating the treasures of my life, do they serve me?* Before Caravan entered my life, I never asked if they served, especially if I thought the answer was no. It takes a clear sense of purpose and the experience of being a long way lost from it to ask this question and really want the answer. Returning from Caravan helped with this. The "treasures" of my life looked so different when I returned.

The question of identity called me to examine what I found in my house for clues. It felt almost as if I were meeting myself for the first time, as if a stranger had moved into my house. Actually, it was more like a long-lost relative coming to visit. I knew we had a connection. I felt our bond. And it wasn't me.

I looked through my books with questions.[4] Who would have this collection, and why? What would be important to someone who owns these books? What would be important to someone who moved into this coach house? What called him to this place? Why is he living this kind of life? Did this make him happy or fulfilled?

I couldn't have a conversation with anyone in my life without asking these questions about him or her. I began to find myself listening to my friends and wondering about what we had agreed to in Caravan. Why are we in each other's lives? How are we doing with these agreements?

I began finding that I could no longer tune into just being in the horizontal world. Caravan had the quality of a dream that is always present. Caravan was a friend always just on the edge of my awareness. Sometimes I could almost convince myself that I dreamt it. The problem was, this life felt like the dream from which I would awaken. Also, if Caravan were the dream, that was fine, because it had changed my life in already profound ways.

I liked the questions I couldn't ignore. I liked the presence these questions encouraged. I liked the appreciation I felt for every person in my life. I liked the way that appreciation demanded that I be present to my life. I liked the levels of awareness that remained without effort on my part.

I did have to choose, and yet this choosing was not something I had difficulty with. Butterflies fluttered just below my radar, anticipating the role for which I seemed to be an understudy. A curtain call seemed just around the corner, a stage appearance into which I needed to be ready to walk. I wanted to understand what was happening to me, and I didn't care to question these changes. I desired these changes. I could not say the purpose of this yet, and I didn't want to stop what was happening.

After only a few visits to Caravan, I felt home was somewhere that included both worlds and perhaps more. I felt so much at home within Caravan. Now Caravan was with me in the horizontal world. This did not create a desire to leave, however; I felt even more love for the beauty of the horizontal world, felt more care for this world.

Maybe it was the ever-present connection I felt between Caravan and our horizontal world. Everything in Caravan is geared to our journey in the horizontal world. There couldn't be one without the other. "Until we all go home together," he had said. So both worlds are tied together by an agreement with the One and Caravan to bring us all home.

I was reminded of Caravan as I watched the United Nations of commuters gathering to ride the El and the bus. I could almost see lines of mounted camels. I saw these long lines of camels in the long winding lines of train cars and buses. I watched people balancing briefcases and portfolios and saw stacks of goods tied on camels' backs, tied in balanced harmony. Camels followed parent camels or friend camels, who in turn followed the guiding hand of someone trusted to guide them. I saw the endless lines of pilgrims winding through Caravan's world.

I could smell the crispness of virtual air and hear the bells singing. I remembered the flowering colors of every nation on earth represented. I could hear the Mediterranean elder asking questions of Caravan's pilgrims, more to tune them as a musician tunes his instrument, than merely for answers. I could feel these worlds crossing over and the music of questions moving through me as I watched.

I had so many questions of my own in those first evenings. I didn't really want to question *if* this was happening. I wanted to know *why* this happened. What did it mean? The more immediate questions surprised me, though. More than *why* this was happening, I now wanted to know *what* was happening here in the horizontal world.

The mystics advise us to die before we die. Some refer to the dark night of the soul, when everything you "know" is questioned to its very foundation. My outlook didn't feel that dramatic, yet in a way it wasn't so far from where I was. The foundation of my world was going through a serious overhaul. Fortunately, not everything was in question at that point. In a strange way, this fit nicely with my ideas about how the universe works. Along with some irritation around what I wasn't being told, I felt a kind of nostalgia for Caravan as I navigated my days in the horizontal world.

Questions floated everywhere just off to the side. The Voice calling was a constant companion, if for no other reason than I expected her at any moment. The questions of my Mediterranean elder in Caravan, ringing, singing, creating, giving form to the weave the children made were almost tangible.

My life was unquestionably involved in two worlds now. My sense of self was forever altered. We're possibly brave about these things when something in us knows it's the only option. This could be a great quality of humanness. Given the chance, I believe most of us will say *yes* to the call to life in the face of challenge and uncertainty. I believe that's why movies and books that ask *What if this were you?* are so popular. I questioned if I wanted this new life, only to say *yes, yes,* over and over.

Caravan traveled under a starlit sky during all of my first visits. It seemed ironic to me, after all the movies I'd seen of caravans moving across the desert, that camels really don't like the heat. Given their preference, they would avoid the heat of the sun. Although they have evolved in every way to accommodate the heat, the sun, and the lack of water, they still protest when faced with the prospect of traveling across the hot desert by day. I've learned since that camels have the intelligence of a three- to six-year-old human child. That's quite a range, I thought, considering the children I've known. Camels do seem to have this same range in personality. The "curiosity that killed the cat" is present to an advanced degree. They can be petulant, rebellious, and spoiled. They can be sweet, too, though I'm told they're seldom courageous. While they're said to be easily spooked in the horizontal world, I've seen little of that in Caravan. The dangerous side attributed to being in their way at mating time is also absent in Caravan. The bells originate from their habit of curiosity that leads them to wander. In horizontal world caravans, the bells help camels find their way back. Pack animals in the long run prefer to stay together. They're never scared or wander off in Caravan. I thought perhaps the bells remained in Caravan because the music helped the people.

I wasn't clear if Caravan ever traveled during the day. I wondered if day ever came to this world at all. I spent my time, even though time was apparently not present to spend, listening and watching. The Voice had said I would be asked to remember in both worlds now. I remembered my recent trips to Caravan after I returned to the horizontal world. My history in Caravan was still a mystery. I only knew what I could see and feel and sense and touch during recent visits.

After traveling for many nights and walking for untold miles, I learned that many in Caravan called my Mediterranean elder Kairos. I thought of him as my guide because he was the only one who instructed me in any way at that point. I seemed to be left to my own devices, and then a feeling in the air alerted me that he was watching. He would stay for what could have been minutes or hours, questioning or commenting, then be gone again.

It was one of those nights, walking under the stars of Caravan, so different from our own, with Kairos walking next to me, silent, feeling the peace and community, that I began to take Caravan in deeply. It felt like home to me, and I watched my fellow pilgrims with a sense of family. I wanted to know them in the way you want to know fellow journeyers you feel you will travel with for a long time. I listened to the soft crunch of sand as we walked, in the same way I used to listen for the sand under my feet beside the rivers of my childhood. Some part of me wanted to imprint those sounds and scents surrounding us so I would always remember the scents of the sacreds in the air even as we traveled. I wanted to remember the sound of the names of the One that surrounded us and moved us forward on our journey. These were the names of the One from every land in the horizontal world. In this land, they blended into a sweet chord. I loved the ethnic colors of the horizontal world in the soft glow of Caravan's night. This was now my family and the home of my heart of hearts.

"Are there other Caravans?" I asked Kairos. "Have there been many? Is Caravan new?" In this world, "new" suddenly seemed a pointless word. Kairos waited for my next question, knowing I wouldn't stop there. "Is there a new Caravan for each age?" I asked. "Or does Caravan start over in each time or age?"

"Caravan is eternal," he said, "as you know, and ever changing, so you could say the answer to your question is both yes and no. There is a collective wisdom passed through time, and your gift to Caravan will have something to do with this."

He pulled long strands of silver hair away from his eyes and forehead and pushed back the hood of his robe. With his strong nose and jaw and his earth-colored robe, he seemed to me at once Jedi knight and Greek statue. "Looked at from the viewpoint of a particular culture," he was saying, "it may appear that Caravan began and will end with the seeming purpose and destiny of that culture. Looked at in terms of the destiny of humankind and all sentient beings, we all move into and out of Caravan over time. We do this as individuals and we do this as cultures."

He stopped, allowing other pilgrims to move around us. Then, as if hearing what he'd waited for, he continued, "Even when you have forgotten, Caravan calls. You can get so lost in your life that you can go weeks, months and even years before you even think about the call you hear in your heart. It may be that pain and life's challenges will remind you. This is not the only way we are called. Joy can call you. Love can call you.

"For as long as the family of sentient beings has been in the horizontal world, Caravan calls. It moves toward the completion of the intention of your world and your homecoming, your return to the One who sent you."

As Kairos shared this, Caravan seemed to breathe through me. I weighed his tone and unspoken words. Lines of camels streamed as far as my vision could touch, my sense of time moving in all directions with no end in sight. I sought the sense of what it meant that all my fellow pilgrims and I have traveled together from the beginning, held by Caravan.

Moving back into Caravan, weaving with, and around the grain of Caravan's flow, Kairos arched his hands across the sweep of pilgrims and continued. "Caravan exists in the imaginal realms, it intersects and runs through your world. It is part of the horizontal world. It underlies the horizontal world and calls you each moment of your life.

"Just beyond the edge of your usual awareness, Caravan has moved since the beginning of time. It moves toward the completion of your story. You are called to remember you have always been part of it. You are called to remember the One that sent you and your agreement to remember, even while you do that which you came to do and be in the horizontal world."

He took my shoulder in hand and steered me around a string of camels that had unexpectedly stopped. "Caravan always moves and is always with you," he said. "By always moving, I mean that it is headed home. Everyone is part of Caravan. Like the Bodhisattvas of Buddhism, many have vowed to stay until all sentient beings travel home with us. The families of human beings and all sentient beings are included in this journey home. Someone is always calling. As long as the created world streams from the void, Caravan travels toward the sun behind the sun, oriented toward home."

Glancing back at the train of camels, he continued. "Caravan is not subject to anything that happens in the horizontal world. It does respond, however. It always responds to the needs of your soul and the help required for the work of Caravan to continue. Guides respond to your insights, to your challenges, and to your growth in the manner most beneficial in all worlds."

I traveled with Caravan, attuning to what it might want me to understand. I sensed that nights were passing, yet tracking its passing was difficult unless it was connected to something I needed to understand in the horizontal world. Otherwise, time in the night wasn't present for us. What seemed to determine our sense of time or the lack of it was the understanding and the situation of our work in Caravan.

Kairos's teachings tuned and held me. Everything in Caravan was new to me. The reason for anything had nothing to attach itself to. This was the world of the desert. That much, I had some idea of. Beyond that, the context was unclear. This was desert, and the extreme heat and lack of water were not relevant. My understanding of the "work" of Caravan still unfolded. My purpose for being in Caravan, I couldn't begin to guess.

Kairos served as an anchor in a world without a map. He knew this world, the landscape, why and how it moved. I imagined he knew the reasons I longed for. I latched on to this possibility with my whole heart. I trusted Kairos.

I loved to listen to the movement of Caravan. I loved to feel the flow of pilgrims as far as I could sense, moving like a single wave in an ocean of beings flowing across an endless plane. Night after night, following silent directions like a flock of birds, we responded to the signals apparently given on a different plane. We all turned at the right moment to move in a new direction that had no apparent reason, and yet it seemed exactly right. I began to enjoy the experience that every movement had a reason; even if I didn't know the reason, I knew it would be perfect. I began to relax into knowing this was exactly right.

"Do you notice the change in pace?" said the man with the long eyebrows from my first night in Caravan. He'd appeared again as if out of thin air. His skin matched both the glow of the night sand and the coats of the camels. "Have you noticed the change in the sand as we walk?" he asked. "Do you notice that even the depth of the sand changes?"

"Yes, to each of your questions," I replied, "and my question, then, would be *why?* In this endless landscape, I know the sand could go on forever without change. For now, I am more interested in why it doesn't stay the same." I said this, knowing that everything in Caravan had a reason. "Could it be that the changes in depth of sand and the terrain in general reflect something we pilgrims are working out together? Or is it something happening in the horizontal world?"

My companion nodded and pointed at another change in the sand. It seemed to me that, just like the first evening, he said what was needed and would say no more. Later in our travels, he would point to a change in the ground and, perhaps trusting that I understood, would turn silently back into the wave of pilgrims.

I noticed Caravan moving slowly enough that nearly everyone now walked with their camel next to them. The pace moved into deep reflection. As much as time did not "move" in Caravan, and a "night" seemed to last for a moment or years, there was no question of getting tired. We seemed to breathe and work got done, and yet getting exhausted wasn't something that happened.

Caravan moved in near silence, a community deep in contemplation. Nearly everyone walking that night appeared to have something weighing on his or her heart. I felt it in the air. We were a sea of pilgrims moving together, more inwardly focused than anything else. I felt the inner communication that directed us. Even the camels knew when to turn. Like us, they were a unified field inwardly guided. Occasionally, direction was given to the lead camels, more as a way of thinking out loud than from the need for it.

My sense of confusion in the horizontal world about what to do with my life blended with the mystery of what was expected in Caravan, and no answer seemed to wait for me around any of the nonexistent corners of Caravan's endless horizon. The collective mood of reflection moved me to ask what the deep ache in my heart meant for my place in all of this. I couldn't reach it, either in this world or in the horizontal world, either for myself or for my family of pilgrims.

For a long time I walked silently, feeling the weight of our reflecting. I wondered what could be happening in the horizontal world to cause this. Then I wondered if it was something that was going to happen. Could we prevent it? Should we? If this something was necessary, could we change how it happened or its severity? Maybe it wasn't bad, just serious.

Did this tell me something of the work of Caravan?

CHAPTER 2

Life Mission, Vision, and Purpose: Assignments and Agreements

CARAVAN RESTED. A VAGUE suggestion of color, omnipresent even, made a sunrise possible, the direction questionable. Where was the east in this world? Is east even where the sun comes up? Now dawn seemed imminent, and still I asked what that would mean in the Caravan of Remembering.

In my previous trips to Caravan, we had always moved, and always at night. I had no recollection of stopping. The work of unloading the camels was already done. For the first time I could remember, tents were set up, and as far as my eyes could see, Caravan was now a tent city. Most of the tents were black or an earth color, though a few were white. As when Caravan moved, colors representing every nation of the horizontal world were attached to or surrounded the tents in some way.

Each tent had a campfire, though, as far as I could tell, fires were not needed for warmth or light. The moons were still clearly present. I smelled the familiar scent of firewood burning along with a cascade of incense. Was it frankincense and myrrh? Was it copal? Was it sage? It was all of these and others unfamiliar to me. It wasn't cold, and a twilight dawn was in the air. I wondered if the campfires would be needed today. I imagined that almost anything might happen.

"You have traveled with us for many nights now, and it is time for me to ask you why you imagine you are here." The Voice, the woman who had called me to Caravan, appeared wearing the same earth colored robe with silver threaded through it. The red in the mix of earth colors in her robe seemed most prominent, a kind of echo of the whispered hint of color in the sky. The impression of silver in her eyes felt more luminous in this ambient morning light, her face timeless, and features universal in impression.

"You met other pilgrims and heard their questions," she said. "You have listened to many conversations, and you likely have more questions now than when you first remember me calling you. Why do you imagine I called you here?"

I didn't feel she truly wanted me to answer this, so I bowed slightly, paused, and responded with a question of my own. "With respect, if I may, why do you always show up like that, unannounced and from nowhere? I think I would like to know more about you. Then, yes, I would like to know why you called me here. And what you want from me. You said I would remember. I'm not entirely sure what that means, and so far I don't think that's happened. Why?"

She allowed my questions to hang unanswered. In the silence I listened, feeling the new rhythms of Caravan at rest, breathing in the scent of blessing in the air, and noticing I could find no shadows produced by the twilight morning as yet.

"You can call me Verity," she said, smiling, touching my shoulder, and gesturing with her other hand toward our tent city. We began to walk. "Wherever I am," she said, "when you need me, when you use this name, I will answer you. Answering will not always mean I will come to you personally. My answer will be suited to your need. Consider this when you call and are surprised by the results you receive. Nonetheless, when you call, I will come to you myself in most cases in this stage of your journey."

Verity continued. "You noticed you are different here. Others recognize and remember their lives in the horizontal world when they arrive in Caravan. They forget their time in Caravan when they return to the horizontal world. I told you when you arrived that you would be asked to remember now in both worlds. Although it is true for you, you see that most of the pilgrims here do not remember in both worlds."

I wondered if children often remember their time in Caravan and are talked out of it.

"In the horizontal world," Verity said, "there is growing interest in the question of why one is born. Growing numbers of people remember they made agreements for their journey in the horizontal world. I ask you now to consider a proposition that is not new to you, though you will only remember saying *yes* if you arrive at that place in your heart. It is possible, of course, that you will not find your way, even after all of this, and with the help given here.

"Everyone has an agreement for their life in the horizontal world," she continued, "though not everyone will remember. Even remembering will not guarantee you will accomplish what you agreed to. 'Many are called and few are chosen.' Many have agreed and few choose to remember, though every one of you is given more help than your personality wants."

"Does this mean everyone in the horizontal world moves through Caravan?" I asked, watching light from the campfires dancing across her face. Verity was the Voice that was always with me, and I felt that my vision of her would be with me in both worlds. I wondered if, like Caravan itself, she reflected the needs of the pilgrims she called. I couldn't feel a place in our world to anchor my way of seeing her. However else the impression of her changed, her eyes were eternity in a moment, the silver luminously alive and infinitely deep.

"Yes," she said, looking into my eyes, "everyone comes. During this time in Caravan, consider the question of why you are here. I want you to also consider the reason you travel in the horizontal world. Consider whom you serve in both worlds, what that means to you, and what this calls you to now."

What she said didn't answer my questions. Her assignment only increased the list of questions and brought my conscious attention to questions I held just below the radar and had tried to ignore. I believed understanding Caravan and the rules would answer my questions. That had not happened yet.

"Verity," I said, "many, maybe most, people in this situation would ask themselves these very questions. As you say, there's a growing interest in both worlds in these questions. Why do you give me these questions as an assignment?"

"You ask yourself these questions," she said, "and you imagine that most people in the horizontal world also ask the same questions. It may surprise you to know some have not, and never will, ask these questions unless something extraordinary happens to them. It is as if they have been asleep in your world for a very long time.

"Although you will hear these questions in Caravan," she continued, "in the horizontal world, asking them is only recently a growing priority. Why do I give you these questions as an assignment? That is a question that may help with the other questions. You can think of it as a clue if you like." She smiled at me. "Enjoy this twilight morning in Caravan." With this, she moved away and out of sight between the tents. This was the first time she left in a conventional manner. I decided not to dwell on that for the moment. Instead, I brooded over the assignment.

I decided to walk and allow that someone or something inside me that knows to guide me. I didn't know where to begin, so movement of any kind seemed like a good idea. I walked through the ocean of tents. Everywhere, pilgrims were sitting around the campfires.

How do I find this inner guidance? This was the first question I asked myself as I moved toward the flickering campfire my heart chose. I remembered when I was first called to Caravan, I doubted myself, my choices, and even my life in the horizontal world. I wondered to myself about the zeitgeist (or spirit) of the time and began to think the zeitgeist of our time might be on good terms with the question of why we travel in the horizontal world. Maybe the zeitgeist of our particular time is an emerging spirit of mission or purpose and vision.

As I neared the campfire, an older man with a northern European appearance seemed to echo my thoughts. "What does it mean to be lifted up by the zeitgeist?" he asked. "Are we called first? I wonder about this often in the horizontal world. Here I might guess that when this person or that one stands out in the horizontal world, it reflects Caravan's calling. It reflects remembering on some level the work done here. How do I remember in the horizontal world? How do I find my place in this current of my time, in this zeitgeist, and the call of Caravan?"

I wondered how many times these pilgrims asked these same questions. How many times do we need to begin in Caravan? We began at the beginning. We looked at our agreement with the One. What might that mean? Why are we in the horizontal world? Whom do we serve?

Why do we run from these questions in the horizontal world?

I moved closer to the fire, which was surrounded by a group of about twenty, drawn in by the resonance of my questions and thoughts. The fire pit was itself a circle in the center of a small sea of beautiful square rugs. This was circle within square within circle. When Caravan stopped, people moved out of affinity groups they'd formed for travel. Here the rugs reflected a more universal sorting of people called personally by the questions in their hearts.

As I moved into the circle, the European man continued. "I have for years wondered what my life was meant to be about. Am I on the floor for the right dance?" His voice was thick, as if he were holding his passion in check. "Something in me will tell me not to ask these questions," he added, "and for a time I'll succeed in exiling them from my thoughts and my life. I don't remember Caravan in those moments, or I would know that these questions will hunt me as long as it takes. Caravan will continue to call me to remember."

He reached down to the edge of the circle and ran his fingers through the sand. He scooped a handful and held it carefully as if listening for a clue. Then, releasing the sand, he knelt down to trace a pattern on the rug next to him, as if sand and rug were connected. "There is a saying among shamans," he said, his voice softer, "that you become what you hunt.[5] Anything you dwell on becomes something you hunt. If you don't ask what your life is for, what its purpose is, then you hunt for something else. It won't be who you really want to become. If it's true you become what you hunt, then what are you becoming?"

What he said caused a subtle ripple around the circle. I imagined I could see an ocean of campfires on an endless horizon, their waves rippling within and then washing over Caravan.

In our circle, as the murmuring quieted, he spoke again. "Around this campfire, together, we are a hunting party. In Caravan, I come home to the true hunt." He looked at the other pilgrims. "I'm afraid I will need your help this morning if anything is going to happen for me in the horizontal world. What I usually find myself hunting in the horizontal world is all the ways I can forget the questions we ask in Caravan."

Silence filled the circle as he finished. Sand and rugs received our inward stares, accepting this space as the fire danced. In the absence of the desert winds of our world, the sand remained in place and the pilgrims' long robes, usually fluttering, were still.

A woman next to the European man, whom I hadn't noticed until now, took the lead. Though she was wearing Western clothes, her features were Eastern. She had an olive complexion and the morning light reflected off the silver in her hair. She seemed both Western and exotic. Now she led this circle.

"What do we know now?"[6] she asked. "Here and in the horizontal world? Where are we now in our calling? These questions are always with us. They are why we return to Caravan to remember. As you begin your pilgrimage, consider how you would like it to end. It is a bit like asking how you want your life to go, what you want your life to be about. This returns us to the question: Why are we here? We begin this pilgrimage to our purpose, mission, and vision, to our agreement with the One.

"It is a journey," she put her hand over her heart, "with stops along the way. It is a journey that will not have an ending you can point to. You may consider death to be an ending, though in our story this would not be true. It is more helpful to look at death as the completion of a segment in the larger pilgrimage of life.

"This much we do know." She traced the lining of her coat, lifting the edge, looking inside, and continued. "When we ask what was packed for your journey, we learn that your provisions were arranged before you began. Everything needed for this journey was sent with you. What you can do is take a moment to look at what you were sent with. In the abundance of gifts packed for you, nothing was wasted. In nature, everything is used and nothing is without purpose. Everything you have in the way of a gift is meant for something you agreed to do during the journey. You were given something for every intention for your life."

She paused and looked around the circle at us. "What blessings did you bring? You came bearing gifts. We all did. Do you remember? Maybe you hope you came with something to give, and have lost or misplaced it. You may never have believed this. Maybe you have an idea you knew when you were young, and then you forgot what it was." Her voice became softer. "Maybe it is time to remember."

Silence enveloped us, one pilgrim shifting his legs, another looking toward the endless horizon. Around this campfire something reached in each of us. The man who had spoken when I joined the circle moved to tend the fire. This felt more like an act to fill the space than the fire's needing attention. I was sure the fire would burn for an endless twilight morning and never need tending. Compliments of Caravan, the fire was a symbol for the work we were to do together.

I felt the woman's presence holding our silence. She began again. "It is indeed time to remember. In fact, it would be good for all of us to remember. When we remember, it is not an accident. It matters that we remember. If it were true that we brought our gifts with us, would it make sense that it was important to remember?

"Some in the horizontal world say it is too much pressure to ask people if they have a life mission. It is too stressful and we would be happier to let that go. The only reason we are here is to be happy. That seems such a lovely thought at first. There is no purpose, so just let it all go. If you do not know your life purpose, then you do not have one . . . or you would be doing it." She nodded at the European man. "Our friend here asks for our help for his journey in the horizontal world precisely because this reasoning calls him to distraction and escape.

"For myself, I feel an innate sense of the meaning of life and the purpose of every being 'in' life. It seems natural to look, feel, sense, and intuit the purpose of every life here and in the horizontal world. It perplexes me that anyone could imagine the miracle of life is an accident with no meaning or purpose. Calling this naïve seems to me an act of insincerity to self. I do not believe anyone who is truly honest with herself feels this way alone at night."

A young woman across the circle addressed our campfire leader by name. "Savitri," she said, "in the horizontal world, some call it fantasy." We knew this one. The response around the circle acknowledged that we all encounter this response to the idea we have a purpose or mission in the world.

"It may seem more realistic," Savitri replied, "to say it is a fantasy that we each have something unique to do in the horizontal world. I say it is just the opposite. I say that denying our unique gifts and the purpose they are meant for is the most impractical thing we can do. We have within us the answer to our challenges. These answers are present in every generation. What every generation does is deny them. Because of this, the challenges of every generation are passed down to the next, usually growing in magnitude and resonance.

"What if we honored the gift and purpose of each person and the answers they uniquely bring? How different the horizontal world would be. What is the cost of so many spending their lives doing things they were never meant to do? What is the cost of so much unhappiness and frustration? What is the benefit each time someone holds onto their gift and purpose, in spite of all those who would say they are crazy? How would their gifts and purpose change the horizontal world?"

She paused now as if listening to something we could not hear. Then, almost to herself, she said, "Even Caravan is changed." She smiled and looked at me for a moment. I knew this was for everyone around the circle and a clue for me. Perhaps her look was so I wouldn't miss it.

"The poet Saadi wrote about a warrior who would not put down his sword and a statesman who would not put down his words,"[7] Savitri continued. "It strikes me that he is saying they recognized the essence of these things for themselves. They recognized there was something essential in their actions. To give up their weapons or words, or 'put them down,' would change who they were. They would cease to be the very men they had come to be.

"For us to make that stand, perhaps it would have to be something we recognize as essential to who we are. It might be there are many things we could be involved in and easily walk away from. What is that something we feel is so much a part of us that we know we cannot walk away?"

Now she turned to the European man again. "My wish for you," she said to him, "is that you feel this way about something. It is my wish that you will know what you would die for and, more importantly, what you will live for. It is my wish that you fill your life in the horizontal world with the right amount of something you know is right for you, with that essential something you will not walk away from or put down."

Savitri, slight and elegant, Western in dress, wore silver jewelry of an Eastern design that reflected the light from the fire and echoed the silver of her hair. Not just her words, her radiating heart held us. "Life in the horizontal world," she continued, "can give you so many things that take you away from who you are. Our friend shared how this was for him. The horizontal world is appealing in its distractions. It can feel glamorous and wonderful as a distraction, or life feels too difficult for you to hold your intention. My hope for you is that you find something you recognize as being so who you are in your core, that you cannot be bought or scared off. My wish is that you find something more important than all of your considerations. My wish is that you fall so much, so much in love, and fall so completely, that you once and for all surrender into your passion and your purpose."

A kind of completion now moved into the space around us as we breathed into her wish for us and her passion. I wanted her to go on. Her words were a kind of air, a kind of food for something in me waiting longer than I could remember. I felt this wave of completion ripple out across Caravan as I searched inside myself for words to continue our dialogue. A child from outside the circle ran up to her. She lifted the girl and looked into the child's eyes.

Then Savitri laughed and looked directly at me. "What is your essential self?"[8] she asked. She lowered the girl to her feet, still holding her. "It could be like asking who you were before you were born," she said. "It could be the question, 'Who are you beyond the masks of your ego?' That is a question worth pursuing, and in this case, I suggest that you ask it in the horizontal world as you seek to express your essential self."

Holding the little girl's hands, she began to rock with her. "I suggest you hold this question in your heart," she said. "I ask you to move this question in the direction life calls you to. Life will help you to discover who you really are in the process of answering the call of your life. When you answer the call of your life, you answer the voice in you that has always wanted to show you the path to your becoming.

"If you are willing to live the question of who you are, life will reward you with a vision of possibility that will bring your life alive. You will come alive in your life because you will be living the life you were perfectly designed for. How could you come alive in a life that you were not designed to live? How could you become the person you were meant to be without the experience you were meant to have?"

"'Why were you born?' is a twin question to 'What is your essence?' What is it that you cannot give up or put down and still be who you are? Still and always, these questions bring us together in Caravan."

I must have reached the point of saturation. In the next breath, I was in the horizontal world. Nice touch, I thought, twilight morning to morning. It felt good to see the sun rising in the sky, even though I'd felt more at home in the timeless night of Caravan. It soothed the disquiet I'd been feeling for some time. In Caravan, the stars felt right.

The sound of Caravan's campfires still crackled in my ears, mixing with park sprinklers and birds playing in the puddles. Surveying the horizontal world, I reflected on campfires with no heat in a desert with an almost-morning that is neither cold from the night nor hot from a coming day. I smiled with appreciation for water that is abundant here and would nourish life for a day that was coming and would be hot.

I could hear Savitri as if I were sitting with her still. Why did I remember the campfire work? Why did I remember any of this? Was I really losing my mind?

The questions of purpose and mission were still a little fuzzy to me as I thought about my recent time in Caravan. Where did vision come into the question of mission and purpose? Returned to the horizontal world, I thought about what I knew about these words. I decided to check the dictionary.

I raced back to the coach house, made a fresh cup of coffee, and went to my Caravan corner. I picked up my *National Geographic* expedition journal and ran my fingers over a photograph of a string of camels. I felt Caravan and heard Savitri speaking in the background. Tracing each camel, I repeated lines from the dictionary and waited for something to settle. I pieced the references together in my mind and worked it out on paper.

Expedition Journal:

Investigating these words: life mission, vision, *and* purpose.

For mission *I found:* "An assignment given to a person or group in an official capacity, a continuing task or responsibility that one is destined or fitted to do or specially called upon to undertake, a lifework or vocation, sent with a trust or a mission, a group of persons sent to a foreign country to conduct diplomatic negotiations." (Webster's New International Dictionary)

The "continuing task" applies first. I feel this deeply in the timeless world of Caravan. For our entire life, we return to Caravan to remember and work on our mission. Next: the specific assignment given, or "responsibility that one is destined or fitted to do or specifically called to undertake." We're sent, given a trust, and charged with a task to undertake in a foreign country, which is the horizontal world.

It's clear in Caravan that this mission is to be the foundation of our life in the horizontal world. It's the underlying grid for the structure of our life. It's meant to be the context for every decision we make in this life.

The definition of purpose: "Something that one sets before oneself as an object to be attained, an end or aim to be kept in view, an object, effect, or result aimed at, intended or attained, an action in course of execution, to propose as an aim to oneself."

The first difference between purpose and mission is the source of each word.

According to Webster, with mission, we're sent with a trust given specifically, called and fitted, an assignment. This isn't something we decide when we arrive. It's a destiny we're uniquely designed to fulfill.

According to Webster, with purpose, "One sets before oneself, the object or result kept in view, the course of action." This would be something I choose. Mission is given, and purpose, I choose.

If purpose has anything to do with my reason for being here, it is because I take the time to contemplate, remember, and articulate my life mission. It's the choices I make, the aim I set for myself, and the person I need to be to accomplish my mission.

Purpose and mission are not the same thing. Purpose can be completely disconnected from the reason I'm here. Mission and purpose are associated only when I've chosen to "set before me" my mission. It seems that mission has to come first. Then I can choose an intention for who I need to be to accomplish it. When what I set before myself is aligned with my mission and kept in view as purpose, then who I need to be for my mission can manifest.

In the midst of this research, the film Lawrence of Arabia appeared on television. When anything connected with the desert shows up in my environment, I jump into alertness. I've cut photos of dunes and camels out of magazines and set them around the coach house. I sense that the story of T.E. Lawrence is the story of someone who lived his vision, his mission, and his purpose. That it was also a story of the desert made the film especially magnetic for me.

Lawrence is alone without his guide in a place in the desert that is completely new to him. He doesn't know where he is, and without his compass he's lost. He doesn't even know which direction to try. The territory is new and unknown. Lawrence is both sent and has personally sensed his deeper mission. He has a destination and no map to follow. In constantly shifting sands that look the same in all directions, it's easy to get lost.

There are no maps of the shifting sands of the desert. They might be useful, for a short time at best. In Lawrence of Arabia, a nation declines even to build roads because they will disappear in the shifting sands. The shifting sands of the horizontal world render all our maps limited. Life mission is the direction we take for the long haul across a shifting terrain, a compass to guide us where only the eternals know where to find landmarks.

Still working this out. I went back to the dictionary for help with placing vision in context with what I'm learning.

According to Webster, vision is "an imaginary, supernatural, or prophetic sight, one that conveys a revelation, a vivid concept or object of imaginative contemplation, a mode or way of seeing the world. It implies some sort of philosophy, unusual discernment and foresight, planning that combines realism with . . ."

We can create a visionary plan for our life that is moral and ethical, that benefits the world and does not connect to our life mission. I would not fault these visions. The confusion starts when we collapse this kind of vision into mission. The distinction comes down to whether or not vision is brought into the context of mission.

Perhaps vision is a kind of revelation about what we're assigned to do that we combine with the reality of our life. This will involve the missions of others. It would include our personal uniqueness, the uniqueness of the time and the environment we're born to, and the involvement of untold numbers of people around the world.

This morning, I think mission is personal, a task or assignment I'm designed for and sent here with, my destiny. Like a snowflake, it's unique, singular, and one of a kind. Vision will include the combining of my unique mission with the missions of others in the world to create the plan to accomplish this vision we share. Purpose will be a choice of who I am and intend to be so that I can accomplish the mission.

In the movie Shakespeare in Love, *Viola says, "I would stay asleep my whole life if I could dream myself into a company of players." I feel the possibility that, in terms of life mission, "a company of players" could be any group that is consciously dedicated to a shared vision.*

Mission, vision, and purpose were coming together for me. I liked the synergy between them and the way they might weave together to form a complete life. At peace for the moment, I wanted space for my understanding to settle in.

I'd spent the whole day in my Caravan corner working it out, and now it was evening. I decided to walk, to allow everything to soak in. Bathed in moonlight, I let go of my research and walked with no particular direction in mind. I could almost feel the pilgrims of Caravan moving across the desert together. I could hear the stories and questions. I could feel the children weaving. Like that first night I arrived in Caravan and with the perpetually grainy voice I'd come to know him by, Kairos's questions moved through my mind. His questions to the children wove themselves into my thoughts on life mission. I could feel the two worlds coming together. I missed my new friends in Caravan and felt myself walking there. I wanted their views of my thoughts. This was the work of Caravan, my new assignment.

I intended to sleep after my walk. I didn't remember the walk at all, much less going to bed. One minute I was walking in the moonlight reflecting on my research concerning *mission*, *purpose*, and *vision*, and the next I found myself walking among the tents of Caravan again. The tents were much the same, and people moved as if their placement were still in progress.

"Welcome to Caravan. What have you remembered?" Verity was sitting on a stack of blankets that created a temporary chair, watching Caravan settle in. Her face seemed lighter; her long elegant features seemed almost those of an elf queen. I smiled. It fit what seemed unsettling about her. She was queen, universally so, of any nation or continent of the horizontal world, only the elf world is another world. Verity visits. Did she ever live in our world?

Oriental rugs, cooking gear, and sections of tents lay all around her. Even though we sometimes ate and drank in Caravan, it never seemed necessary, and I saw no food or water stacked with the cooking gear. Tea, coffee, and other cultural favorites seemed to appear when they facilitated the work of the campfire. Even though Verity was perhaps just a few inches taller than most pilgrims, she gave the impression of being more. Even then, in the chaos of the camp setup, she was regally calm and as powerful as a full moon.

I wondered if our talk would determine my next campfire.

"Your next campfire will be one you choose," she said.

I hadn't responded to her first question. She responded to the question in my mind that I hadn't voiced. What was she telling me? She guided me with the voiced instructions that said something else not spoken.

"Our talk may influence it," she continued, "and it will be a choice you make consciously this time. I want you to continue weaving through the camp setup until you find your place. It is a kind of dialogue, like the children's weaving. Of course it is different only in the stage of your work here. Remember, if you can attune to the campfire calling now, you may feel your horizontal-world self connected to the work done in that circle."

Not knowing where to file this information, I answered her first question. What did I remember? "I spent the day in the horizontal world looking up definitions and thinking about aspects of mission, vision, and purpose," I told her. "This search came out of the last campfire. I felt a flow and I continued from there. What I remembered first was not to forget my time in Caravan. Then I continued to contemplate our dialogue. Now I'm here again and it feels like I never left."

Verity turned on her blanket to find my eyes. "It is not the first time you remembered when you returned. You notice your fellow pilgrims do not remember Caravan in the horizontal world. What is different in this observation?"

Returning Verity's connection, I looked within for the thread she pointed to. "I was just trying to find my place," I replied. "Unlike the others, I didn't remember time in Caravan before I arrived in Caravan. Then, also unlike the others, when I returned to the horizontal world I remembered Caravan. I now remember both in a linear way that seems natural to the flow of life in the horizontal world. My reverse situation is not remembering any of my time in Caravan before the first call. The whole of those first nights was about figuring it out, finding my rhythm, learning the ropes. Then suddenly it's twilight morning and time to begin my work, which has captured my whole being and remains with me as I move from world to world. Actually, this was the first time I have felt close to real answers, so I can't say it will continue. I think your assignment made the difference."

"Then allow this insight to guide you as you weave your place this morning." Verity's glance embraced twilight morning in Caravan. In a moment, or an eternity, her eyes found every gesture, every word, every intention. As if she were reading the face of a dear, old friend, she smiled in recognition.

Together, she and I watched tents rising from the desert floor. Persian and Turkish rugs, Oriental and European tapestries, and textiles from around the world adorned floors and walls and surrounded campfires. Everything was placed with great love. Laughter born of work repeated mindfully sprang up. As if waiting for a sign now given, Verity nodded almost imperceptibly and rose to her feet. After holding my eyes for a moment, she walked away. I wasn't surprised when she disappeared into the movement of pilgrims.

I felt she'd said just exactly enough to guide me without giving away secrets. Her assignment excited me. She had told me to consider why I was in Caravan, why I was in the horizontal world. Whom do I serve in both worlds? What does this mean to me?

Now I was beginning to enjoy this game. I was uncertain how I felt about the way I found myself in this arrangement and how it seemed to be set up. I was uncertain about my level of choice, and Verity's mystery appearances gave rise to a vague sense of unfair advantage. A part of me felt concern around the edges of my mind, while at the same time I felt inspired to go deeper into the mystery. Her sudden appearances and disappearances annoyed, fascinated, and amused me all at once.

The man with the long eyebrows and deep-set eyes, invisible against the background of Caravan until needed, had answered my first questions. Now he appeared again. Uncannily, though always perfectly, he seemed to be in the area on cue. Was this weaving of Caravan in both worlds a kind of assignment for him? Almost the desert itself at times, he was the color of sand and night. In this twilight morning, he was the color of sand and camel. He could disappear in front of your eyes, though he never gave the impression he was up to anything. In the way that both Verity and Kairos seemed timeless, this man seemed to be without race or nation. He was Everyman. In this Caravan of every race and nation, he was all and none. Like Verity and Kairos, though more subtly, his hair had the silver hint. His robe was earth-colored without the silver threads. He moved in silence across the sand and among the pilgrims. I wondered if anyone ever saw him unless they were meant to.

"You are wondering if you should help someone set up camp," he said, his voice musical, a harmonic counterpart to the hum of Caravan setting up. "That is a good first question. The intention to be of service is a worthy thing. It is a fundamental quality of your life mission. Anything you consider will not be your life mission without this quality. Also, yes, we will share this journey together. The name you will know me by will be Amar Nen Alam Tabari. We will discover together if you are Tabari. Alam is a kind of title, and during our time together you may call me Amar Nen."

"How did you know my question?" I asked.

"It was in your expression," he said, "though it is more the way you move from tent to tent, leaning forward, then back. Just when a collision seems inevitable, you dance with inspiration. Your nature, like your intention, is good, and that means something. Do not worry about setting up for now. Your time will come. Listen to your nature first. Then you will know how to navigate both Caravan and the horizontal world. Listen to the nature, of this twilight morning in Caravan."

Amar Nen began to blend with Caravan again. "Breathe into this dialogue," he told me, "and you will recognize your next appointment. Remember that your intention is to be of service as you breathe into your work here your nature, and the sweetness of this twilight morning."

I relaxed into my breath as I watched him walk away. I watched his robe flowing in a way that blended into the sand and Caravan in a breath or two. He disappeared seamlessly, sand on sand. He had the best qualities of a leader, though I never saw him lead. I wondered if I could follow his movements through Caravan or watch him from above. As I thought this, I got that impression for a moment. Though he hadn't said goodbye, there was always a kindness in his no-nonsense answers to my questions.

I found Caravan peaceful now, even in the random order of the pilgrims setting up. It was like the silence present even in the middle of rush hour on the subway you can experience, in a moment important to the soul. Standing there, I remembered moments of epiphany I'd received while walking with sidewalks full of Chicago commuters, each of us navigating our route through the subways to our homes. Yes, I shared this inner call of the soul with untold numbers of pilgrims. We navigate our commute home.

As I breathed more deeply into my heart, I bathed in the shadowless, ambient, all-pervading twilight of this morning in Caravan. This light was unchanging, day did not come. I felt the usual pleasant crispness of the air on my skin and across my face that I'd come to remember in the horizontal world whenever Caravan called. As I followed my breath, I felt my counterpart self in the horizontal world. I heard his conversations. I saw events overlapping of friends and colleagues over meals in restaurants and across studio drafting tables and computers.

This movement of life in the horizontal world faded into the background as I watched rugs being spread out to create our floor in the desert. Great tent apartments of many rooms bloomed as far as the endless horizon like flowers after rain. What I called our camels, now freed from their work for the moment, created gatherings of their own in scattered packs. The thought that I didn't have a personal camel yet brought a smile to my face.

Everything that had been on the back of a camel was now in orderly if incomprehensible stacks. There were rugs of every nation. I saw rugs with rich earth tones, with highlights of vibrant purples, reds, and blues. Other rugs had muted yellows and greens with reds and blacks. Patterns of squares and circles, patterns of plants and animals, and tapestries illustrating stories from myths and many cultures were stacked everywhere and waiting for their moment of use. Tripods meant to hold cooking pots displayed elaborate design and ornamentation, and others, the sheerest simplicity. Pots were decorated with the symbols of every culture, those known and those yet to be discovered. I saw chests of every size and shape. Stacks as far as the eye could see in every direction gave a kind of warmth and homelike feel to our tent city. It seemed likely that things would stay where they were. Just like this twilight morning in Caravan, they would remain suspended in timeless potential. With unpacking complete, such as it was, I remembered to attune to the campfire that called me.

"It is true that dharma means duty. It also means nature."[9] Savitri, who had emerged from the circle to lead the work during my first campfire, now led this campfire. She now wore an earth-colored robe with a hint of silver in specific places. I wondered if the silver indicated a position in Caravan. I remembered her sharing the poet Saadi's story of the warrior who wouldn't put down his sword and the statesman who wouldn't put down his words. She had asked us then to find what was essential in us, what was so much who we are, that we couldn't walk away from it or put it down. I thought she could now say this essential us is our nature, perhaps our dharma.

Savitri turned, drawing our attention to the fire, which bloomed into multiple colors reflecting the way wood of differing natures will create different colors of flame. The rhythm of the fire foundation, her voice a plainsong accompaniment, she began again. "Our duty arises out of our nature," she said. "It is not imposed upon us. This is duty that arises from the blueprint of our being and essence." Remembering that in Caravan our guides hear our thoughts, I smiled. "It is the nature of seeds to grow according to their destiny," she said. "An acorn will grow into an oak tree, and not a fig tree, a call the acorn is designed to answer. This acorn is sent to serve and is perfect for the environment it is born to. The acorn says yes to the One that sends it. The acorn says yes to the agreement it has to serve all the beings it shares life with in the horizontal world. If it had an agreement with other beings in a different place, it would grow to be a fig, a palm, a cactus, or a redwood.

"We grow in exactly this way in accordance with our nature," she continued. "Our nature holds the blueprint of our duty, our agreement of place and mission in the horizontal world. Dharma is duty arising from our nature. Everything we find in our nature, in our dharma, is inscribed for a specific service and need."

Savitri paused here in what I know now to be that subtle picking up of the question not asked out loud. As she waited for the question, she rested her gaze on the teenage boy I had met walking with Kairos. I'd guessed that he came from South America in the horizontal world, though now I supposed he could be from anywhere. He was quite tall, seemed strong, though very thin, and I thought, archetypically a dancer. He seemed to surprise himself by asking aloud, "And what of karma? How does this play into dharma? Does our assignment come from our success and failure in a previous life?"

She nodded. "Lucio, I could ask each pilgrim around this circle what he thinks. Instead, I ask you to hold this question in your heart for now. You might contemplate what that would mean for you. I ask you to consider karma moving in your life in the horizontal world. One definition of karma tells us that our action creates a seed reply or a cause in motion. The reaction to the action is always in kind. This is the acorn becoming an oak instead of a fig."

She paused again. "You arrive in the horizontal world with an agreement to serve. You agree to serve according to your nature, and duty is created from the destiny you are designed to serve. You say yes or no to this destiny every moment of your life. Every thought, every feeling, every action, every intention leads to your choices, and each choice creates a seed. Each choice moves you in the direction of your mission or away from it. Each choice creates resonance for the next choice and the next seed. You will be accountable for the growth of each seed."

Savitri turned to watch the fire for a moment. Then, as if hearing something land in us, she went on with the lesson. "This is one way you might think of karma. What if for each choice and decision in your life you had a context to choose from? Consider this question as that context. Ask yourself with each decision you make if this will move you closer to your agreement with the One or away from it. Ask yourself where the seeds you create will take you as they grow. What is the chain of events that grows from the possible choices you must choose from? How would life in the horizontal world change if you asked these questions first?"

Circling the campfire, she stopped behind me, and I sensed the web of our choices and decisions. I could almost hear the hum of connections singing toward and away from the metaphorical tree we were meant to grow into. "A great deal of grace moves with us in this process," she said, "and the threads of missed agreements are opportunities for the One to create another call. 'Come, come again,' Rumi says, 'though you have broken your vows a thousand times . . . Ours is not a caravan of despair.'"

Savitri left me to circle the campfire again. She knelt beside the fire and waited for the next question. It came from the Polynesian teenager I had met walking with Kairos. Savitri smiled at her. Already, the seed of Savitri's difference as a Caravan guide had emerged in this girl's appearance. I could see the slightest beginning of silver in her long dark hair and sensed that she might follow Savitri and lead a Caravan circle herself when her time came.

As the girl stood up, the silver traces in her hair sparked light out of proportion to their number. "Could we break to walk with this and come back?" she asked. "I feel many places in my horizontal world life, possible turning points, each a seed of something. I hear a thousand voices calling. Who made those choices? If my horizontal-world self considered any agreement, it was only the obvious one of the moment. My horizontal-world self doesn't remember to ask the question of mission. If she remembers that, she may remember to ask your question."

"Yes, Alika," Savitri answered. "Walk until you are ready to return here. Or if this is all you need from me this morning, go to what is next for you."

As everyone began to walk away, I watched Savitri as she went inward. I thought she would sit in silence for as long as it took for us to return. I felt that Caravan also holds us in its eternal breath, creating the perfect virtual curve, a gentle wind blowing in the direction of our next appointment. I wondered if she had hinted we would "return" to a different campfire when we were done walking with what she shared. Would anyone walk a little and return to this campfire? How many would return to the horizontal world before the next campfire?

It was morning again when I returned to the horizontal world. I was surprised to be back, apparently for an intermission. As I took my time getting ready for the day in the horizontal world, I paused to appreciate the beauty of early morning. It was reassuring to see the sun rising in the sky. It was even more reassuring to see it higher above the horizon after my shower and shave. Verity, Amar Nen, Kairos, and especially Savitri's questions lingered in my mind, figuratively joining me as I sat down for breakfast.

As I weighed what might be my priorities for my day, I also thought about choosing each moment in the context of my mission here in the horizontal world. Still needing to identify my life mission, I asked myself if my to-do list would bring me closer to the manifestation of that mission or take me further away. I thought about what choosing life mission first would mean in this world on a day-to-day basis, on a practical level.

As I thought about Savitri's homework questions and Verity's assignment, I went to my dedicated expedition journal corner. As I surveyed the new pictures and postcards of camels and the desert, I felt like it was a kind of family album surrounding me, as I did my best to integrate my two worlds and anchor the work in some way.

Expedition Journal:

I want to get this down before I forget. It helped bring together all these categories going around in my head. Savitri said, "It is significant that it is called a life mission. I encourage you to think of it as something that relates to your whole life. It is not just your career or a particular project. Your life mission is your spirituality, your family, your community, your service, your creativity . . . everything your heart is called to. Your life mission is everything in your life being in alignment with the reason you are sent. Life mission is something that moves with you in your life. It is synergistic and dances with the changes that life always brings.

CHAPTER 3

$\star_\star^\star$

Life Mission, Spiritual Agreement

IN DEEP CONTEMPLATION OF life mission and my life in the horizontal world, I heard the now familiar calling of Verity's voice. The next thing I was aware of was the sound of camels wanting my attention. It was still twilight morning in Caravan. Camels of every color and purpose surrounded me. Having read about the names given to camels in the Arabian Desert, I remembered their owners gave them names for every period of their life, for each kind of job, and the kind of camel that traveled each terrain. It's said Eskimos have more than two hundred names for snow that describe subtle differences in wetness or weight. Sand, and, it seemed, camels perhaps have an equal number of names in the Arabian Desert.

It seemed to me that Caravan moved in all directions and in no direction. It felt as if Caravan were moving in some direction, yet I could never tell which direction that was. Whatever non-direction it took when it moved again, I was at the edge of it.

As I sat and watched from a kind of outside-looking-in perspective, I began to wonder how an early explorer of the horizontal world would have felt standing just past the known area of a map. His map would have indicated that something was beyond, and perhaps implied that "past this border you are on your own." I felt a bit on my own out there.

How did I fit into this family of pilgrims and this being called Caravan? Was Verity asking me to go beyond the boundary of who I thought I was? I decided the answers to this and other questions on an expanding list would appear when I was ready for them.

It was peaceful at the edge with my new view of the flow. Although I was unable to see others arriving and departing, I could almost feel them. Something told me where they arrived from in the horizontal world. With no felt sense of where they'd go after they arrived, I listened for Verity's voice, thinking she must also be calling them. I almost thought I could hear her for a moment, and then her voice was gone.

I watched countless stars and listened to the calls of pilgrims coming and going from Caravan. I felt the inhalation and exhalation of Caravan as a being. Something in me would stay on the edge forever, I thought, and maybe I could in a place where time doesn't exist. Instead, I walked toward the dynamic heart of Caravan. I dived into the bustle of Caravan's shifting tides of pilgrims moving from campfire to campfire like students between classes on a college campus. Exactly, I thought. It's a life-mission academy for the horizontal world, and I am barely out of orientation.

As I rounded a corner, I could see only three or four faces I remembered from my last campfire. Then I heard a voice that held my attention, and resonated in my heart. Savitri was speaking. "We often call my friend here Bede," she nodded toward him. "For those of you who are new to me, my name in this circle is Savitri." Bede looked right at home, barefoot and without a tie in a well-cut suit. He fit the mold of guide in Caravan, as he had the requisite silver hair and his eyes carried the hint of silver.

Savitri continued, "The journey to becoming human, moving toward human being in the horizontal world, seems a very long road.[10] Each of you receives a task in the horizontal world, and this gift helps you find and keep your way on that long journey. When you remember your life mission, then you have at least found the path. If you can follow your life mission, it will take care of you on the journey to becoming a human being."

Bede joined in. "When I asked my life mission what direction I should take, it moved me every time in the direction of life and Spirit.[11] It saved my life and gave it meaning." He reminded me of an actor who always plays the part of an elder statesman who understands what is happening more than others might. Regardless of his role, this actor carries the archetype of mentor and spiritual guide in his very presence. Bede had this presence. He sat next to Savitri in a way that hinted they were a team. "It is true," he added, "that while the journey is not made easy for us, help is given."

He shared a silent moment with Savitri, then continued. "Life mission actually takes care of us. When you give your intention, attention, and life force to something long enough, it comes alive. You may have heard that when authors work on a book long enough and with enough life force, the world and the characters of their book come to life. They direct what comes next. You can have that kind of relationship with your life mission. If you are willing to give yourself to it, it will take on life and give back to you."

At this point, I asked myself how much life force I'd given to my own life mission. Where might it have whispered guidance to me?

"You are sent with a purpose in this life," Bede continued. "It is not so much that your Creator needs you to perform, build, change, save, connect, stop, or end something, because you are the only one who could do that. It is more about your opportunity to do what is asked, for what doing it creates in you. The journey of holding the intention to become the vision of what is possible for your life, of living the question of why you are in the horizontal world, will in itself transform you."

Savitri and Bede leaned back so we could breathe this in. Surveying the circle as I digested what they'd said, I noticed that Lucio and Alika were in the circle, though not together. Kairos had said that first night that they had found me and that was enough. Now we were also finding our way to Savitri's circle together. In the all-pervading ambient light of this endless twilight morning, we were now silent around the campfire. We smiled at each other. I thought there might be a hint that Caravan and a mutual life mission were taking care of us.

Bede stood up then and walked slowly around the circle, stopping to connect with his foot the interweaving floral patterns of one rug to the geometric pattern of another, and again to the men riding horses on another rug. Then he began speaking again. "When the psychologist Viktor Frankl looked at the survivors of the death camps of World War II, he found a sense that their life had purpose made the most difference to their survival." He paused. "Could this sense of meaning save you?

Isn't this what we all cry for? Isn't this what the angry person in the street cries for when he or she turns to violence? What if we all thought the discovery of our life mission were the most important thing we could do, and the most natural?" He looked at Savitri, and they turned and looked at me as he continued. "What if our life mission were Spirit's way of helping us to become human beings?"

The chorus of the fire's flame gave me the impression of a distant wind rising, though Caravan itself was still. I felt a subtle impression of distant thunder, just barely audible hours before a storm. I felt it calling me. Bede brought me back. "In order to be fully who you are meant to be, you will have to answer to what you are designed to express. In order to fully express your gifts and abilities, you must prepare to embody this design."[12] He looked around the circle again. "You were not given all you were given, each in such a unique way, to watch someone else do the thing your heart calls you to. Because you were perfectly designed for your life mission, no one else can do it in the way meant for you. In the end, if you do not do it, it may be left undone."

Like complements on a wheel, Savitri and Bede now moved around the circle. "Living your life mission," Savitri said, "is a way of living your life that requires the very best of you. It brings out your best qualities. In the Sufi tradition, there is a practice of remembering the Ninety-Nine Names of God. In this practice, the focus on these names of God asks that you hold the qualities of God in your conscious attention. As you hold these qualities in your awareness, consciously and over time, the qualities of God are naturally assimilated in your very makeup. In a sense, you become these qualities. They become part of you."

I felt something building across the fire as Savitri continued. "You live your life mission for what it changes in you. Living it is the process designed to create your highest possibility. It is, in fact, the only way you can achieve this highest possibility. As Rumi wrote in one of his poems, 'It is as if you have done a thousand other things and not the thing you were sent to do.' Only the one thing you were sent to do will create this highest possibility."

Looking out at the endless horizon, then closing her eyes, she continued. "If we choose not to take that path, we pass on God's greatest gift to find Her. She is holding Her hand out to us, and sending a messenger to point the way. The message is our life mission. In the end, this path will require everything we have. That is the good news. If we can give everything of ourselves, then just maybe all that will be left in us will be Her."

It was as if we had been collectively holding our breath, and now we slowly let it out. Some of us stared at the fire, and some looked across the circle without focusing. I couldn't help watching Savitri and Bede. I could hear pilgrims moving in Caravan as if it were time to move on to the next "campfire class." I didn't think anyone in our circle was ready to move.

Bede traced another pattern with his feet on each side of the circle. I wondered if this was instruction for another part of us. Then he spoke. "Life mission is the opportunity to remember the part of us that touches greatness. Answering the call of our life mission is the chance to meet the very best part of us. If we can hold on to our intention to answer that call, we may find that part of ourselves that can only be found down the narrow road."

He continued, "We move in the horizontal world for such a short time, and it is so easy to forget our possible greatness. It is easy when life happens to forget how much in us could be passed over. What happens in moments of greatness that overrides our smallness? If we live in the horizontal world for a purpose, then those moments could be waiting for us around the corner or the next bend in the road.

"Like a cork floating in a river, when we default on destiny, we go where the river takes us. Not choosing is still a choice. We are sent to our life mission and destiny. It is meant for us, and will not happen automatically. We must choose."

By now, Savitri was standing next to me, and Bede was directly across the circle from me. The fire was between us. Something about Savitri's standing next to me held a line of intention through the fire to what Bede said. This would happen often in the circle due to the physical nature of the setup. I hadn't noticed it before, and now I wondered what that line could mean. One thing it meant was that one of them was facing us at all times. Perhaps it meant we couldn't pretend we weren't seeing the call to our life mission.

I watched reflections of the flames moving across Bede's clean-shaven face. Then I found myself watching the woman next to him. I felt that her horizontal world life might be very different than mine. The stylized elephants on her dress suggested Africa, or at least an African heritage she honored with her clothing. Her eyes were full of life and her beautiful dark face was full of spirit, yet I felt a great sadness surrounding her and her life in the horizontal world. I guessed her to be in her mid- to late forties in the horizontal world, and although I thought she probably did well enough financially, I felt a hard edge in her life.

It didn't surprise me when she spoke up. "It would be nice at turning points in the horizontal world," she said, "if someone would come to me with a sign from Spirit. It would be so nice to have that kind of certainty about destiny and not just live in the tides of fate. I would like to know that I'm heading toward my life mission, even if it's painful in that moment.

"It would be comforting to know what's expected of me,"[13] she continued. "My heart seems as confused as my head around this question, and this is not only uncomfortable, it's not comforting." She stopped and looked at each of us before continuing. "There's no peace in my heart," she said. "There's been no peace for years now. It tears me apart, for sure. It's killing something in me. Is that actually the idea? Is everything taken from us so we'll surrender? If I don't surrender, am I passing up my opportunity to die to who I think I am?"

Bede touched her shoulder for a moment. That was a kind of comfort, I thought. Then he began to circle. "It is true," he said, "that it is difficult to know if you have made any difference in the world. You may never know. You have to live with that possibility and still ask yourself how your best instincts, feelings, rational mind and connection to spirit can guide you. If you do not ask, you can say to yourself that you did not interfere. You will have to face the voice that asks you if *not* asking was just your excuse to not get involved. Doing nothing about what is put in front of you, about what you are called to, is so easy. It sounds justifiable. Doing nothing can be defended in so many ways. We have all heard it said, 'There is nothing to do. It is already done. You are always already the One.' While this is true on a refined level of spirit, at the end of the day, does this excuse quiet your heart? I do not think that those who made that point wanted it to be used as a reason to sit it out.

"If, at the end of the day," he continued, "I followed my heart, mind, soul, spirit, and gut feelings to make the difference I could make from where I was, then it may be that life is not what I thought. It may be that I am misled about what so-and-so needed. I could be way off. All of that may be true, and still I would do what I did again in a heartbeat and feel really great about it, even if life is way out ahead of me. Even if it were way more complex than I can imagine, I would say I was glad to risk it."

Bede fell silent for a moment to allow what he had shared to settle in. "Where do these intuitions and inspirations that call us come from?" he asked. "How do these situations appear in our life? It is a mystery, and we are called to be present with it. We are called to do our best with the mystery of what we are best able to bring to our life. In bringing our best to each moment, remembering the One that sent us is a kind of peace."

Bede now brought his lecture to an end. "Contemplate your call and what it might mean in the horizontal world if you follow your heart in that call. In our limited understanding in the horizontal world, there is a value in even the smallest gesture when our hearts remember. It does make a difference. Remember, the One is always with you. Be at peace."

It had been twilight morning when I arrived in Caravan, and I wasn't surprised to find it was morning when I returned to the horizontal world. It felt good to be able to shower and jump into my work life. Again the two worlds blended as I shared my pilgrimage to my studio with my fellow commuters. My traveling companions on the train could have been anyone in Caravan.

I worked straight through till mid-afternoon, skipping lunch to complete thumbnail sketches for a presentation due in a few days. I was now a regular at a table in the first-floor restaurant in the tower that housed some of the studios I worked in. I ordered a late lunch just to be able to sit and write. I didn't want to go back upstairs to the studio, and by this time I was in a position to call it a day if I wanted to. The sketches I'd done gave us enough direction to proceed and there was more then enough time to put the presentation together. When I wasn't working up in a studio, I usually gravitated to what the servers in the restaurant now called my journal corner.

After a few bites, I pushed the food aside and pulled the journal from my case. I sat there, watching the foot traffic, listening for what Caravan wanted me to remember. Such thoughts had been just outside my awareness while I worked all morning.

What have I learned? What do I remember?

Expedition Journal:

Before getting to work, I heard a story on National Public Radio about how someone's life was affected by the times and places in which he found himself. The true story of Varian Fry was about a journalist who went to France during the occupation by the Nazis to help refugees escape. The commentator said he was an American Schindler.

Like Schindler's, Fry's personality, talents, gifts, and style, perfectly fit the challenge of that moment. Establishing his rescue network became his moment of greatness. In the 13 months that he was in charge of the operation, he was fearless and in his total optimum embodiment. Also like Schindler, he found it difficult to find a similar combination later in his life.

If Fry had lived in a culture that took it for granted that attention to life mission was essential and required ongoing attention, would the rest of his life have been different? If the map for finding an ongoing and continuous relationship with his life mission had been available to Schindler and Fry, would they have continued their journeys and built on the great experiences they'd had so far?

The problem in situations like theirs is that when people find themselves in situations called on by life, they respond. When the crisis is over, they're left trying to figure out what's next. If they weren't sure why and how they got there, or why they responded the way they did, then how will they know where to find the next thread of their life mission?

A second story on NPR was about a man who was an advocate for the arts in our time of declining support for the arts in general. He lobbied Congress and spoke on the radio about the importance of the arts for development of citizenship. He talked about the decline of awareness of history in our country and pointed out that in most cases it was possible to graduate from high school with a single history class.

What made this a life mission story was the moment in a college history class when a painting elicited an epiphany in this man that changed him and occupied him for the rest of his life. Art plus history became the foundation for his work in the world. He championed the arts in the context of history, stressing the importance of this integration for our development as people and citizens.

He said that when we initially encounter a work of art and become engaged with it, if we follow this call, it will take us into its relationship to the time, place, and culture in which it was created. We're drawn into the context of its creation. Then we can return to this work of art with deeper engagement as it changes us and enhances our understanding of ourselves, our world, and our place in it.

For one's life mission, the point is the moment of epiphany.[14] *Does every human being have moments of epiphany in his or her life? Is it possible to look back years later and identify this moment of epiphany?*

These two stories have me thinking about life mission and our place in our moment in history. Life mission and the moment in history come together in both of these stories. Each is about this intersection. There is a constant intersection which our life mission is meant to steer us through. Perhaps when such moments of great decision come, what we learn in the stories is that guidance comes to help us see our way.

Now I feel that the work in Caravan takes on a new level of importance. Work done in Caravan becomes fundamental to life in the horizontal world. I feel new respect for the work done in Caravan. I begin to see why Caravan travels with us, working with us and helping us remember why we've been sent.

Three women from the studio I worked at that day joined me for a mid-afternoon coffee break. I put my journal down and started picking at my food again as they resumed an earlier conversation they'd had as though I'd been in on it. One of the women, twenty-something and newly married, turned to me. "We're talking family," she said, "and making it in design and advertising. I want that success and a meaningful career. Now I'm wondering how my desire for family would be interpreted."

One of her friends neatly folded her jacket and stacked it on top of her briefcase and portfolio on a chair she stole from the next table. Then she said, "I already feel a 'less than' status given to women who choose to sacrifice career for children. The official line is that if I'm determined to go for the dream and still try to carry both work and children, my career will lose its momentum."

The third woman pulled her chair forward. "A study about gender issues of career and children found women are mostly ambivalent about career," she said. "It reported we feel betrayed by biology. I often feel that way myself." She waved toward the corner where the servers were taking their break and added, "It said a woman's dream might be sidetracked by the very idea a woman may someday have children. So why train her or give her too much responsibility?" One of the servers walked up. The woman looked at her and said, "I'll have . . ."

While they were ordering, I watched the stream of workers going on their ways to their next appointments. Then I turned back to my three friends. This was the tip of the iceberg, I thought, and I dearly wanted to ask them if they remembered Caravan. I imagined that somewhere in Caravan, some part of each of them had shared this concern about women and careers around a campfire. I wondered if I might be able to find them in Caravan if I held the intention to do so. I wanted to introduce them to Verity and Savitri, that is, if they didn't already know and work with them. Not everyone in Caravan does. And this reminded me of my thoughts about the two stories on NPR. With questions of tools and process coming up again so soon, I couldn't help but look around the restaurant for Verity. What if I could help these three women? Was their concern a deeper question than either career or children? Perhaps both career and children were life missions for them. It doesn't have to be one or the other. How can we know?

I jumped into the conversation. "You all know who the mythologist Joseph Campbell is, right?" They nodded. "When Campbell wrote about this question of the role of women and the issue of career, he wrote first that it was a matter of fulfillment, not achievement. He wrote that the decision of whether or not to go for a particular goal is often a question of achievement we hold out to ourselves as some great touchstone. In the end, unless it's the answer to a need of our soul to express itself in some way, it won't bring us what we hope for. The question of what is important to 'go for' will in the end be most fulfilling if we instead ask, 'Why am I here?'"

Turning to each woman in turn, I said, "Campbell was teaching at a women's college at the time, so I imagine the question came up often. He wrote that it's not a question of a masculine or feminine approach to life. To first ask what is our life mission gives a foundation to the question of how to live where you find yourself."

The server arrived with the coffee pot, so I held my cup out for a refill and continued. "I believe Campbell said the question of family would be better left till after the question of what we're here for is answered. It was a question of life work, not career. If you can find your work in the world, the question of career and family would answer itself."

The first woman laughed. "I'll have to think about that one," she said. "It sounded good as you said it. Work in the world, then career and/or family as a distinction is a little fuzzy."

I thought about that for a moment. "Perhaps the work in the world question, or why we're here, creates space for the rest to unfold," I said. "Your work in the world, or life mission, might be to have a family. It might be to have an avocation or volunteering or a career. Or all of them. Or something else. He might have been saying that putting the question of your work in the world first creates a container for choosing the rest."

I shared more about my research into life mission. Echoes of Caravan surrounded us as we talked about it. Something was set in motion.

This time, I clearly heard Verity calling me. As Caravan came into focus, she nodded to me. "Come," she said, "come, wanderer, worshiper, lover of leaving . . . come and sit with me." She wrapped her robe in waves around her as she sat down. I felt she was the ocean itself at times, and I could hear it calling as she arranged herself. It was still twilight morning. Now, however, I found coffee, tea, and other drinks brewing on tripods over the fires.

Looking out over Caravan, Verity said, "There is so much in the air now. Do you sense it?"

I breathed in the scent of strong coffees and teas, the scents of their herbal and nutty flavors swirling with copal and frankincense also being burned. The scents of sage and sweet grass mixed with myrrh and prayer.

Verity traced her fingertips along the outline of a silver phoenix in the purple of the rug we sat on as our fellow pilgrims were serving and being served. "Go deeper," she said. "There is more. Breath deeper . . . Include everything."

I did go deeper. I did include more and still more, until the perfume of this twilight morning in Caravan was . . . everything. Verity whispered as if far off and yet right next to my ear, "Yessss."

I didn't notice the circle forming around us. I wondered if these pilgrims had been with us all along. Then Verity leaned in again and whispered, "This is my friend Jun. Listen to him."

It was as if we had arrived at something already in progress. Everyone had their eyes closed as they listened to an Asian man. Jun had what I was coming to expect of the archetypal guides in Caravan. He could have been fifty or fifty thousand years old. Though he didn't look tall, his limbs and fingers seemed especially long. He wore the same earth-colored robes with silver threads as the other guides, his eyes shone with the telltale silver glint, and of course his hair was also silver. Most interesting to me was the dragon cane he ran his fingers over as he spoke, though it seemed unlikely he needed it to walk. The entire cane was a single carved dragon.

Jun pulled a handful of something from his robe and threw it into the fire. A rainbow cloud of smoke and sparks swirled upward, holding enough form for us to follow it skyward. He waited as we watched. I have no idea how long we watched. When he spoke again he seemed to begin again from some place outside of time. "Life mission," he said, "is Spirit immanent in the horizontal world. It is the breath of the One embodied and calling us to rise up. To accomplish what you were truly sent to do, life mission asks you to bring everything to the table and hold nothing back. Life mission means transcending in life and being completely present, saying yes with every breath you take. That is why it brings you in the end to God. It asks everything of you, and in the end it will not by itself be enough. Always, you will be asked to do something just beyond your capability. Such a task is given to remind you that when you give everything, and it is not quite enough, it brings you back to the One that sent you. You need to remember. Life mission is a spiritual agreement."

After a pause, he continued. "Arriving at this moment, you are stripped of all that is between you and the One that sent you. It is your journey that brings you back to your Source. Living the question of 'why' will remind you of your agreement. It is both the source of joy and the foundation of meaning for your life in the horizontal world."

Now he lowered himself until he was sitting on his knees. He traced a golden dragon pattern in a deep red oriental rug for a moment, then looked up. "That you feel your life has meaning is a foundation to life. That this way of living is an inspiration and a joy is also important to the journey. What I want for you is that you feel that your journey or pilgrimage in the horizontal world is the most exciting adventure you can imagine. Living your life mission will have its challenges, of course, and it is possible to experience joy even in difficult times. This is the good news! It is this very challenge in each of its facets that will do the work of transforming you to the highest possibility you are here to become. There is a joy in this work, even though it is hard to measure in horizontal-world terms. You will find joy in ways that will surprise you.

"Your work is to transform within," he said, "to prepare the container for the Beloved. The days when you bring yourself back are the days when you face your fears and doubts and the depths of your shadow. Everything that keeps you from your brilliance will be there in front of you. Every time you bring yourself back to your agreement with the One, that is the moment when something really happens."

Jun leaned back on his heels. "The horizontal world beckons, shiny possibilities calling simultaneously from every direction. Life mission is a narrowing. Life mission will call you to make the tough choices. It will always test you. It will make you choose, and it will ask this every single day. The deciding factor in whether or not you will manifest your life mission is your ability to choose every day. A life mission is never decided by a single decision. Even the big, seemingly crucial, decisions are based on the thousand small decisions that lead up to it."

He stood up and raised the dragon cane into the air. "I invite you to do this consciously," he said. "I invite you to bring everything to your life mission every single day. Bring all your imagination. Bring all of your creativity. Bring all of your so-called faults and turn them into gold. Bring your fears and use them. Bring everything you have ever been or known or experienced. Bring it all to your life. Bring it strong and bring it every single day of the rest of your life in the horizontal world.

"All of what some in the horizontal world call the 'unfairness' of life," he went on, "the disappointments, the abuses, the betrayals, and the endless list will create either bitterness or beauty in you. Beauty is what it is all for. Your life mission is your opportunity to transform bitterness into beauty."

Jun now began to circle us as he spoke, looking briefly into the eyes of each of us. "Your life mission is the great story of your life. It is the story you tell yourself. It determines the life you will live. This is your chance to live the high story.

"Your life mission is a trust given to you by Spirit.[15] It is a steward-ship. If you take care of it, is will take care of you. Empires rise around a trust given by the One only to crumble when they are abandoned in moments by moments of accumulated forgetting. You are carried by this trust. You are protected in many ways, from events you may never know consciously.

"There is a greatness you are meant to be part of. This is a quality that surrounds a human being. It is the presence of the One visiting the moment. A moment like this can go unnoticed in its elegance. It is the seed that moves a hard heart. It is a long, very slow, very gentle rain that remembers and falls long enough to bring life to the absolute desert."

Jun stopped in front of me. He looked for a moment at Verity, still sitting next to me, then looked directly into my eyes. "When you return to the horizontal world," he said, "remember that your life mission is a sacred trust and spiritual practice. Your work this twilight morning in

Caravan and for eternity is always this. Remember as you work with your campfire. Remember as you move through your days in the horizontal world. Each moment is the opportunity to embody your greatness. Each moment is a container of Divine intent, an opportunity for the One to touch your world, to breathe eternity into a moment."

I looked into Jun's eyes as he spoke. Then he went silent, and I returned to the deep inner listening. I could hear Verity calling in my head and heart. "Go deeper . . . include everything . . ."

CHAPTER 4

⋆⋆⋆

Committing to the Process
of Life Mission

WHEN I OPENED MY eyes, Verity, Jun, and his campfire circle were
gone. Jun's words floated at the edge of my mind: *Life mission as "sacred
trust and spiritual practice."* Now in another location in the vastness of
Caravan, I was surrounded by the tent city. I decided to wander and
wait for Caravan to signal the next move.

As I walked I allowed a stream of questions to float in my mind.
What did it mean? Verity called me, then immediately we called Jun's
circle to us. By going within, I now found myself in another location in
Caravan. Had I missed something? What should I notice now?

I noticed it was quieter than usual. Caravan's pilgrims seemed
more reflective this twilight dawn. In my mind I watched Caravan from
above. What the horizontal world considered to be normal everyday
activities seemed out of place to me here in Caravan. Pots for hot drinks
of endless persuasions steamed away. The aroma of familiar favorites
reminded me of holidays in the horizontal world. Camel handlers were
going through their timeless routines, as if the camels actually needed
to eat here. People were moving bundles around the campsite in that
abstract way we do things when we do them as a way of thinking. Men
and women were mending gear or materials, as if this was needed.
When something is needed in Caravan, it's simply there, including tent
sections that did not need to be mended and the beautiful kilim rugs,
and blankets of every persuasion. Even the weaving in and out of the

children had a contemplative quality, slow, steady, and tentative. Campfires were smaller and seemed to have a personal or family quality.

Everywhere smaller groups gathered if a group formed at all. People did individual tasks. Not since the long, quiet walks of night had it been this silent in Caravan. It would be a morning to watch the dawn if morning ever arrived in Caravan, with a rising sun to turn toward. I didn't notice tension in the air. No questions were asked. This morning hinted it was a time to go within.

After the way I entered Caravan, I welcomed this inward time. I'd spent many quiet moments in the horizontal world lately, sorting through what I knew of the work of Caravan and doing research for my assignment. Verity's assignment, to ask why I traveled in each world, who I served, and what this meant to me, stayed with me. Quiet time in Caravan had a different quality. It might arise from the untold number of beings quietly traveling with me and engaged in the same inward dialogue. It reminded me of our connection. I was struck by the timing. In Caravan, there was community work that we did together. When it was time to go within, as far as I could tell, we collectively went within. We did this work with a kind of shared connection.

I wondered if something had happened in the horizontal world to call for this collective inward movement. Was something about to happen? Were we collectively at a turning point we measured within ourselves? Did something wait for a collective choice? Each of Caravan's guides I'd known said, in their unique ways, that the connection to the horizontal world was fundamental to Caravan's purpose. In the short time I'd spent in Caravan, I'd discovered the connection to the horizontal world at every turn.

Individually and as whole cultures we worked through how we would meet in the horizontal world. Around the campfires, moving in the night or thinking it over on quiet mornings like this one in Caravan, we sorted out what we were discussing. We were told that everything in our work was connected to the mission and purpose for our lives in the horizontal world and to everything that happened in Caravan. Understanding this connection led me to feel that as everyone in Caravan moved inward, something in the horizontal world collectively held its breath.

And this feeling led me to wonder why I so often had the impression of arriving just after something had happened. Was this true for each of my fellow pilgrims? Did this prevent me from imagining I could plan or control my experience in Caravan? Did every experience in Caravan come about as the result of Caravan's response to our needs in both worlds?

I found myself winding my way toward an edge of Caravan, searching for something on the endless horizon. Standing on the edge felt perfect in that moment. The endless silent horizon matched the space within. For a time without time, I watched the unbroken horizon of the ever-twilight morning, endless unfolding space only occasionally broken by an event. A pilgrim might move into my peripheral vision, then back into the fold of Caravan.

Looking outward, I listened inwardly to memories of pilgrims sharing their stories. It was like a movie montage flashing across the screen of my mind. I reviewed every moment I'd spent in Caravan and every moment of my life in the horizontal world. I imagined the life review at the end of my life would be very similar. I didn't feel this as any kind of judgment. That someday I might view this as a kind of judgment did not escape me. Now it felt more a way of making space for what I might do about it. How many times in our lives do we wait until someone tells us we have a month or six to straighten out our affairs? How many times do we arrive at this point in Caravan, where we have a chance to change our lives in the horizontal world before the pronouncement, before the dramatic event?

For the first time I discovered I had an expedition journal in Caravan.[16] It had the same illustration on the cover as my journal in the horizontal world, though the pages of explorers were blank. The names and stories were not yet filled in. It felt perfect this morning in Caravan. I looked around for Verity. "When something shifts, she shows up."

This time when I found her, she looked freeze-framed, for only a moment. She waited just long enough for me to see her, then turned and disappeared into our tent city. I whispered, "Thank you," as Caravan reclaimed her, convinced she heard me.

I stopped for a moment, and a woman clothed in deep blue handed me a cup of the strong coffee of the desert. I said thank you and moved to a place on the sand next to her tent. I noticed that Caravan's pilgrims took personal space. I enjoyed her coffee and again entered into the inner world of the expedition journal of Caravan.

Great inventors, visual and performing artists, scientists, detectives, and those whose vocations or avocations involved creativity often carried notebooks. Entries in my journal were quick summaries, as I was hoping to get the gist of things while I could. The unexpected timing of movement in Caravan created a tentativeness, a vulnerability around my Caravan journal. How long would I have this journal? Would it show up with me every time I arrived in Caravan? Where would it be when I was in the horizontal world?

After writing in my journal, I felt called to return to the flow of Caravan. As I stood up, the lady in blue appeared next to me as silently as a summer breeze parting the curtains. I handed her my empty cup, and she reached for my journal. Experience in Caravan demonstrated thus far that when something was needed it appeared, so it seemed natural enough to hand it over to her. She turned without a word, and I bowed, wondering if she heard the thank you in my thoughts.

I returned to threading the edge of Caravan, holding memories both simultaneous and layered. What Jun had said earlier moved deeper into my heart. I thought about life mission as trust, vow, and spiritual practice. I thought about my life in the horizontal world and the tests of life mission. I felt the weight of the life force necessary to show up every day to my intention to live my life mission.

I sensed the draw to my company of players.[17] In the movie *Shakespeare in Love*, Viola says, "I could spend my whole life dreaming if I could spend it in the company of players." I love that line. My company of players weren't who I thought they would be at this point in my life. I told myself I would figure that out. I committed to giving myself the time to discover what was next for me. I just didn't have a sense of what to do with the rest of my life. What I did know was that I couldn't continue that life. The all-night jobs, and the pointless assignments for clients I wouldn't choose to give my life force to under other circumstances, were costing me in ways beyond health.

The sound of sand crunching under foot broke the silence surrounding me, as I left Caravan's edge. Walking back through Caravan, I noticed people talking again. The atmosphere was calm and casual, and yet I felt the work of Caravan in the air. The questions of the campfire threaded though every conversation. I knew so little and had so much to learn about Caravan's work. Verity's assignment, the questions of life mission, who this mission served and what it meant to me—all these questions moved together in the same direction, and I could start with that. I felt lighter and at home in this, and allowed my destiny to draw me to the conversation with clues to the quest.

The bearded face of Kairos greeted me as I rounded the corner of a tent that drew me. Running his hands along the surface, leaning in, he created, then transformed images as he touched the tent's surface. The tent's surface displayed complex, many-colored symbols that felt to me like designs or spiritual logos. My days in advertising colored my perception. Thinking about it, the idea of spiritual logos didn't seem so far-fetched. Actually, the symbols of each of the traditions in the horizontal world were kinds of logos. They wouldn't call them that, even if they did serve in a similar way.

"How do these symbols function for you?" Kairos asked. "What ideas do they hold for you? If your life mission is spiritual practice, and the symbol of a tradition is a container or logo of that tradition, what is your logo? What is the logo of your tradition? What idea does it hold?"

I thought about this and could have said many things close to expressing the idea. I felt many things no words would describe. The symbol better carried the ideas I had no words for.

Kairos continued. "As you attune to the symbol of your spiritual tradition, it may help to use your experience as a graphic artist to consider the logo of your life mission.[18] When you consider the relationship of your agreement with the One that sent you, spirit and life mission may come together in the form of symbol before the words come to you. What qualities will your logo represent?"

With my eyes I traced the patterns and symbols on the tent as I thought about the exercise he'd given me. Kairos sat among rugs scattered around him and pointed to a place for me. Now he silently ran his hand over many of the patterns intersecting as the rugs crossed over each other. I thought about the night I had first met him, when he had directed the weaving of the children. This had brought Lucio and Alika to me. What did it mean that Kairos seemed to guide all three of us? Where were the three of us going to wind up, and would our traveling involve all three of us together? Watching the patterns of the rugs and the symbols woven into them, and patterns on them overlaying each other, I thought he was showing me a weave of a different kind. I wondered what additional weave he would direct me to.

Kairos stopped tracing patterns for a moment to look at me. "The power of ideas in the horizontal world moves the tide of nations," he said. "Each individual is designed to embody a quality and an idea in a way that is unique to them. Each country is called to embody qualities and ideas unique to them. You may have heard it said that America is an idea as Rome was an idea. As you consider their separate missions and question the degree to which they were accomplished, consider what this means in your time. Consider what this means to you.

"What idea would you give your life for?"[19] he asked me. "Some of your holidays are to honor those who gave their lives for the idea your country embodies. Do you know what means enough to you to give your life for it? What is the highest story you can imagine? What is the most extraordinary life this highest quality and idea can create for you?"

Kairos paused and ran both hands over the patterns of different rugs, giving me time to follow the connections, then continued. "Your life mission grows out of the central idea of your life, which makes beauty and truth in a recurring wave. What is this recurring theme of your life? In your world, chaos theory calls these patterns, which are endlessly recurring although never exactly the same, fractals. What is the fractal flowering pattern of your life? The perfume of the theme of your life can be found in these fractal trails, like tracks in the snow. These flowering fractal patterns call you to make your life the most you can imagine, and more. This call is the possibility to be exactly what you hope you can be in your best moments. You are capable of great love and great deeds."

As I listened to him, I remembered the day I noticed one of the veins on my arm had become an inflamed red line. It snaked up my arm in small but inevitable increments. A spider had bitten me earlier in the day and I hadn't thought much of it at the time. Then as I watched the red inching up my arm, a friend who worked in the medical field told me if it reached my heart I would die. Standing outside the emergency room afterwards, I thought about what was important in those moments when death seemed a real possibility. What I cared about in those moments is what I still cared about as I sat with Kairos.

I had something real to do, and though some part of me wanted to rebel, that something was always there. Real to me outside that emergency room and with Kairos, that something the heart of hearts knows and calls to, that transcends who I think I am, what I think I know, and especially what I fear. Longing and a sense of calling had tugged at me, and because I could never definitively describe to myself what that meant, I had applied myself to the goal of never doing a job I hated. I hadn't known what I would do, but I'd promised myself that what I did would always be creative and that I wouldn't sell my freedom. Art and music seemed to fit, and something more called. Talking to Kairos now, several years later, as a student in Caravan, what had been important after my visit to the emergency room was still important to me.

Kairos stood up and reached to help me up. As he stepped over the rugs, he said, "Come," and we navigated through the tents and pilgrims of Caravan. I followed the stories of the changing cultures illustrated on tents and by the people as we moved among them. Pots decorated with sterling silver and jewelry made of wood and various metals displayed the trademark signs of their cultures. Blood reds and indigo blues, contrasting with subtle hues of earth and plant colors, embodied their culture's symbols. Drums, flutes, guitars, veenas, and harmoniums accompanying chants from every tradition filled the air. Even in the midst of all the life of Caravan, silence reigned inside me.

Then, without glancing back, Kairos asked me, "Do you know when your inner beings are on the move?[20] Who is it that rebels when you are inspired and say *yes* to something? When you commit and believe, do you watch for the part of you that says *no*? In the horizontal world, there is a force within you that tests you to be sure you mean it. There is another force within that tests if it can stop you. One of these forces wants you to push past its resistance. The other only wants to stop you. It is important to notice where and when these two forces show themselves in your life.

"What can be frightening about life mission," he continued, "is what people think will be asked of them, what changes they will have to make in their lives. Your expression is 'If you always do what you have always done, you will always be what you have always been.' So, yes, you will have to change your life. Others in your life may find this change uncomfortable. There is no way around this."

I followed Kairos as he surveyed the horizon of Caravan's tent city. Inwardly, I saw many of the horizontal world cities I had lived and traveled through, sensed in the vastness of the silent space this created.

While still surveying Caravan, he continued. "If you have a sense you have something real to do, and the world is counting on you, past the times when it seems like pressure, the feeling that it matters may keep you going. That may be the only thing that will keep you going or make any sense to you. It can be a scary world. It can seem like everyone is really kind of off out there, and what's the point after all. Then, in a moment, you see you make a difference to someone. And everything shifts.

"Viktor Frankl wrote that courage is directly proportional to our sense of meaning. If our sense of meaning is larger than our sense of self, then do we not automatically reach for a larger vision? If it is true that we can *imagine* it, then we have the ability to *do* it, then it only makes sense that we reach higher if we dream higher. If our sense of meaning is larger, then our courage will also be larger."

When I returned to the horizontal world, the intensity of my travel in Caravan remained with me. When I thought about the life I had been living before Verity called me to Caravan, it was like recalling a past life. I felt as if I were a million years old as I reached for my journal, feeling both worlds as I ran my fingers over the camels in the picture, questioning which journal was more real. I felt the paradox of my life and the rising tide of both, the possible deeper meaning, and the growing list of unresolved questions.

Expedition Journal:

The sculptor Henry Moore said, "The secret to life is to have a task, something you bring everything to. And the most important thing is that this task must be something you can't possibly do." Isn't this precisely what I've felt the absence of, what I'm looking for now?

There's a scene from a movie that's stayed with me. At the end of the movie, The Replacements, *the coach talks about the fact that the strike is over, hence it's over for the replacement players as well. What's important, however, is that they've been part of something great.* [21] *He says that once you've been part of something great, even for a moment, that stays with you for the rest of your life. What is the something great I would choose to be part of?*

There's a story that when you go to heaven, there's someone you'll meet who wasn't talked about much in your family. [22] *That person is the person you were meant to become. How would it feel to become that person now, while I'm still living? How would it feel to become the person I've always felt in my heart I was called to be? What would that mean in my life?*

"For the Love of the Game." I used to hear that phrase in reference to Michael Jordan. I thought he represented something that was important for me to understand. Can we really do our life mission without on some level being in touch with this "love of the game"?

When I think about why I'm here and how I would bring this love of the game to my work in the world, the love of the game begins to breathe in me. [23] *I've felt that missing for longer than I can remember. Maybe it's always been missing. I long for the passion and joy that the "love of the game" symbolizes to me. I want it to radiate and inform my way in both worlds. The being of my life mission deserves this. We all deserve to have this love of the game in our life.*

It was time for me to remember what to do with my life. I was burned out with its pace. I'd enjoyed my work in the studio to begin with, yet I never thought I'd stick with it. How did it happen that I was still there? Maybe the studio work was something to get me to the next place. It was a challenge, and I enjoyed being challenged. It was creative, and I enjoyed that. I enjoyed the completion of a project and seeing it in print. Graphic design and illustration had been a way to get out of the music business and make a decent wage. It had a lot going for it, yet I knew it wasn't what I wanted to do with the rest of my life. Recently I'd transitioned more to illustration and had moments when I thought I could do that long-term. Illustration felt more in keeping with what I'd felt drawn to when I majored in art in college. Just as I'd had to leave the music business, the feeling I needed to leave design and illustration nipped around the edges of my awareness. That brought me to this juncture in my life.

I thought about taking a sabbatical from my work to sort it all out, and as far as the studio was concerned, it wasn't a good time to take off. It was difficult to care about this. At the same time, the thought of my studio partner's growing impatience gave me pause. I didn't want to rely solely on Caravan. Still, if I wasn't also supposed to do Caravan's work in the horizontal world, why did I remember it in the horizontal world?

I decided to work on Verity's assignment in both worlds.

I did a round of the bookstores, new and used, then sat down to read. I bought a few days from my partner with promises to make it up to her, and created a mini-sabbatical. She wasn't pleased, yet I needed that time off. The expedition journal became my constant companion, carrying it from room to room, ready for any insight. I held it even as I read, shifting it back and forth to write, then read and write again.

Expedition Journal:

Reflecting on Verity's assignment, and the possibility of a real sabbatical, I'm thinking about what we call work, and the ideas of vocation and avocation. I can sense the many ways we work out what has meaning to us in the world in the sense of vocation or calling and jobs. It isn't just that we spend so much of our life working, though that would be part of it.

Work is many things to many people. It's where we experiment with who we think we are. It's where we test ourselves. It's hell for some of us, something to get through. For others, it's where life is good. It can be where we make a difference and see goodness manifesting in the world.

For some of us, our work is where the creativity within us can be served. We can find challenge after challenge and, meeting those challenges, move to the next test of our ability, finding a creative answer to the question at hand. For some of us, work is a way of testing ourselves against the world or a group of people, in order to come out on top. For others, it's a way of pitting ourselves against nature.

The Sufi Master Pir Vilayat Inayat Khan wrote that what we take with us when we leave this world will be the "quintessence of our experience." [24] If we've been a carpenter all of our lives, what we take with us will not so much be the knowledge of how to build a cabinet as our knowledge of the essential nature of creating form. I wonder what the subtle differences might be for each of the visual and performing arts. Form is created in all the visual arts. The form of the performing arts can be transitory, and still would be the experience of creating form as performance, even if that performance isn't recorded. The quintessence of the experience I'm called to suggests a place to look for clues to my life mission. What does the quintessence of what I've done so far tell me? The quintessence of what I'm called to do is something I look forward to finding.

If we say then that our life mission is our agreement with the One, then that agreement may be returning the quintessence of our particular life mission experience, as part of that agreement. If we say that we do our life for what it creates in us, could we say we do it to create that quintessence in us?

We're told we travel for eternity in Caravan. We adjust as many times and as often as we need to. This leads me to believe that living my life mission is a process, not the end product. Life mission is a journey, and preparing the container for Spirit. It's not so important that the big dream becomes a reality in this world. It's important that we're about the business of moving toward that vision or mission. If it's for what it'll change, transform and create, then life mission's goal is to be a vehicle, not a destination. Quantum physics would say the end is present even in the beginning, calling us like a great attractor. It's the journey.

When we row to the other side of the river, we're meant to get out of the canoe and leave it on the riverbank. When I get to the end of this journey called my life mission, I'll need to leave the vehicle on the side of the road and move on. What's important is that I use the vehicle of my life mission to transform the container for spirit. When Spirit comes in the end, I'll be able to hold this knowing as I move on.

Jonah's story reminds us of how often we can feel unqualified for our life mission. Jonah didn't believe he could do what God called him to do, so he ran away. Like him, we think there must be some mistake, that we aren't enough. Even after his experience in the belly of the whale, grace brought him to the fulfillment of his life mission. How much added grief and sidetracks could we save ourselves if we believed we could do what we were called to do?

I'm writing this down here so I can process it next time I sit around the campfire with Savitri. I believe her teaching partner Bede gave this lesson:

"When I think about life mission and the basic goodness of people, I wonder how anyone could be doing their life mission and not be in a space of gratitude and kindness. Life mission brings out the goodness of life. Life mission keeps our eyes full of wonder and the beauty of life. If I think of all the times I looked around in the middle of my life in the horizontal world, in the midst of doing work I loved, I always feel enormously blessed. Doing the work we love always blesses us with the gifts we give. I can see the very thing we give is the gift that life mission returns to us.

"It may be that the gift of a life mission is that it's the closest we can get in this life to seeing the face of God. I see the face of the One every time I make a decision to listen to the call. When I see someone answer the call, I look up and I smile and I say thank you for the privilege of witnessing it. I feel that humanity has a chance, after all. I see a great deal of that. Maybe that is one of the greatest gifts of doing one's life mission. I see such longing in people. I see such heart in people and the pain of wanting to do more. I hear such longing to make a difference in life.

"It is good to see that in people. It is so easy to come to think people don't care. It feels so good to experience someone willing to make great sacrifices to make the world a better place."

As I do Caravan's life mission work, I see more of what Bede meant. It isn't that I didn't see it before. Now when I'm present to what Bede was pointing to, when I notice this in my day, it stands out more and stays with me. It does give me hope.

I remember Savitri saying that when the general tone is confused and down, "One of the journeys to life mission is the road down and through chaos." That makes sense. Robert Bly wrote, "We must go down before we can go up. If we want to ascend, we cannot escape the ashes work. The underworld cannot be by-passed."

Savitri also said, "Our life mission may be born from our wounds."[25] This certainly seems to be true for many people. It may be true even when it doesn't seem to be true in the moment, when we're in an "ashes place." Sometimes when we find the inspiration for our life mission, we find it in the wounds of our past.

Savitri also said, "Down and through the wounds, the shadow, and the ashes lies a path we have to follow. In that way lies chaos certainly. The promise is there is something in our underworld worth finding. There is our golden shadow and our redemption."

I began to feel hope as I listened to Savitri and Bede. The underworld was always at hand in my musical years. Temptation and distraction accompanied every gain. Why did I want to write and perform music? Who was it in service to? How far would I go and what price was I willing to pay? I wanted to believe there was a reason. And now I look at all the wasted time, the pain, and the confusion I had and caused, so many years disconnected from Spirit, and I wonder what it meant. What could redeem those dead ends, that wasted time?

I wondered how many times I shared these wounds around the campfire in Caravan. I thought Verity must have called me and Kairos must have guided me through all of it. Remembering in both worlds will not excuse me from facing my ashes.

Still as Pir Vilayat wrote, "If life is creative, then we are not simply the effect of our past." We're capable of creating a life mission from the song of our soul that is not the sum of our wounds, even if our life mission is a solution to a wound.

I want to do this ashes work. I want to honor the gift in the underworld and its place. I want to remember I'm not the sum total of my past. Without attempting to deny a part of me, I want to remember the whole. Creativity honors and is present in life and gives us a new choice. Creativity says the result is not always preordained, that something new, unforeseen, and unrelated to the past can emerge.

I remember a woman around Savitri's campfire asking, "Can this idea of life mission survive hard times? Is this an idea that only works in a good economy or for the well-off?"

Savitri answered, "It is tempting to think so. Yet this is only the apparent side effect of your current culture. Having a purpose in life is as old as humankind, as old as the universe itself. It could be argued that the universe itself is purposeful. The One sends us with a purpose and, as you can see, people from all lands and cultures of the horizontal world come to the Caravan of Remembering. This is the work for all of us."

Savitri surveyed every direction of Caravan as she said this. I remember everyone joined her, most of us turning 360 degrees, witnessing the vast expanse of pilgrims doing Caravan work. People and the signs of all humankind were abundant in every direction.

She waited for us, then continued. "When you arrive at the crossroads, or turning point in your life, how do you decide?[26] When it is time to decide if you will say yes to an opportunity . . . to leave or stay with someone or situation . . . to have an operation . . . to give something . . . to take a risk that could change your whole life . . . to allow someone his or her choice—how do you decide? What are your criteria for making such decisions?"

Corporations and life mission

When Savitri said "corporations," we were all surprised. We all turned to her and listened more carefully. She said, "It takes a great will to hold an intention of many years as an individual. Corporations can hold in their charters a written mission that, if necessary, can unfold over many generations. It may even be several people's *jobs to watch over and decide if the company is stewarding properly and is aligned with the vision of its founders.*

"For an individual, however, this is not the case. As an individual, we are likely the only one watching over our vision . . . at least at first and until we find others who are willing to give their lives to our vision. As individuals, we are the ones who will have to decide on a moment-by-moment basis if what we are going to do is in alignment with our purpose and vision."

Savitri on people in our lives and our environment:

She said, "When we look to this vision of our purpose and mission, and who we surround ourselves with, there is a correspondence between them. It makes a difference in the end. It changes the course of our lives. Our mission simply cannot be done without the influence, inspiration, and support of the right people.[27] The question of whether or not we manifest our mission will come down to the environment we create for our life. Who is in that environment with us will be the most important question to ask about that environment.

"It is true that we can always transcend the environment. When you see examples of people who do this, you can ask yourself a couple of questions. Did the challenging environment itself create the motive to succeed in the dream? Did this person or group have to expend exponentially more life force to succeed in spite of it? In either case, the environment has a great influence on the life mission.

"If the environment is that important and the people in that environment are the most important elements in any environment in terms of life mission, then how we approach relationships may be crucial. How would we have to respond to the people in our life for them to help us create the possibility we imagine for our life mission? Who would we have to include in our circle of friends and colleagues? Who will we need to become? Manifesting life mission in this world often comes down to a community that believes in and wants to support your mission."

As I remember that campfire with Savitri, the movie Life as a House comes to mind. What I love about Life as a House is that it *shows how much going for our dream can mean to everyone else. It's never just about us, even when we think it is. It's impossible to really go for our dream alone if we do it for love. We all wait for someone in our life to go for his or her dream with love, for love. I love how the movie shows how people are just waiting for someone to go for it. The main character changes so many people around him. The son, who doesn't want to help with his father's dream to build the house, is pulled in by love. Being pulled in by love is exactly what I'm longing for.*

CHAPTER 5

Life Mission Across Culture and Over Time

"GOOD MORNING. WHAT DO you remember now?"[28]

Verity had taken to asking me this whenever I returned to Caravan. It was almost her way of saying hello. It surprised me a little that it was still twilight-dawn morning in Caravan. The familiar scent of frankincense and myrrh hung in the air. Sage and sweetgrass, along with copal and sandalwood drifted in what I felt was heavenly breath, even though Caravan didn't actually breathe and didn't actually have wind as we know it in the horizontal world. There was an impression of a breeze, however, which I welcomed.

It seemed in that moment that the scent of sacreds burning would imprint forever with my sense of Verity. When I encountered incense burning in the horizontal world during that time, my thoughts turned to Caravan. Moments later however, my thoughts would anchor to Verity. I wondered if the rainbow of sacreds in the air signaled her presence and if in the horizontal world I would always wonder if the scent hinted she was about to call.

In that moment, the signal was the hint of a near smile. I suspected she often listened to my thoughts. The earth colors of Verity's robe reminded me of riverbank browns and tans with the threaded silver carving multicolored yellows and reds into canyon walls. There was almost a whitewater effect to the movement of the silver as Verity flowed with me through Caravan. Verity stopped to look directly into my eyes.

"Even if it seems you are more confused," she said, "you know you are getting close to something. What do you imagine you are close to? It is all right to wonder. It is all right not to know." She looked quietly at me as if to allow a thin strip of something to break gently.

"I wish I could say what I feel close to now," I replied. "I'm grateful for my time here. I'm grateful I can remember in both worlds. Since you gave me your assignment, I've found everyone here seems to be working on this assignment. The only thing different is the rest of Caravan's pilgrims don't appear to remember in the horizontal world. I've been working hard on the question of why I live in either world. I'm still working out what exactly my mission in the horizontal world is. I want to find it. I feel more confident now that I will find it.

"It started with your assignment," I added, "and I want to know for myself now. The dialogue around the campfire always takes me deeper into the question, *do we have a purpose in the horizontal world?* Walking the desert of this world with my family of pilgrims, sitting at the camp-fires, listening to the conversations, everywhere this question is present. Being in Caravan is itself a confirmation that the answer is *yes*. This *yes* feels as eternal as Caravan's movement across this timeless universe. It's only in the horizontal world that we ask if we have a life mission. Now I know this in my in heart of hearts."

Verity seemed pleased, and reading her reactions was a subtle art I'd far from mastered. It was hard to tell. I'd not seen her show obvious emotion, yet I didn't think it out of the realm of possibility.

She answered in a softer voice. "You have taken part in many campfires on the subject of life mission, vision, and purpose. You med-itated on their meanings and you hold the question in your heart as an ongoing priority. You recognize its importance to yourself and the horizontal world. The campfires you find now will move you to another place in this dialogue." With this, she bowed her head ever so slightly and walked into the flow of Caravan. I watched her for the moment when she disappeared. I was sure that if I didn't watch her, she'd disap-pear into thin air.

Scanning the pilgrims in Caravan, I noticed they were dressed differently from each other. A collage of people in period clothing sur-rounded me. I wondered why. This nod to time in the horizontal world piqued my curiosity, and again I felt like I was on a Hollywood movie set. Having a sense of the evolution of fashion in the West, I guessed a span of hundreds of years surrounded me. Floor-length dresses, pants of different lengths, jackets and shirts of different styles displayed a range of periods. I felt uncertainty about the time periods of Eastern clothing. I wondered if they appeared as they were in the moment they left the horizontal world, meaning they were coming from across time into my "now moment" in Caravan? I wondered if they were all coming from our "now moments" in the horizontal world, and the period clothing had to do with something else we would explore collectively.

The possessions and tools people used seemed to be tied to different eras in the horizontal world. It reminded me of an event in the horizontal world called a Rendezvous, where a group of people dedicated to reenacting a specific time in history gather. Meeting for a weekend, sometimes longer, they wear clothes in the styles and fabrics of the period in question and use the appropriate tools. Everything has to be of that period. Nonmembers of the group can visit and learn from a Rendezvous, but they have to leave at the end of the day if they don't have the proper gear and clothes. Seeing what looked like a Rendezvous felt like déjà vu. This would be a super Rendezvous in the horizontal world, with pods of time reenactments of different periods everywhere.

As I walked through the camp, I noticed the difference the time-referenced clothes and gear made to the camp. I found myself surprised I hadn't noticed it before. I knew Caravan was eternal and timeless; traveling in Caravan, it was easy to forget the apparent passage of time in the horizontal world, an artificial marker we set for ourselves.

For a virtual eternity, the question of our purpose in the horizontal world was the operating question of Caravan. My impression was that for thousands of years the injunction was: Remember who you are and why you're in the horizontal world. I wondered if this had to do with what I was seeing.

"What is it?" I asked myself. "What's up this morning?" As I wound my way through the tents, I found myself once again with Savitri. As far as I remembered, she had led every campfire I'd participated in. With me, there were perhaps ten people in the circle. Informality was evident in the casual way everyone leaned or even lay down if it felt right.

Savitri was timeless in her earth-colored robe, and everyone else seemed to come from a particular time. Looking around this morning's circle, I guessed that we represented many centuries.

As I entered the circle, Savitri said, "Do you remember Rumi, the Sufi poet of the thirteenth century? In one of his poems, he said that each of us has a task we are to perform. He indicated in this poem that we each have a mission and a purpose unique to us. It is as if we were sent by a king to another land to perform a task. If we perform a thousand other tasks, and not the one we were sent to do, then it is as if we have done nothing. Is he saying our life mission is an agreement with the One that sent us?"

She paused as we thought about her question, then continued. "Hazrat Inayat Khan, an early twentieth-century Sufi, said we are each like pieces of a great puzzle. If we are not willing to take our place, then the puzzle will never be put together. Some of us are the edge pieces that others need to see in place in order to imagine their own places in the puzzle. Wherever your piece is meant to fit, if you do not take your place, someone will be missing his or her connection in the completed picture of life. The Sufis also have a saying that for every person that finds their place in life, ten thousand people will have an opportunity to find theirs."

Savitri paused to drink some tea and watch us for a moment. It was the first time I'd seen her drink anything. I smiled thinking this was a Sufi pause.

"For thousands of years, spiritual traditions considered pilgrimage an important element of the spiritual journey of life." She looked out toward the sea of campfires and continued. "For Muslims, it is one of the obligations of their faith that at some point in their life they will make pilgrimage to Mecca.

"What makes a journey a pilgrimage and not a vacation is a sense of purpose for the journey. It is holding an intention and an awareness of our connection to Spirit. This is the sense in which we journey through life if we have a sense of our life mission."

I felt Savitri was laying the foundation for the journey we were about to take together in this campfire. We began with a king sending us to a foreign land to perform a task, and we were led to this journey as sacred pilgrimage. We were to find our place in the puzzle so that others could find their place. I knew by this time that we would be traveling vertically. In Caravan, we called the other world horizontal because time moved horizontally across its landscape, literal, linear, and in one direction. This twilight-dawn morning I'd been directly reminded that time is subjective, multilayered, and, if need be, overlapping or vertical.

An Asian girl sitting next to her spoke now as she accepted a cup of tea. "I remember reading that the Buddha said, 'Your work is to find your work and give all of yourself to it,'" she said. "I didn't make the connection to it as specifically life mission at the time. If it was 'my work' then, wouldn't it have to be my life mission? That would make sense, wouldn't it? She looked around the circle as if she expected us to decide.

When we didn't, she was silent. Her face clear and unlined, her hair hung to her waist. She was probably in her early twenties in the horizontal world. In the silence I thought about what I knew of the Buddha. I also wondered if this girl had grown up Buddhist. I wondered if she'd grown up in a Christian country with questions about her cultural and ancestral heritage? Although her clothes seemed to be of another time in the horizontal world, they were Western.

After a moment she continued. "As I think of it, it seems to me the Buddhist concept of Right Livelihood indicates something about life purpose."

This animated a young man sitting next to her, dressed in what I guessed to be Middle Eastern clothes of a period I felt unqualified to guess. His jet-black hair, glasses, and manner suggested he was a university student. "I thought that was about doing no harm in one's work," he said. "I thought that meant you were to consider the consequences of your work. Would harm come to someone directly or indirectly from the product of your work?"

The girl studied him for a moment, then responded. "Right Livelihood is the fifth of the eightfold path of the Buddha. My impression so far is that while Right Livelihood means work that does no harm, it also includes using your inborn talent, heart values, and a quest for meaning. To me, it speaks to our differences as well as the universal in each of us. It honors that we have only a short time here and that the individual and unique natures of our mind streams will call each of us differently." Looking away from the young man to the rest of us, she continued. "Right Livelihood calls us to be of service to something larger than ourselves. The Eightfold Path also calls for the liberation of all sentient beings. I feel that this path also reminds us that to be here at all is a great opportunity. Wouldn't that make it important that we honor our reason for being here?"

Watching her as she talked, Savitri replied to her, "Yes, the Buddha is quoted as saying 'Your work is to find your work and give all of yourself to it.' When the Buddha says this, what is he saying? Is he asking us to find something or anything that we can do and give all of our self to? Is he saying we should attune to the nature of our mind stream, or to the essential nature that is each of us and give all of our self to that?"

Sparks flew up as Savitri moved logs in the fire. We watched their upward motion toward the star-filled sky. Looking at the stars, Savitri said, "When the ten thousand things—which is code for the multiplicity of the manifest world—have been stripped away . . . there is something that remains." Her voice quiet, meeting our eyes, she said, "There is an essential nature that is the unique nature of your Self.[29] The way this essential nature meets the world will be the way you can be of service to all sentient beings. This essential nature holds the gift of your call."

I looked around the campfire as Savitri spoke. Everyone was sitting up now and leaning toward the Asian girl. She scanned the circle. As I watched her, I thought she might be gauging how conversation in Caravan and her life in the horizontal world fit. I wondered what it meant to the rest of us around the campfire.

She looked at Savitri. "In *The Diamond Cutter*, I remember a point made about the benefactors to the Buddha. It said in the commentary that these benefactors were included for a reason. This point would never have been an accident. It was said to have been included to show that those first to be instructed were the leaders."

Tucking her long hair behind her ears seemed to center her. "This means to me," she added, "that not all the Buddha's original students were poor beggars. They had already demonstrated leadership, courage, and attainment in their lives. Some had become enormously wealthy in their own right. It said they had incarnated in order to be in that position to help Buddha."

Savitri waited for us to respond, then said, "Just as you can never step into the same river twice, you can never drive down the same street twice or do the same work twice. Each event in our life makes an incredible difference if we can be present to it. Is it possible to be that present to our life? This is something the wisdom traditions have been telling us for thousands of years. If we can treat the moments of our life in all of their display as extraordinary, this may help us find our way to life mission, by this alone."[30]

Although moments in Caravan have a timeless nature, I got the point and decided not to wait until I went back to the horizontal world to practice being fully present. I listened for the nature of life in Caravan in that moment. The low hum of conversation around other campfires blended into a background of melody. I noticed the scent of sacreds again and that already I'd begun not to notice them. I reached down to move my fingers through the sand and remembered I'd stopped noticing the difference in the sand as I moved through Caravan. As I took a sip of tea I consciously breathed in the aroma, and compared the taste of the tea to the coffee I'd drunk during my last trip to Caravan. As I took the space to linger visually over each of my campfire mates, I recognized the unique moment. I fell in love with life and was inspired with the idea of this mindful practice as a signpost for life mission.

Savitri, reading my mind, turned to me. "Remember the Rumi quote, 'Let the beauty you love be what you do.' If you treat everything in your life as extraordinary, and the journey of your life as an extraordinary life, you will find it beautiful.[31] This love and beauty will lead you to your life mission. If you follow the love and the beauty, it will always lead you there."

The young man who'd been surprised by the relationship of Right Livelihood to life mission, with hands animated, agitated and perhaps anxious, jumped in. "I listened to a *Tibetan Book of the Dead* talk on tape. It seems to make the question of the life mission less compelling. First of all, there is the matter of coming back over and over. Next, there is the matter of making the best case for nonattachment you can make so that when the moment comes you will be ready to move on. It also teaches that attachment is the single greatest cause of suffering, according to the Buddha."

"Do you remember the Boddichitta vow?" Savitri answered. "*Boddi* has to do with primordial essence, and *chitta* has to do with the heart. The Boddichitta vow is coming from the primordial essence of the heart with compassion for all sentient beings. This is a fitting vow for life mission work. It isn't a requirement to be on the path of your life mission, and it would certainly be in harmony with it. I can't imagine any life mission that wouldn't resonate with that."

"Do you remember the talk about the bardos in the *Tibetan Book of the Dead?*" She looked from the young man to me, then the rest of the circle, and continued, "The bardo is a place of transition. Your time from birth to death in the horizontal world is a bardo. Each place you move to afterward is a bardo. The Tibetans would say you might move through several immediately after death. By this definition, your time in Caravan would be a bardo."

As she spoke, I remembered wondering during my first night in Caravan (the first night I remembered, though I was coming to understand I'd been here before) if I were dead and traveling to my next life. I was still working on what Caravan meant to my soul and where it led. This experience in Caravan was indeed moving between lives, and the person I was before that night had passed away.

Savitri continued, "In the confusion of the passage through the bardos, to even remember that your intention was to serve the freedom of all sentient beings would move you in that instant to a different experience of the bardo. It is even possible that that alone might result in a favorable rebirth so that you might indeed be of service. This is the very thing that you pray for in Phowa. Phowa is a training to consciously make your transition at death. You might pray that you will be instantly reborn into a life that would make it possible for you to actually make a difference and be in service."

It was as if everyone in the circle were asking himself or herself if they'd made that prayer. Silent and searching inward, no one moved. In a whisper, Savitri asked, "What if you made that vow, received the answer to that prayer, found yourself in a life in which you actually could make a difference . . . and then allowed yourself to be talked out of the importance of doing what you came to do? Perhaps that would make for a bit of a slide in the progress of your journey. Would that be denial of life mission?"

The Asian girl, eyes unfocused and looking inward, ignoring the hair in her face, in a voice softer even then Verity's, said, "When I think about what the Buddhists say about the odds of even ever becoming a human being, it makes me even more determined to fight for our remembering and awakening. It's difficult sometimes to believe I can really be of some service that will make a difference. There's a strong part of me that would like to believe I could. If I convince myself I can't make a difference, then I won't have to go for anything in my life and I can go back to sleep. That would be a great mistake."

We all nodded in consent and leaned back. It felt as if we'd waited together to exhale, and with a collective sigh relaxed into whatever we could lean our weight against. Savitri, in keeping with the informal nature of the circle, leaned against the Asian girl for a moment. They both laughed and we followed their gaze upwards as they looked to the stars again.

Encouraged, I shared, "Houston Smith wrote that for Hindus, there are four paths to God, or four yogas. The four yogas include (1) the yoga of devotion or guru yoga, (2) ascetic or renunciation yoga, (3) wisdom yoga or study, and (4) work yoga. Would you call work yoga life mission yoga?"

Savitri pressed her forehead to the Asian girl's forehead for a moment, then stood up and began walking around the circle of our campfire. "The path of work yoga acknowledges that to be in the world is an opportunity to experience Spirit in motion through work. It asks that our work in the world be dedicated to spirit. It is a way to check our spiritual progress daily as we work in the world. It is acknowledged as a Way or path to enlightenment and freedom from the wheel of life.

"If you choose the path of work, and use your work as a way of checking your progress with Spirit, do you think the work you do will be important? Do you remember that I started this morning quoting Rumi as saying, 'It is as if a king sent you to a foreign land and you do a thousand things but not the one thing you were sent to do, then it is as if you have done nothing'? Do you think using work yoga as your path to enlightenment would call you to align your work with your life mission?"

The circle was quiet. I watched as our unofficial tea server walked around with refills. I occasionally looked out toward the other circles, allowing our talk to sink in. I watched women dressed in saris and burkas and men in robes of Asia and the desert. As I noticed a small group walking among the tents, I wondered if they were biblical monks. I got up to stretch, feeling my legs as I dug my heels in the sand and I watched the men file past us.

A man sitting next to me, dressed in what I guessed were the robes of the Middle East, spoke now. "Christ says in the Gospel of Thomas, 'That which you do not bring forth from within you will destroy you. That which you bring forth from within you will save your life.' Christ also said all that is not given is lost.

"Sitting in Caravan," this man continued, "I can't help but think he refers to our agreement with God. If, as Rumi said, we're sent to do one thing and not the thousand other things, and that one thing isn't brought forth, would not bringing this forth indeed destroy us? I feel that conflict in my horizontal world life. I've felt that my whole life there. Savitri, how do I remember our campfire in the horizontal world? Without remembering I feel sad and lost there."

Putting his hands on his knees, he pushed himself to a standing position, then leaned forward and spoke again. "Growing up in the horizontal world, as children or young adults, our life mission is not a part of our discussion about our future life. We are told in a thousand ways what is expected of us. My parents had a very definite idea of what I should do."

As he talked about his parents, I recalled my parents' ideas about my future work. It may have been the era in which I grew up, and yet it seems parents projected their own expectation of their children's future careers onto their sons and daughters. I remembered a talk by Cynthia Tobias I'd heard on the radio. She was speaking to a group of parents. I paraphrased what I remembered of her talk. Cynthia said, "In Proverbs 22:6, it's written, to train up a child in the way he should go and when he is old he will not depart from it." She went on to say (still paraphrasing), "Context is crucial in understanding the actual translation of what is written. In this place in Proverbs, the Hebrew word that's been translated as 'train' is actually a usage that comes from midwifery. It's the only place in the Bible this occurs. It describes a process used when a baby is first born to clear the mouth. It literally means to create an environment for life. Also in the translation, the context of 'in the way he should go' would more accurately mean 'according to his/her gift or bent." Putting this all together, Cynthia said she would more accurately say, 'Create an environment for life for a child according to his or her individual gift or bent, and when older, he or she will not depart from it.'"[32]

I told the man how grateful I was to hear that, as I was still digesting my own parents' disapproval of my decision to go into music. "This is not an injunction to parents to decide what their children should do with their lives," I said. "This does not give them permission to choose what their children should do to make their way in the world, because parents know better. This verse in Proverbs asks parents to create an environment in which their child's nature, gift, or bent is called forth and nurtured, and when the child becomes an adult, he or she will not depart from it. Here in Caravan, I might say this is an injunction to parents to consider the question of the life mission of their children."

Savitri picked up this thread of the conversation as she was making her way around the circle. "The 'wisdom' book of the Bible, which is what Proverbs is often called, perhaps tells us in this verse that it is important to live into the nature, the blueprint in which we are designed. It is important to honor the call of God that imprints us. The stories of the patriarchs and matriarchs of the Bible were built around the principle that God commissioned them with missions, that God has a covenant with humans. The lives of all of the great prophets of the Bible were built around their callings from God. These prophets were not always confident of their ability to carry out their missions, however. Even running away, as Jonah did, did not save him from carrying out his mission."

A man I guessed to be American, dressed in a brown suit from the 1930s or '40s, added, "In the wisdom stories of the Jewish tradition there is the story of the great Hassidic master, Rabbi Zuza. The story goes that Rabbi Zuza was very sick and was being carried on a stretcher to a more restful place. He seemed very distraught. Someone asked him, 'What is the matter, Rabbi Zuza? Are you afraid that God will ask you why you were not more like Moses?' 'No,' Rabbi Zuza answered, 'I am afraid God will ask me why I wasn't more like Rabbi Zuza.'"

As this story settled in our hearts, we became restless. Savitri suggested we walk a little and return. Threading my way around tents and through the pilgrims of Caravan, I guessed from the period clothing that I was walking among the traditions we'd just talked about. I saw what could have been Buddhists, Hindus, Muslims, Christians, Jews, Sufis, and more. I wondered if everyone dressed in period clothing was also having the same kinds of talks in their campfire circles.

During our break, I was grateful not to have to go back to the horizontal world. I was in the flow of life mission, moving through time and culture, wanting more.

Savitri was speaking as I returned. "Plato told the story of the journey of the soul and the daemon that accompanies us. He said that when the soul is about to come to earth, it is given a life mission. It was believed that the soul will tend to forget its assignment in the process of being born, so an angel or daemon is assigned to each soul to remind it of its life mission." This story of daemon comes from Plato's *Republic*. As she spoke, I imagined the daemon assigned to remind us of our life mission might be like the parents in the line from the book *14,000 Things to Be Happy About*. The line describes parents steering children around the grocery store by their heads. I imagined our daemon trying to do this to us for most of our lives.

Everyone from the campfire circle was back again. Now the many varieties of tea from before were augmented by coffee. Several options suspended by tripods hung above the fire.

The man I'd guessed to be an American from the 1930s poured himself a cup of coffee and began to pace within the inner circle of the campfire. "Freud, who is arguably the father of psychology," he began, "theorized that within us are really only two motivating forces. Most all of us are familiar with his theories on the importance of sexuality in our lives. The other main force, the one we've not heard as much about, is the importance he accorded to work. Freud placed work equal to sexuality in the power to create mental and physical wholeness. He also cited how doing the incorrect work, or being unable to do the work we're designed to do, is equally harmful. He seemed to be saying that doing work you weren't designed to do, and that in fact is wrong for you, is an invitation to psychosis. Is this the domain of psychology talking about life mission?"

I answered him in my mind. *Yes.* We were spiraling through the spiritual traditions to what some might think of as Greek philosophy, also to psychology. And why not? We'd done significant time travel around this campfire for a world outside of time.

Savitri picked up this thread, too. "Viktor Frankl spent his career as a psychologist looking at the reasons some people survive great traumas and hardship while others do not. Frankl survived the death camps of Nazi Germany. After the war, he felt compelled to explore the question of survival. Frankel concluded that a sense that life has meaning was the biggest factor in surviving the death camps. Those who felt their lives had meaning and that it was important for them to survive fought to survive. This feeling of meaning in life seemed to give them an extra something that enhanced their chances and they tended to survive.

"Frankl also found that courage was proportional to meaning. The courage we have to face our life and move through it is proportional to our sense of our life having a reason and a purpose. Our sense of our life mission is our greatest source of courage."

The American from the 1930s leaned in her direction and said, "Frankl founded Logotherapy around the principle that human beings have a fundamental 'will to meaning,' which is a dynamic underpinning everything in our life. There is a kind of tension between life and the will to meaning. Deprived of this kind of positive stress to find and create a life of meaning and purpose, humans will compensate by creating negative stress. Frankl proposed that we are healthiest when we live with a sense of meaning and purpose."

Savitri paused, then opened one hand across the fire as if to hand the line to him. With a subtle reception of the offer, he continued the thread. "Psychiatrist Erik Erickson, in his psychological stages of development, included a stage called generativity. One of the characteristics of this stage is the desire to leave a legacy."

As I had seen Bede and Savitri orbit in Caravan's work, Savitri, moving gently clockwise, responded, "Consider the question of dealing with generativity and legacy. Developing consciously through Erickson's stages to the ability to be generative in the world, what will we choose to generate? This is about more than our personal self at this point. When we consciously decide what our generative legacy will be, what criteria will we use? Here in Caravan, I ask, is there a life that makes sense to live that does not include the reason we were sent? Can you conceive of choosing anything but your life mission?"

The man replied, "Depth psychologist James Hillman addressed this question in his book *The Soul's Code*. He referred to what he called the acorn principle. I think he is saying the code of our life mission is within us, and like the mighty oak tree is waiting to unfold over time in the course of our life. He wrote that it is inherent in us from birth, like the acorn, and isn't created by our life in the horizontal world."

Savitri thanked him and said it was time for another break. She told us to come back when we were ready, then sat down at the edge of the rugs and went inward. It took a few moments before any of us moved. I went inward myself until I felt the call to follow the silent dialogue of Caravan's flow. In the eternal timeless world of Caravan, it's difficult to know how long I moved through the tent city of Caravan.

Suddenly it was morning in the horizontal world. Back at the coach house, I found myself still surrounded by the stacks of books I'd found during my bookstore tour. After my first journeys to Caravan, I'd sought inspiration for Verity's questions in the pages of those books. Now I wanted to go deeper. This created an excitement in me for another tour of the bookstores. Around the campfire we'd talked about life mission as a current moving within the world's spiritual traditions. We'd talked about Plato and the field of psychology. Now I wanted to know more.

It felt good to shower and feel the water running over my physical body. It felt good to be back in the horizontal world, and I was inspired by my trips to Caravan. Moving between Caravan and the horizontal world, I could no longer ignore the call. I knew my life wasn't right. I wasn't happy. Still, I avoided the tough questions. I hadn't recognized that I'd been in survival mode. I had enough of the basics needed to live and was in survival mode, emotionally and spiritually. Ironically, almost because of a kind of abundance of the basics I had purposely disconnected from the real questions.

Beginning with Verity's assignment to discern my reason for being in both the horizontal and vertical worlds, I was ready to look at my personal life mission. As Savitri had led the talk about life mission as found in world religions, I felt the personal nature of life mission through their founders. I felt the founder's life mission of these traditions thread through the lives of those who continued them. Then as she talked about Plato and the correlation of life mission through the development of psychology, I felt it point even more in the direction of the personal.

Of course, I said to myself, life mission is personal. That's the point. We each have a unique, one-of-a-kind mission. I felt individuals interacting with the question of life mission and the legacy left to the world as a result of that enquiry. I wanted to go further. What else have individuals contributed to the dialogue of life mission? Something in me moved and I felt more alive than I'd felt in a very long time.

Returning from another tour of the bookstores, my car's trunk was filled with books from all over Chicago. On the way home, I grabbed a burger and fries from a room-sized, not nearly big enough restaurant that I loved and called "the place on the corner with no name," because it didn't seem to have a name. When I got home, I set the food next to the stacks of books as I unpacked, getting ready for the next journey inward. I'd found several new books by Joseph Campbell, so I opened the expedition journal and went back and forth between writing in the journal and reading, annotating the journey.

Expedition Journal:

Joseph Campbell is best known for his injunction to "follow your bliss." Most people interpret this to mean "do whatever you like." In his deeper description of what he meant, Campbell said, "It's important to do the archetypal and mythical deep inner work that's necessary for us to claim our humanity and adulthood."

Reading Campbell's Hero with a Thousand Faces, *I see at least six aspects: (1) the hero/heroine's journey, (2) the time in the wilderness, (3) the time of doing ashes work, (4) the time of facing our shadows, (5) the time of wrestling with the archetypal world, and (6) the testing of our ideas about who we are.*

After I've passed through each of these stages (or steps) to reach my deepest self, perhaps then I will come to my bliss. This isn't meant to be in order or to be the complete list. I think he meant that if I'm willing to go through the whole journey, it will bring me to my life mission or bliss. I must do this work. Even then the journey isn't complete until I bring the gift of my adventure back, and give it to the world.

It seems that Campbell meant finding my life task was paramount to living the archetypal myth of my life.[33] *Before I can really get the gifts of this archetypal movement in my life, I need to contact where the gifts live in me. Finding my life mission is a way of contacting how my gifts wait to act in my life.*

What an incredible notion! "Follow your passion toward fulfillment, in the way the innateness of who you are leads you to. Then you will find the archetypal moving in your life." When this happens, then even though I may have to endure sacrifice or even pain, it will nonetheless lead to my bliss.

To first ask about life mission is to give a foundation to the question of how to live from where I find myself. The cultural context I find myself in will give form to the question of how I navigate my life mission.

Campbell also wrote that to live this vision-mission, we may need to go against the conventions of our culture, or our culture may accommodate our life mission without a problem.[34] *Either way, if we look first to life mission, it may save us from unneeded battles.*

Even the fields of medicine and healing now acknowledge the importance of a sense of purpose and meaning to our health. This sense is seen in the tendency of people to fade quickly in terms of health after "retirement" if their job isn't replaced by work that speaks to their soul.

In many cases when someone gets a diagnosis of only weeks, months, or a year to live, they feel a kind of permission to do what they've always imagined they'd like to do. Often when they orient their life around this soul desire, suddenly there is remission of their illness. One thing is certain: Doing our heart's desire has a powerful healing effect on every level of our health.

The effect of work poorly suited to us can be seen in reports of our uniquely human choice of the hour between eight and nine o'clock Monday morning as the time when more of us die than any other hour. That this is widely believed to be true may indicate a general feeling that many of us would rather die than face another week of work disconnected from our essential self.

Science, which has focused mostly on the facts of how things work more than why, or if we should care about it, avoiding ascribing philosophical or spiritual meaning, begins to honor intention in the formation of life. Through the observer effect in physics, the characteristics of attractors in chaos theory, the formation of peptides in the body, the movement of electrons from the void and throughout all life, the extremely intricate interconnections necessary for the balance of the universe in general, and our planet in particular, and the awesome wonder of the human body, science is now having to at least consider that purpose may be somewhere in the equation.

Current work on spiritual intelligence shows the unitive nature of brain frequencies that are tied to the question of meaning and purpose. The work of spiritual intelligence is to tie together information spread across the brain (and the field informing the brain). Spiritual intelligence asks of information moving across the brain, "Why is this important? Why do I want to know this? How does this apply to everything else I know and believe? What should I do with this, and why?" We have an innate intelligence, and its function seems to me to be navigating the questions of meaning and purpose. Does lack of connection to meaning indicate low spiritual intelligence?

I listened to a tape of a Sufi named Llewellyn Vaughn-Lee referring to life mission. He said that we have an outer life mission and an inner life mission. That's an intriguing thought certainly. Hazrat Inayat Khan also writes about this inner and outer life mission. How does this relate to Caravan and my assignment?

Hazrat Inayat Khan also writes that everyone has a place in the orchestra of life. Each of us is an instrument in this orchestra.

Finding our place has to do with getting tuned up for our place in the performance of the piece.

According to Hazrat Inayat Kahn, all things, even electrons, have their very specific, unique place in the scheme of things. Not only does each and every human being have their place in the Divine plan, with a mission that is unique to each, every electron also has a uniquely designed place in the plan of the universe.

In this line of reasoning then, photons would have a mission to carry the information of the life mission of the electrons they've been in contact with. Certainly the bottom line for this would be the message of the One. It would ultimately be the message of the Great Sacred Mystery that we all have the opportunity to take part in consciously.

The other thing that jumped out at me while I was reading Hazrat Inayat Kahn was the part about God having this design for every being in the universe, even subatomic particles. All beings, really everything in the universe, would have to come to its place eventually. Significant to me was the idea of God moving the pieces when they needed to be moved.

It's so often true that we know exactly what to do, and we know it almost immediately. We know this in spite of how much we really don't want to know this. We know this and then convince ourselves that we're confused, and this gives us a great deal of time to stay when we should be gone. It means we get to pay a great price and also get very off-course.

It would be situations like these, I think, that Hazrat Inayat Khan meant when he talked about God moving to bring the pieces back into place. I think it's this that we talk about when we say we get a nudge first, then a push, and finally the big event in our life. There's a great deal of compassion in this on all three levels, though it may not seem like it at the time.

* ⋆ *

CHAPTER 6

Life Mission—Individual

IT WAS STILL TWILIGHT dawn in Caravan as Verity came into focus. She didn't ask me what I remembered. She didn't ask me what I'd discovered. Her face and hands almost floated, the earth-colored robe and her form within nearly translucent. I watched threads of silver weaving in her eyes as she enquired about something within me, quiet and surrounded by silence. Everywhere around us, pilgrims did the work of Caravan, yet the silent, deep calm enveloping us felt like the eye of an ocean storm hitting landfall. She found what she was looking for, passed her hand left to right in front of me, and as the sounds of Caravan rushed forward, she moved into it. I followed.

We stopped next to a campfire and listened as an elegant Black man completed a story. The pilgrims of Caravan appeared to have returned to dressing in more or less modern attire.

The work with life mission moving through time seemed to be complete for the moment. As the man finished speaking, I realized it was his story. His was a story of a life between two worlds. He asked what it meant to be of these two worlds in the horizontal world. I wondered if remembering being part of the horizontal world and Caravan helped him. As he finished, others sitting around this campfire said nothing. The woman in the earth robe standing by the campfire next to him put her hand on his shoulder and said, "Tell us again. Find the highest thread of calling in your story."

Everyone in the circle leaned in. I could feel their presence to his story. What were they listening for? He started over, taking more time, weighing his words. He seemed to listen and watch for their response. As he told his story again, I remembered something James Hillman wrote. "It is not so much the damaging things that happened to us, as the damaging way we tell ourselves the story of what happened." I wondered if this man would now tell his story differently.

His story of the journey between the traditional and the modern, African and European, ancestral home and city, community and isolation, secular and sacred life interested me, and stayed with me as Verity signaled to move on. We moved slowly through Caravan, weaving like the children from my first nights in Caravan. Stories of the horizontal world swirled around us as we walked. Voices hung in the air, a chorus of the song of humanity. Around each campfire, we heard someone telling his or her story. Women's stories mingled with men's stories. Children and adolescents shared their stories with the adults. I had the feeling Verity didn't want me to get involved just yet with any story in particular, just to listen.

Verity moved to a private campfire next to one of the tents. This was a family, or personal campfire, not meant for the circle of teaching. The fire was small, quiet and unattended at that moment. The flames were low to the ground with little flickering. The illumination from the fire, lower then usual, was ideal for going within. I thought Verity would question me. Instead we sat in silence watching the fire as stories of life in the horizontal world danced through my thoughts. The rich tapestry and vast creativity of human expression took on a new meaning, though locating why was just out of reach. In between this collection of short stories I sorted pieces of my own story. This twilight morning walk was making clear the patchwork-quilt nature of my life story. If anyone had asked me to tell the story of my life, I would have been confident I knew what it was. Now it was clear to me that whatever my story was, it changed every time I told it.

Verity apparently waited for this. She looked up. Our eyes met for a moment and I felt like I was meeting her again after a long journey. Meeting a friend after a long pilgrimage, we see they're no longer the person we knew, however long they've been in our life. We wonder who they've become, and how much of the person we knew is still there. I wondered, as I looked into her eyes in that moment, how long she had been my guide and teacher.

She smiled a little and added the aside she used to make me smile. "Come, wanderer, worshiper, lover of leaving." She was standing then. I completely missed seeing her get up. Already she moved back toward the circles of campfires.

As we joined the circles, I felt we moved in the circle of life. The family of life on earth flowed from circle to circle. Tents thinned out as we walked until it was only campfire circles as far as the eye could see. In each circle someone was telling his or her story.

Something different was in the air this time. It was more electric, more alive. We walked for a long time before I recognized the obvious. Now there were only teaching campfires, and each one was focused on the individual's story. I felt a wave move through my body. My curriculum in Caravan, my place within Caravan had moved from the work with the foundation of life mission as an idea, to what life mission means to the individual. At least the idea it might be so, and curiosity about what this shift to the individual would mean, made me hope so. The excitement I felt in the air around the campfires sparked, as the work moved from the abstract to the personal.

As I felt this difference, Verity moved into one of the circles. I joined her in the circle where an older woman was telling her story. She was wearing a black skirt with a light blouse surrounded by a shawl of black, red and green. I guessed she might be South American. Although we understood each other's languages in Caravan, there were many cultures, and cultural context still led to questions.

Unlike in the last group, listening in silence, now asking questions was part of the process. This group didn't bother to wait until the end of the story. Our group asked questions as we went, as soon as we thought of them. Often several questions asked at once led to laughter and smiles. Alive and energetic, this story-telling felt like something in the process of birthing.

The South American woman was talking about her life in the horizontal world and we questioned her version of the story. When she told us about growing up in her small village, we asked her what that meant to her life. She said the challenge of the "two worlds" was a large part of both her personal story and the collective story of her village. This reminded me of the story the elegant Black man of the first campfire that morning had told, and I thought the meeting of the old and new worlds was paradoxically as old as humankind. She told us that in her early childhood she'd experienced the trust of living a life in many ways unchanged for as long as anyone could remember. Then, gradually, the modern world crept into her village. At first, it was someone leaving and not coming back. Then people and objects from the modern world began to change their way of life. The certainty of how life should be lived fell from her so gradually she couldn't describe how that happened. This uncertainty colored every decision in her life and her village, or at least it felt that way to her.

The background anxiety, change and modernity affected her place in the village. She believed it changed the choices her parents made for her as a young woman. Decisions made mostly for her in terms of marriage and family would've gone differently in the old life, she felt. The old map for living no longer guiding the villagers, and the new map still unclear, she said her voice was lost from her life. She was lost from her life and questioned why life should turn out like it did for her, her family, and her village. We asked her what it meant to her life that she felt that. We asked her what it could mean if there were more to the story. We all shared questions from our hearts as we looked for what might be unexplored in her story.

The campfire guide asked her what her intention had been at each stage, working slowly through her life story. Survival was often the first answer, though as she retold her story she got in touch with deeper intentions. She remembered intentions surrendered then, coming alive in the retelling of her story. She wanted so many things, tentative longings and dreams. A different freedom in her person and a very different kind of marriage were longings entering adulthood. Some of her longings seemed universal to me, made tentative by changes in the world of her village. "Why" questions came from every direction of the circle. As we continued she began to backtrack in her story, which now became a kaleidoscope of moving threads to us. I guessed it seemed so to her as well, to listen to her voice, and watch her face.

Always our questions led her to a higher way of telling her story.

Each time she retold a part of her story, she seemed wiser, more alive, more magical, and more empowered.

I began to see the work we were doing in this circle. The spirit of this work and the wonder of the horizontal world caught me as we worked with her. I was caught up in the wonder of the magic of her life. I felt the perfection of life in the horizontal world.

In these circles, the guides were occasional catalysts, sometimes leading the questions, though sparingly, or encouraging the storyteller to tell the story again from the beginning. Even if this was version twenty or thirty, the guide said, "Again please." I began to realize that in Caravan we have eternity to tell and retell our story. We're always telling our story, even though we're most often completely unaware that we're doing it. Caravan asks us to tell it consciously until we move toward the most empowering, most life-enhancing, most meaningful version, that hints of the "why" of our life.

As I considered this, the guide said, "Listen for the highest story of your life.[35] If we were sent to the horizontal world to embody a particular mission, what in the story of our life tells of that? Listen for the clues the teller of this tale is missing in his or her own life. We create our life in the sharing of our stories about it.

"In the telling," the guide went on, "we find the pattern in the tapestry of our life in the horizontal world. We see a thread moving through an event, and see for the first time, perhaps, why we made the choice we did. Witness the context of the larger weave of your life that you use to create the story of a life mission embodied and lived. Even if you do not remember this work we do together here, when you return to the horizontal world, perfume of the highest version of your story will be with you. You may feel a sense of peace or the rightness of a direction. Watch for this now as you listen or as you tell your story. Each time, feel your way through. Help each other and watch for your part in the story."

The South American woman began again. Everyone shared the story now as we were with her, breath for breath. Someone would question a detail as if he were sharing the story of a family picnic we'd all been to. Though we kept mostly to her story, occasionally someone would volunteer something from his or her own story if it helped her tell her story differently. More and more our story, it became enriched as her personal story.

With an almost imperceptible touch, Verity returned me to the walk through the teaching campfires of Caravan. Here was the great melting pot of life. We heard every kind of story for life in the horizontal world as we walked. What was the difference, I asked myself, between these stories and fiction? These were real stories of real lives in the horizontal world. Yet, as they were retold, they changed until they almost seemed to have become someone else's story. Then, paradoxically, they became perfectly their story. In this great cauldron, life alchemy was in process.

Caravan asks what our highest story is. Caravan asks us to imagine what it might be to see it as better than we remember it. Caravan asks us to seek the life mission the story is calling to. One of the campfire guides asked the people in her circle to remember their stories as greater possibilities. "Now go inward and remember what is possible for your story in the inner world of your imagination," she said. "What if this is not about escape? What if you used this inner world to create possibility in your outer world? What if you can create resonance for your life in the horizontal world here in Caravan, finding answers, inspiration, and awareness?"

The guide continued, "Tell and retell your story until it comes alive with the resonance of the imaginal realm. Find the place of the mythic, magical, alchemical, mystic, and heroic qualities you wish to embody in your life."

It was time for a break apparently, as I found myself back in Wicker Park. I thought perhaps the idea was to "go home and practice" for a bit. I stood in the rain contemplating what would bring my story alive. The mythic, magic, mystic and heroic life sounded good. I thought I could practice that on the El on the way to the studio I was booked to work in that day. That thought reminded me both of how unromantic, not mythic, and not magical the work in the studio felt lately, and how late I was likely to be for the work waiting for me.

As I walked home I considered the part of my story that told about living in Wicker Park in a coach house.[36] The soundtrack of that morning in the park, and the scent of the city magnified as I tuned into my neighborhood, in a way I hadn't since moving into it. Maybe I'd never really tuned into my neighborhood. Who would live here and what story would go with that? I wondered what my neighbors' stories were.

In the first days back from my first trips to Caravan, I had looked around the coach house and wondered who this guy was who owned these things. Why these possessions and what did they say about me? I sought clues for who I was, partially because I couldn't believe Caravan had happened to me, so I must be clueless or crazy. I asked these questions, to anchor myself in some way. I asked because Verity had given me an assignment that mystified me. Looking around that morning I wanted to know what kind of story led to what I was seeing. What kind of guy owned this story and what was the highest way of telling his story?

I worked next to an artist named Arist that day. Born in Poland, he was a wiry-bearded, red-headed firecracker of a guy with a square jaw and deep set eyes that flashed wildly, as if he were up to something, which he often was. At least a foot shorter than me, he had attitude, exuberance, flair, and a confidence that wanted to occupy everyone's space. I might have admired him if his attitude didn't carry a self-destructive kind of recklessness and a combination of qualities that sometimes created great and surprising work, and just as often a costly disaster that might have worked with just a bit more forethought and planning.

My personal challenge with Arist wasn't this so much as it wasn't my studio and usually we weren't working on the same project. My challenge with him lay in what seemed to be his total disregard for the studio's tools, including mine. It seemed disrespectful, mindless, and cavalier that his use of them often left them ruined. This was an everyday affair. He was always unrepentant and couldn't seem to understand why I was upset. I decided that morning to find the higher story . . . if I could.

When I asked him to tell me his story, he became serious in a way I'd never experienced with him. He had grown up in Communist Poland, something he'd never revealed in any of the times we'd worked together. He told me he had never wanted to be a designer. If anything, perhaps a fine artist, but he wasn't sure about that, either. He'd shown a

certain aptitude when he was young and had been sent through chan-
nels accordingly. It wasn't like he had to do something he hated, but he
didn't feel as if he had really decided. He had "talent," so opportunity
presented itself. He'd had some luck, but advancement wasn't just given
to him. Once his career direction was set by the system, his tendency
to take risks developed as a response to his sense of now or never, as
openings appeared.

He implied that growing up in a communist country cultivated
a disregard for property. If he had something nice, it was taken away
or destroyed by someone else who didn't care. No one had personal
property that was nice for long. Mostly no one had personal property.
He needed to stand out to have any kind of life, so he took chances. In
the system surrounding him, no one else seemed to care if things went
wrong or instruments or materials were ruined, because "the people"
owned them. At any rate he said, "the people" had stopped caring years
ago. He was lucky often enough.

He didn't want to talk about his family except to say he hadn't
trusted them growing up and wasn't close. He didn't want to talk about
how he'd gotten to America. His marriage to an American wife was new,
so I thought a green card marriage might be involved, and let that go.

To practice the story work, I brought him back to his childhood
in Poland. I asked him to tell me what he'd been dreaming about, or
was afraid of at the time when the sorting and decision-making began
that set him on his journey. I asked about his training as an artist and
designer. I asked him at what point he thought he might prefer to be a
fine artist. What were the turning points? Then I asked him to look at
his story from different perspectives. I hoped to help him see what possibility, what higher story, might have been working in his life. (I also
wanted to get some practice working with the higher story.) I couldn't
tell if he was happy or if he would even recognize it if he was, but he
seemed to have landed in a good life, from the outside looking in.

He seemed to have more choices now than he'd had in his former
life, and a decent level of abundance. I hoped he loved his wife. I wondered if he needed to be a fine artist, and let that go. If he did, I thought,
he needed to come to that realization on his own. Where he was in his
life at least gave him that option.

Looking at his life from my side of the fence, I thought there was a higher story than he was seeing. I could feel a shift in perspective around the edges and sensed something might come of it when he suddenly stopped, and stared out and over the towers of the Chicago Loop. He just stopped. As if something in him was saying, "No more." He shrugged his shoulders, tilted his head in the way he used to disarm people, and said he'd better get back to work. I wondered still, however, if something would change about the way he told his story to himself. What I knew was that my own story about him had changed. I still didn't want him to use my tools, and I wasn't angry with him anymore.

Walking homeward through Wicker Park that night I wondered how many of my neighbors had stories like Arist's. As my mind moved to the coach house, moments away, my thoughts returned to what it could tell about me. Practicing, I asked myself what the highest story of my life would tell me about my life mission. The scent of sage mixed with frankincense and copal stopped me and I laid down my portfolio. Verity called . . .

Back in Caravan, I found myself in the same campfire circle I'd been in just before I'd returned to the horizontal world. It appeared that no time at all had passed since I'd left this circle. It was as if the campfire guide had just asked the questions that sent me home. I felt the power of Verity's look, and turned just in time to follow her to the next circle.

Jun guided this circle, and it struck me that he and each of my guides in their ways all embodied the mythic, magic, mystic, alchemical, and heroic qualities previous guides spoke of. I thought Jun reflected the best I could imagine in a peaceful samurai. Wise and fierce in the inner peace he radiated, his dragon cane seemed more to consider than any sword. I realized this may have been a projection coming from my Western background. I also believed that Jun not only transcended any one tradition, he also had that presence.

He asked the group, "When you told yourself the story of 'how it came to be this way,' whose story were you telling?[37] How many stories make up the story of your people? Who exactly are 'your people'? As we shared campfires in Caravan, was there someone there you thought was not 'your people'? In the horizontal world, each culture has its version of how it came to be or how it should be. As we tell the stories of our lives, our own place within the stories of our culture was nearly invisible. With help around the campfire, this surfaced to some degree."

This stopped me for a moment. I had been looking forward to focusing on how life mission applied to my life as an individual, something that held some prospect of answers to Verity's assignment. Just when we seemed to be headed in that direction, we moved to the stories of our culture . . . and looking over my shoulder to Caravan . . . and our place in it.

"Now," Jun continued, "I want you to tell the story of 'how it came to be this way' and 'how it should be' from your cultures and traditions. As you tell these stories, the life missions of your cultures and traditions step forward from the background. What is the myth of your culture and tradition in the horizontal world?

"If the tradition you entered in the horizontal world is purposeful, then what is essential about your nature that called you to it? When all the stories we tell ourselves about how it is and how it came to be are gone, essence is what remains. It is my belief that there is something that is eternal and held hostage to our stories. I believe it responds to our life. What is the essential nature or dharma of your culture? What were the agreements? What is the great myth of your culture and your part in it?"

As I looked around the campfire, I noticed that Alika and Lucio were sitting on just the other side of Verity. Was it my imagination? Did I see a further hint of silver in Alika's hair or was it just the way she tied it back? Lucio seemed taller. He and Alika both felt older, less teenage. Was this the movement of Caravan or my imagination? Our pilgrimage was bringing us together in the campfire circles with increasing frequency. I wondered if we would soon meet in the horizontal world.

I also wondered about the natures of our different cultures and how they'd be brought together. Knowing very little of their cultures, I thought their stories might surprise me. In that moment, it felt likely that I would eventually know both the stories of their cultures in the horizontal world and how I fit into their personal stories. I committed myself in that moment to do what I could to create this high story together.

Alika smiled and looked to me as I made this commitment, almost as if she, like Caravan's guides, could read my thoughts now. Those first few strands of silver in her hair sparkled in the light of the campfire out of proportion to their number. She looked more grown up. Already? I smiled back.

Jun paused for a moment, then nodded to Verity almost imperceptibly, and continued. "What of the great stories of life? In the great stories of the horizontal world, what are the great mythic qualities carried in the blueprint of your culture? If the stories of all people are added together to create the great story, what is the role your culture was meant to play? If all parts are valuable and necessary, what is the life mission part of your culture? What is your individual part?

"The questions themselves are like threads of the fabric. They hold a place in the tapestry of our life and yet we find they are part of the weave of others we are joined to. Everyone on the journey in the horizontal world is part of this Caravan . . . though not everyone remembers. It is important to hold to this shared connection.

"Somewhere in the place where all stories are connected is the personal story. It dances with all other stories. It holds others in their places like a great puzzle we all share. It is a mystery that need not be solved, only lived."

Jun used his dragon cane to adjust the wood in the fire and looked into each of us, one at a time. In my mind, I saw a view from above Caravan, of seemingly endless campfires. The campfires formed patterns within patterns, as if zooming outward in a computer-generated animation. The Caravan of Remembering moving home, together telling the great story of the One who sent us, was embodied in endless variations. The symphony felt infinitely sweet to me then and has ever since.

"The stories of your cultures move through many tributaries," Jun continued. "In the highest sense, the myths and fairy tales of your cultures carry the blueprints of information of who your culture is and the higher stories of possibilities. These myths and fairy tales hold the blueprint of what it means to be a whole and healthy adult, capable of service and being a loving person in your culture. This blueprint carries instructions for life within the context into which you were born. It carries the context for what is and has been possible for a man or a woman in your place and time.

"I ask you now to hold in your heart the question of your place in the myth you were born into in the horizontal world. I ask you to consider the myth you live now in the horizontal world. The collective myth carries the collective wisdom as well as the collective ignorance. Of what is good in the myth of your culture, what are you called to uphold? What needs to change, and what part will you play?"

Jun traced rugs pattern-to-pattern, African to Asian, South American to Middle Eastern, European to Indian with his dragon cane, then began again. "You might ask if you are meant to play a part in the myth of the culture of your birth, or that of another culture. This will bring you to questions fundamental to our work here. What is the myth you live now? What is the myth you are called to live?

"We will break now and I invite you to walk. Return when you are ready and we will continue. Do not concern yourself about this. When you are ready, you will find your way back to this circle."

At this, we all stood up. Verity connected with me for a moment, then moved to the center next to the fire to talk to Jun. The question of the myth I'm living followed me as I watched the milling about between campfires. This reminded me of the time between classes on a university campus. Some campfires were in session, and elsewhere streams of people filed toward their next place on the schedule of their curriculum. Caravan is itself mythic, and the display of people from all corners of the horizontal world felt like an epic myth in motion.

The unfolding collective high story moved into multiple exposures. I moved slightly in a directionless direction, and the sounds of Wicker Park anchored me. I didn't immediately reach for my portfolio. The park was surprisingly empty, and I took a moment to appreciate the grass, the trees, and the rain. Then I headed home.

I wanted to know more about myth, especially the myth I lived. Earlier I would have said I knew. Thinking about the myth I lived was both more real and less certain. I realized I didn't know what asking this question meant. Now I wanted to know in a way that helped me understand my life, and what the One who sent me called me to.

As I drove toward the used bookstore section of downtown Chicago, I thought about the myths of the world I knew. I thought about classic myths of Greek gods and goddesses. Inwardly, on the screen of my imagination, I reviewed Arthurian legends and the myth of the Wild West that were so much a part of my childhood. I retuned to the aspect of myth I encountered in the first round of Joseph Campbell's books. I thought about the myth of America, the myth of Africa and of the Orient, as we know them in the Western world.

Jun wanted us to look at both the myth of the culture we were born into and our personal myth, which seemed closer and dearer to me after my time in Caravan. Perhaps it was the constant reminder that this pilgrimage in the horizontal world is only one of the places I live. My time in Caravan was placing everything in the realm of a myth I live.

I concluded that taking responsibility for our agreement with the One that sent us is another way of defining the myth we agreed to embody. Jun asked us to consider what larger myth we agreed to take a place in. When sent to the horizontal world to embody a mission, is this then the embodiment of archetype and myth?

Turning again to the used bookstores, not entirely sure what I was looking for, I didn't want an academic version per se. I found several more books by Joseph Campbell that intrigued me. I felt something was still missing, though. The books I was holding were too specific. I kept looking until I found books by Robert Bly, Marion Woodman, and C. G. Jung, and his students' books. I found a book on the skill of writing that described the movement of archetypes in traditional mythic stories and modern fiction. I was now caught by the possibility of this archetypal movement to help me answer the questions of the high story of my life, and the personal and collective myth of life mission I was called to live.

Inquiring into the myth we're living, I focused on the primary archetypes moving within my culture. Inquiring into the myth I was living, I asked which archetypes moved with me personally. As I browsed, I found a writer quoting Jung as saying, "The most important work we can do is to discover what myth we're living, and if this is the one we were called to live." This led me to look through a shelf of books on Jung for the source of the quote.

This inquiry was divine dialogue and divine disclosure into the question of life mission. The work of Caravan is the work of this question. We're sent with a mission to embody. Standing there with a couple of my fingers in a book, I looked out the window and smiled as I saw others also shopping in the rain. I thought about the millions of fellow Caravan pilgrims with whom I shared Chicago and its many cultures. I thought that our life missions would be embedded within the myths of our cultures and the personal myth we chose, or inherited by default. Jung said our work is to discover our myth and choose consciously.

I thought about the possibility of the high story work we do in conjunction with our work to understand archetype and myth and choice. I was so excited, I almost engaged a total stranger in this dialogue. Instead, I paid for the books and dashed through the rain to the coffeehouse on the corner. I wanted to jump into the books I'd found as soon as possible. I also wanted to stay in the dreamlike atmosphere of that wet day in Chicago, watching people in the rain, doing Caravan homework.

I had an immediate impression that the teen who took my order was Hawaiian. I asked, and it turned out to be true. When she gave my order to the boy making the drinks, I felt 'South American,' though it wasn't obvious. He confirmed my guess, and my mind returned to Caravan. Were these two Alika and Lucio in this world? My heart told me no. I didn't yet know the rules and whether people might look different in the horizontal world than they do in Caravan. Again my heart told me *no*. A hint of something? If so, what? Like that first night Verity appeared, I smiled and decided I was fine with the mystery.

I found a corner table mostly out of the flow of customers, and dove into my books. I found the mix of psychology, philosophy, sociology, anthropology, spirituality, self-help, and personal growth an intriguing mix. It was hours before I surfaced.

When I finally looked up, I noticed a woman with bags from the same used bookstores. She was sitting at the next table, also reading and taking notes. I wondered if she'd been in the bookstores at the same time without my noticing it. Then I realized we'd been reading next to each other for hours. Just as I was wondering if she was also doing homework for Caravan, she looked up and smiled. She lifted her bag with the bookstore logo to acknowledge that she understood. Then she went back to her reading. In my mind, I went over the campfires I could remember, then let it go.

I found the archetypes of the royal court: king, queen, warrior, wizard, sorceress, jester, prince, and princess. I found gods presented as archetypes of qualities. I found the general life archetypes of virgin, maiden, crone, wild man, wild woman, wise fool, and so on. I found psychological archetypes like id, ego, inner critic, shadow, and inner child. I found the modern archetypes, including the movie or sports star, nerd, geek, yuppie, hippie, politician, tree-hugger, entrepreneur, CEO, insurgent, reporter, and more. Each of these archetypes is embedded in the myths of our culture and our time.

I knew I needed time to digest what this reading meant to me in order to know how to use it. I knew understanding archetypes and the myth I was meant to live was going to be a key to Verity's assignment, remembering what I'm called to do in both worlds, and why I don't forget as I move between them. As I gathered my things to leave, the woman at the next table looked up, smiled, and returned to her reading. For a moment I wondered about the coincidence and if I was meant to talk to her. Maybe, if she'd held my gaze a moment longer, if she hadn't returned so quickly to her reading. I felt drawn in a way that said I knew her, and I couldn't place where. This being the classic "Don't I know you?" line, I left without pursuing it.

I didn't hurry through the rain. I held my head up to receive it and enjoyed feeling it wash over my face. I enjoyed the sound of the rain. I'd enjoyed my search and being out in my city. I'd enjoyed reading next to the stranger and felt she was still with me in some way as I got into my car. Verity's initial assignment ran in the background as I turned Jun's assignment over in my mind. I looked in the rear view mirror as I parked the car by the coach house and asked the reflection I saw, "Okay, who are you, and what did you do with David?"

I looked for the woman from the coffee shop as I walked back into Jun's campfire circle. Verity leaned next to my ear and whispered this time, "Welcome to the Caravan of Remembering. She isn't here just now. You are remembering high story and the possible myth. Put this together with your assignment and listen to your heart of hearts."

Verity guided my arm as she moved us to a seat next to Alika again. Lucio wasn't present in the circle this time. I realized I'd begun to think of them as a unit. I knew it wasn't as simple as that, and yet it was so natural to assume. Kairos had first brought the three of us together, and now Verity had brought Alika and me to sit with her twice in Jun's circle.

I didn't have time to go far with my questions as Jun began to animate the circle. It felt like we were coming off a moment's pause. "You have considered how your life mission is embedded within the story of your cultures, and the mythic movement they are in turn embedded within," he said. "We talked about how your personal story and mythic pattern, in turn, are embedded in the culture and myths. Now I would like to talk about the container.

"The highest story you can embody and the highest mythic blueprint together form a container for your agreement with the One that sent you.[38] That container holds all of these relationships. The highest story and the highest myth together form a container for the Self in the horizontal world. This forms a container for your pilgrimage, a place for who you think you are to safely remember and transform. Held and carried within this vessel, the alchemical process of the pilgrimage can do the work of your assignment and preparation for the journey home."

Jun looked past us, past our circle, and out toward the ocean of campfire circles, doing the great, mythic, high story work of remembering. Raising his dragon cane, Jun looked out. He walked around the inner circle between the fire and us, carrying us with him to all the other fires, to the feeling of the one being of Caravan, traveling home.

I felt our horizontal world spinning in the grand matrix of the One sending us forth then calling us home: the outward then inward breath of Creation. I felt civilizations rise up and fall away. I felt the rise of nations and the fall of nations. I felt the river of ideas cross-pollinating, seeding, roots interlacing, growing, and bearing fruit. I saw that sometimes these ideas were harvested, sometimes destroyed, and sometimes left to die on the vine. I felt the shaping and reshaping of the stories we told ourselves about this calling into being and the return to the One that sent us. There have always been as many versions of this as there were cultures and traditions.

I saw Caravan moving through this universe outside of time, holding us, calling us to honor our agreement with the One that sent us. I felt the unending patience and grace of the work in Caravan. I felt the currents of collective mythic and cultural stories moving through the personal life missions of the hundred billion lives said to have lived in our world over its history. In a way that I have no words for, I felt my place in that stream, and a great peace moved through me. We all go home together because there's never been a separation between us. We're all held in the arms of the One, the One who sent Caravan to bring us home. A million million years is but a breath to the One who sent us and calls for our return.

A quiet pervaded every corner of Caravan as I returned. Verity moved around the circle opposite Jun. They slowed to a stop and Verity returned to the place between Alika and me.

Jun moved wood in the fire with his cane as he began again, his voice just loud enough to be heard. "Our work in Caravan assists our horizontal world selves in the work of embodying our life missions.[39] Together with the One that sent us, we create a container for the work in the horizontal world. There is another kind of miracle that happens with this. Something is created that is a kind of life. We co-create the being of our life mission. Like our self, our life mission is a being that lives in both worlds and moves with us. Our relationship with this being is as ancient as our relationship with Caravan and the One that sent us." He paused and looked at each of us. "Your work, at least here in Caravan, requires your conscious participation in this relationship. Your conscious relationship here will affect your horizontal-world life, even if you don't consciously remember it there."

I watched the co-creation of Jun's dance with his dragon cane. Point by point, from one hand to another, close and next to his body, then outward beyond our circle, tracing a pattern in a rug, then the head of the dragon against his heart. What if the connection to my life mission could be that natural and well-synched?

Jun said, "The relationship you have with the being of your life mission is connected to your relationship with all of life. It is directly connected to your agreement with the One that sent you. You have direct agreements made with other pilgrims in Caravan about your work in the horizontal world.

"The being of your life mission travels with you for your entire journey. It can be your closest friend and greatest protector in times of danger. In fact, the safest place for you in the horizontal world is traveling with your life mission. It will be the safest place in a crisis. It has most likely saved your life many times you are not even aware of."

All the while, as Jun told the story of our partnership with our life mission, dragon and Jun danced the possibility of this co-emergent unfolding. I looked within for examples of what he was saying in my own life.

Jun said, "The being of your life mission is on intimate terms with the Divine Spirit of Guidance. It is close to the Spirit of Guidance because it is your life mission.[40] It doesn't have all of your personal resistance in the way. There is a principle of resonance here. The more you give your time and attention to your life mission, the stronger your connection is. The more you give your time and attention to your life mission, the more beingness it will take on. When you stay present to the guidance you receive each and every moment from the One that sent you, you will have more certainty about your destiny.

"Your destiny has beingness. If you open your heart to the manifestation of your life mission, it will walk with you. If you hold it in your heart, like all relationships, it will respond to your call. Your life mission has called you every moment of your life in the horizontal world. If you open your heart in the horizontal world, you will hear your life mission calling you."

As Jun talked about the being of my life mission, I thought about all the times when guidance felt almost tangible. I thought it was a kind of intuition, as if Spirit were tapping me on the shoulder. Sometimes I listened, sometimes I didn't. I know for sure I was given inklings to not do things. When I went ahead anyway, I always regretted it.

I wanted to be able to go inside myself and call the being of my life mission. I wondered if we would be taught in Caravan how to do that. I felt a sense of its presence and wondered how it related to Caravan.

If the being of my life mission is present in my time in the horizontal world, then is it also with me in Caravan?

Jun stood next to me then. He touched my shoulder for a second as he continued. "Yes, the being of your life mission is with you here in Caravan.[41] It is a part of you, has been with you from the beginning, and does this work with you. It also is a being with its own integrity. It is timeless, as you are. You can ask for its help here as you can in the horizontal world. Your work in the horizontal world is done through this being as it is done with and through the One that sent you. Yes, it is of the One that sent you and has a kind of angelic presence in your life.

"If you are wondering if you will be shown how to contact the being of your life mission, I will say yes, though the instruction will be indirect. You will be your own best teacher in this. I advise you to hold the intention to be aware of your life mission. That is enough, just now. Your life mission is holding you in this work now, just as Caravan is holding all of us in this work. The One that sent us is in turn holding all of us and calling."

Verity looked at me. Jun and the rest of the circle were far off in that moment. It seemed that even in timeless Caravan, time had stopped. Verity pointed to several patterns in the rug, and they lit up. The sand under the rug gave the impression of mountains and valleys with light moving along highways of threads. I could read unfolding stories, although I couldn't be sure who was telling these stories. Was Verity the narrator? Was this one of the ways the One told our unfolding story? Verity touched her heart to remind me.

As I breathed into my heart, I heard the voices returning to Caravan. I heard stories being retold, being shared until each person's story was deeply a part of everyone in the circle. I felt the high story spiral, and I began to see the community it formed. I felt the mythic patterns weaving, watching the light move along the patterns of the rugs. I saw patterns within patterns moving to form larger patterns that made rugs that were identifiable as from particular cultures. I saw beings created by the weave, very much a part of the stories of the rugs and the cultures that told their story. The rugs were themselves containers for all of this. Everything I encountered in the horizontal world, in Caravan, in life, lay and lived in these patterns the light wove, the co-creation of the great story.

The sand of Caravan's world felt tangible beneath us. Rugs and sand were flexible, moving as we moved, supporting our campfire work. The high story, the mythic and archetypal patterns, our collective and individual stories weaving throughout, and the beingness of our life mission contained within the weave of life in the horizontal world, created the very foundation of it all.

Verity smiled and touched her heart again.

I continued to watch light moving along the weave of the rugs. I felt the great love of the One who sent us and the beauty of the great tapestry of the horizontal world. Everything since the first night I remembered in Caravan had led to this moment. All of it was foundation. I realized I understood the language of this unfolding story. I understood the language revealing itself as light moving through the rug, and surprisingly, I knew that some part of me understood the language of Caravan. Though I couldn't exactly translate it yet, I knew in that moment the language of Caravan was threaded through my very being.

Jun came back into focus. It felt as if he were sharing my thoughts.

"I know that most of you here have spent the largest share of your recent campfire circles developing high stories," he said. "Most of you in this circle gave support to someone putting his or her story together. I encouraged you to do this, and also to think about the story of your own culture and the myth underlying it. Along with this, I asked you to consider the myth you personally live in the horizontal world. We have talked about how these together form a container for your life mission. This container holds this and the being of your life mission. All of this together is a kind of foundation for the work you will do next in Caravan. Allow this to go deeply into your heart, and it will help you with what is next."

Jun turned to the fire, and once again Verity moved next to him in the center. If I was sure of the myth I was called to live and the highest possible story of my life mission, I would have a north star to guide me in the horizontal world. I looked up at the still unfamiliar stars above me and wondered if one of them remained stationary as we moved. I realized I didn't know if any of them moved.

I wanted that star, at least metaphorically. I wanted that foundation to build on. I wanted that foundation to work the assignment Verity had given me in the beginning.

This is the work of Caravan: Each pilgrim is to bring back to his or her life in the horizontal world the high story of his or her life mission. Everyone there was working to build enough resonance to carry over to his or her life in the horizontal world.

I felt the foundation Verity and the others had given me to begin this work. Still, I felt there was something more. Verity had given me a specific assignment in both worlds. If this were preparation and foundation for both worlds, it didn't seem to answer for both. It fit the work we all do in Caravan.

The other piece of the assignment was still a mystery.

CHAPTER 7

Considering Your Life Mission

VERITY CALLED AND ONCE again it was night in Caravan. The startling nature of this realization brought me to attention. I remembered wondering if day ever came to Caravan. I still had no answer. I could only say morning almost came to Caravan. I'd spent every one of my recent visits in the endless twilight of that almost place. Verity welcomed me back to night in Caravan. She gestured toward the open desert and began to walk. Caravan was in the very first stages of moving out. Camels were packed and waiting in lines to begin. As I walked with her, Caravan began to move between two fires and out. The threshold guardians bowed to Verity as we crossed over and out into the desert of the endless night of the Caravan of Remembering.

She turned to me as we passed the fires that formed the gates that Caravan moved through. "It begins," she said. For a time without measure we walked. Behind us, the lines of pilgrims extended as far as the eye could see. In front of us lay the desert, an ocean of space. The horizon, empty of anything or anyone and ever receding, appeared endless. Again we walked in silence. Breath slowing, mind slowing, walking and quieting, breathing and letting go. Forgetting all except to walk.

As in my first nights in Caravan, there would be no way of knowing how long we walked. Like emerging slowly from delicious sleep, I noticed without noticing when it happened, that Kairos walked with me. Like my first nights in Caravan, my mood was to have forgotten to have a mood. My thoughts moved out ahead of us and didn't return.

When thought returned, I wondered about Verity walking with me out and through the gates. I wondered about the amount of time she spent with me. Now I wondered if she had handed me off to Kairos. Though I was sure by now that Kairos could hear my thoughts if he chose to, he said nothing, walking silently next to me.

"It begins," Verity had said. The first night, I remembered, she had said, "Welcome to the Caravan of Remembering," and disappeared. To-night it was, "It begins." I asked myself what it meant to begin now after my many trips to Caravan.

As I thought about this Alika moved next to me. Barefoot, in jeans, with flowered shirt and hair tied back, she felt both American and Poly-nesian. Holding my arm, leaning in, voice quiet, she said, "Just like the night we found you. Here we are again. I'm still wondering why we seem to be doing the same work, even though I would guess you've already done this. If this difference is a marker for our horizontal-world selves, I want to know more. Don't you?" She paused to wait for a response. When I didn't respond, she continued, "Time to go to work. How are you doing with your high story?"

Kairos smiled and put his hand to his heart. I was sure he'd brought Alika to give me the work, and now it was time to go in to do it. As we walked through this endless night, this time my heart was filled with the question of the high story calling me.

It was time for my high story.[42] I realized all the different ways I told my story, even to myself. It was no longer an abstract idea. It was time for my life mission. I began to see images of all the places I'd lived in growing up. Sometimes my family had moved every three months. For most of my childhood, I felt as if we were always moving. I went inside myself to experience this. As memories moved inside I felt the movement of Caravan outside. I realized that my whole life had and was moving in both worlds. When I realized this, I felt a kind of peace realizing I felt very at home with this. From the beginning, my journey, my story, was one of a pilgrim. The story of my life as a pilgrimage in both worlds felt very high story to my heart.

I thought about all the people I'd met in the many places my family had lived in and traveled through. The countless people, touring with music moved through my life, came to mind. I turned to look at my fellow pilgrims in Caravan, moving like ocean waves, wondering how many I touched or passed by in the horizontal world. How many would I yet meet there? Would we be able to remind each other of our time here? Do we make pacts to remember?

As we walked, I began silently telling myself the story of my life, sometimes stopping myself in the telling, asking the questions asked around the campfire. I asked myself what something meant to me by the way I told it. I stopped myself to ask if the way I told the story was really true. Did it help to tell it this way?

I heard the voice of Kairos in my head, "Again please." I began again, and each time I did my best to tell my story in a way more alive, more empowered, more embodied, more healing.

This was the work of Caravan.

I witnessed those nights around the campfire, the retelling of a life that remained true even when the telling changed. I remembered as I listened, something I'd heard in the horizontal world: Facts and the truth are not the same thing. In relationship, it is more important to look for the truth than the facts. I felt as I listened that facts are of the head. The truth is heart.

I looked for the truth of my life now. I wasn't sure if I even knew the facts. Whatever the facts were, they hadn't helped me much. What I often thought were the facts turned out to be, more than anything else, the voice of someone in my head. The facts were often the voice of a team of inner critical voices or the denied self turned shadow.

I recognized the way I used my story of the facts to keep me from sticking my neck out and going for my dreams. In this way, I supposed, the facts were the weapon of choice for my comfort zone. It kept me safe. It also kept me from my life.

This time I wanted my heart of hearts to tell me the story of my life. I wanted the truthful version that created courage from its meaningfulness. I wanted to be astonished by my life and the way it revealed the One who sent me. Most of all, for Verity, I wanted a revelation of what the One who sent me prepared me for and called me to.

I paused in my inner work for a moment to follow the direction Kairos indicated. Within the movement of Caravan, I saw children weaving as they did those first nights. With the children weaving, and

Kairos and Alika walking with me, it felt almost as if we were back to my first nights in Caravan again. Though I felt I knew more now, I still felt young in Caravan's ways. That first night I'd met Kairos, Alika, and Lucio, and I had watched Kairos tune the children. Alika had been further along than the children, though she had also been weaving. Then we had all walked together. Now we were walking very much like we had that first night, she and I further along and doing the same work.

Kairos pointed again. "As you watch the children weave tonight and retell your story, do not hurry through the weaving of your childhood in the horizontal world. There are important clues for you there. You can imagine watching them now, how you also did this weaving to prepare your childhood for your life mission. Imagine the people you had to find to set it all up. How many agreements would it require to prepare a life mission?"

"Kairos," I asked, "are you tuning us also with these questions?"

"Again please," was all he said as he held his hand to his heart, looking to the horizon moving ever out in front of us as we walked toward it.

I watched Alika for a moment, then returned to thoughts of my childhood. I saw myself skating around large rocks, down a stream frozen with ice. I saw myself moving among plants several feet over my child's height, thick with branches filled with what seemed like millions of bells. I thought I walked in a magic kingdom.

My story began in the desert of Texas where I was born, and took me to nearly every state and culture in our country and a few others. Though I experienced the desert first, I lived in nearly every environment offered.

I saw myself once again walking the beaches of both oceans and the mountains of Colorado. I remembered walking in the dunes of California and the deserts of New Mexico and Arizona. I saw myself walking the rivers of Wisconsin and the redwoods of California. I walked the mountain forests of both coasts and the Everglades of the South. I walked the prairies of the West and the cornfields of the Midwest. My family visited an endless stream of states and national parks. I walked in winter snow in drifts over my head wearing layers of coats, and through mountains of fall leaves. I walked next to ocean palms and winter sands where fall and winter never visited. I walked in concrete canyons made by skyscrapers and through rivers of people. My family lived with every race, religion, and culture. We had a million neighbors and none for miles.

In each world we entered, I found something that came alive, every new place a world to discover. I knew there wouldn't be enough time to get attached, and remembering, I could almost hear my father telling me those very words. This gave me a great deal of freedom to experiment, because I knew I wouldn't be around long enough to care about the local clique. This allowed me to make friends as the moment called.

What clues were in this? Why a life like this? I experienced nearly every environment and culture in America. We stayed just long enough to get a feel for them and not so long that I was constrained by them. I found people and aspects of each place to love, memories that have stayed with me my whole life. I never stayed long enough to feel slighted by anyone there, that I remember.

As I thought about this I looked around Caravan. I wondered how many walking with us then were people I had met in the pilgrimage of my childhood. If my childhood pilgrimage prepared me for anything, I thought it was my travels in Caravan. That made me smile. I watched my fellow pilgrims moving ever on through the night, as the movie of my childhood moved ever on inside. What clues, I asked myself?

"Again please," said the voice of Kairos in my head.

I thought about the way Spirit moved in my childhood. I found Spirit in the many places more than in the people. I was more often confused in my childhood by the way people related God to me. I thought people in general were also confused by life. I heard so many conflicting ideas on the subject of God and what our life was meant to be. I was presented with every religion in one way or another growing up, though my family was officially Christian. My time in nature felt more straightforward. There was a kind of attunement that came naturally.

The paradox was how this moved to its opposite over time. As I grew older, I retained my respect and reverence for nature, and spent less and less time there. I found a new kind of nature. I found the unlimited nature of inner space. I found myself spending more time drawing and painting these inner worlds. Also I wrote music that I heard inside more than the music of the outside world.

I smiled to remember that already I felt comfortable moving between worlds. I wondered to myself if I had visited Caravan then, and didn't have the understanding of it to remember it was Caravan I visited. I was comfortable with people of all places, cultures, and religions. I was comfortable with ideas that were different. I learned to be open to any world. Again, I thought my childhood had prepared me more for Caravan than the horizontal world.

I moved to thinking about the schools I had passed through. There were so many. Unlike my current friends in the horizontal world, I have fewer memories of particular teachers from my childhood. My family moved too often to remember any one of them changing my life greatly. This had more to do with my life than any of the teachers. The ones I found inspiring were always the rogue teachers. They were the ones who still seemed alive. They were the ones who called us to stay awake. I remembered Miss Wilson actually saying that to us. As young as we were, she knew we were already going to sleep. She rewarded independent experimental thinking. I found this way natural and we got on well until it was time to leave again.

Yes, I could see patterns in the kaleidoscope of my childhood and the teachers I gravitated toward. Always my life and my heart created situations that called me to stay awake and say yes to life. I was looking for something, and my childhood had been designed in a way that kept that alive.

My childhood resulted in my spending years in the fine arts and more years on the road as a musician. I could have settled into the world of fine art. Instead, just as that was about to happen, rock and roll took me on the road. Echoing my childhood, I traveled to new places day after day. I felt this pattern. My life of pilgrimage had been designed for something. Kairos had told me to listen and look for the clues. What did this life prepare me for? What did the One call me into life in the horizontal world to embody?

I thought about the subjects that interested me. Surely this would be a clue. I was good at science and math, though more interested in science. I found history and the social sciences intriguing, and the arts exciting, although I studied music with private teachers. Learning languages made sense, and new schools and some awkward teachers made languages difficult. As I thought about it, I realized I'd enjoyed all my classes and found nearly every subject interesting. I wanted to know about everything. That did not seem helpful in my search for the high story or my life mission.

Different environments, cultures, races, financial status, politics, careers, schools, subjects, and disciplines—I thrived in all of them. I didn't have a favorite. I didn't long for one over the other. I found a place in each of them. I found comfort in all of them. I felt I understood all well enough to fit in as a child. Where were the clues in this?

Kairos must have sensed that I felt stuck. He pointed toward different groups of pilgrims. "Just now you were telling yourself the story of your life. What moved you through the stages of growing up? Over there, do you remember being in that period of your childhood?" He pointed to a group of children who seemed to be deadly serious about something they were looking at. Apparently, each of them had a different idea about it, and it seemed important they all agree on the truth of it.

"Actually," I replied, "I don't remember ever caring about that. I do remember being caught in the middle and looking for the diplomatic solution. I might be still working on that more than I would like to admit. I don't remember looking for the one right answer. I liked to find several."

Kairos pointed to a group of what appeared to be teens. Though I hadn't noticed it before, I could see that even in Caravan they were working out what it meant to be one gender or the other. This, I thought, must be particularly complex in Caravan. At least in the horizontal world, we're given social, cultural, and religious clues as to what is expected and accepted. Here in Caravan, all possibilities were present. Some kind of inner resolution must be worked out here to prepare and inspire the life mission in the horizontal world.

As I watched them I nodded to Kairos. "Yes, I remember that, and yes, I remember there being many stages. I am sure that will continue as long as I travel in either world. How to be a man in the horizontal world is a question of many stages. How to relate that to being with women in the horizontal world is another world in itself. Yes, I painfully remember some of those stages. Thank you for that."

"Think about each stage and what moved you through it, and the direction it took you. Think about our work in Caravan." Kairos continued to point out different groups going through a variety of life challenges. "In your travels here, you have witnessed the work of moving the life in the horizontal world. If what happens in your life there isn't an accident, if you helped to set up the events and intentions, do you think the particular situations of your initiations are accidental?

"The rites of passage in terms of gender and sexuality will likely stand out for you," he continued. "If you look for them, you will find the rites of passage in all areas of your growing up in the horizontal world.[43] When you tell your story, what determines the kinds of initiation and rites of passage you experience? What determines the direction they take you in? If your life mission is a resonant attractor, calling your life in a particular way, why this turning point versus some other? Why this initiation? Why this rite of passage?"

I felt he was speaking to Alika as well as me. I thought about how fresh this must seem to her. I felt that although I might have more perspective at this point in my life, I might also have many more layers of defense and emotional padding. Again I circled the question of facts or truth. Did I get closer in each telling?

"Again please."

I thought about the many kinds of initiations and rites of passage we might have in a lifetime. Passing from grade to grade in school is a common rite of passage. I realized looking back that who was there and where it happened held a great deal of meaning. Who was there and where it happened determined in many ways how we let go and moved forward. Within any grade of school there were many rites of passage. Again, who shared them with me, and where they happened formed my idea of myself in ways I only understood years later. I could see specific moments along the way. This was the first time I'd thought about my life in this way.

Just as Kairos had said, there are many rites of passage moments of gender and sexuality. These show up at many points in the year. Others are learning initiations, team rites of passage, and initiations of money and its consequences. There are initiations of work and play, both public and private.

I found initiations and rites of passage working together to both mark and direct my life. I couldn't separate this process from Caravan however. This was just as much true here, and I wondered who directed this process in Caravan. Then I looked at Kairos, thought of Verity, and smiled.

I started again. I started with the first moments I could call rites of passage and initiation.[44] I supposed that losing the first tooth could be called a rite of passage. Would a first birthday party count if you didn't remember it? I thought the first anything you can remember might qualify. What influence did my first grades in high school classes have on how I thought of myself? What influence did the reception of my first music recital or first garage band's dance have? How did the reception of my first paintings shape my identity and what I thought was possible for my life? The question was how had these served and what did they call me to.

In the work of identifying my life mission, I looked for the footprints or fingerprints of the guides.[45] I looked for the impressions of the invisible hand. Here in Caravan, I realized that the guiding hand was often myself, doing the work of Caravan. The work I was doing that moment would create the foundation for the invisible guidance I would whisper to my horizontal world self's inner ear, if I didn't already remember my time here.

Now that I understood what Kairos was pointing at, I needed to return again to my story. What had the invisible hand been directing me toward? What did it mean that these significant rites happened when they did, in the places they did, and with the people they did? How did these rites relate to my story, the myth I lived, the container created, and the foundation laid?

I thought about this boy moving from place to place, environment to environment, culture to culture, and state to state in more ways than geography. I thought about my life mission being created by all that traveled with me. Yes, initiations and rites of passage were part of the process; they formed the container and foundation for life mission and the man I was becoming.

I knew this would help me with Verity's assignment, if I could stay with it. I knew I was getting to something. The great *Aha*, however, was not yet in sight. I could feel the answers around the corner of my awareness. The work made sense to me, and I couldn't bring it all together yet. I decided to let go of guiding the story and allow it to percolate and flow freely for a bit.

I breathed into the flow of Caravan. I savored the environment, the perfume of crossing the night sands. Those first nights on the move with Caravan came back to me. I felt a little of the peace of thoughts moving out toward the empty horizon, disappearing, and not being replaced by other thoughts. I felt the peace of walking in time outside of time until thought returned as I remembered moments of my childhood. I wondered if I had walked in Caravan then and didn't remember it. I knew I could find an initiation or rite of passage this walking helped me through if I looked for it. I decided to leave that for later.

Then I thought about my current life in Chicago. Sometimes I went to Lake Shore Drive. I liked to walk the beach at night, next to Lake Michigan. This was reassuring in its way. Every time I returned to the horizontal world it was raining when I arrived. It felt like a balance to the absolute desert of Caravan. I liked walking the sands in both worlds now.

Even in Chicago, the others on the beach held themselves in a place of quiet reflection. We walked silently together enjoying wind and water, sand and stars. It reminded me of Caravan when others walked the beach with me. I experienced a kind of paradoxical nostalgia for nights in Caravan, walking the beach next to the lake with my fellow Chicago pilgrims. A million lights to one side and endless waves to the other, and still I would get lost in walking the sands.

I could see this ritual helped me with Caravan. If my first nights in Caravan were initiations or rites of passage, then those nights on the beach in Chicago were part of it. Those nights walking the beach in Chicago helped me to ground my life in the horizontal world. It seemed less real than Caravan, even as I realized it was the point of Caravan's existence. Even if Caravan was given for our work in the horizontal world, the horizontal world seemed less real to me. The feel of sand between my toes, pulling my feet as I walked, kept me in the horizontal world.

In the horizontal world eventually we get tired walking the sands. Then there's the life we're called to embody, to return to. I would walk to the El, and the first night Verity visited would come back to me. Then getting off at Wicker Park, I would stop for a moment to look toward the place I always returned to in the rain. If I walked the beach long enough, I would be tired enough to accept the whole thing in peace. I would return to the coach house and collapse into my corner chair to rest or write in my expedition journal.

Those nights of walking the beach in Chicago, and returning home to write in the expedition journal, moved gently through me as I walked in Caravan. I allowed them to take hold as I let go of the story of my childhood. Now I saw the rituals I created to ground my movement from one stage of my life to the next. It struck me that if I could identify these rituals in my childhood, I would be very close to identifying the initiations important to my life mission. They seemed like clues, footprints in the sand.

Caravan slowed in that moment till we stopped completely. This was the first time Caravan had stopped without setting up camp. Those who were riding stayed on their camels, who seemed content to remain motionless except for an occasional step forward or back. In Caravan, the only way to tell if we were moving in any direction was footprints in the sand. Now with Caravan at rest, I could see clearly the direction we traveled, and the direction we moved toward.

After a moment, Alika whispered to me, "It is perfect, isn't it? I never get tired of that. You're looking at the tracks, right?"

"Finding the direction . . . yes . . . footprints in the sand.[46] Finding the direction for everything we've gone through, to what end we are led. Where is our pole star? In addition to these questions we ask, there's the presence of Caravan directing behind the work. Yes, I was looking for the direction."

"Looking at the sand," she said, "I see the direction we travel, will travel, assuming we continue. Are the tracks of your life mission direction so far, as clear to you?"

"No. Just this minute I feel they will be. Everything in Caravan stopped to witness this for us. Now I see the direction was there for us the whole time. Caravan didn't need to stop for us to see it. The direction is clear even as we move through it, if we look. Though Cara-van just showed us it's okay to stop to look if we need to, I know now we can see it even as we move. What I want to get really good at is seeing the direction calling, without looking back. I want to see the direction calling from in front of us."

At this we both turned to look in the direction Caravan had been moving. As we did this Caravan did indeed begin to move. It was slow in starting, yet slowly and surely we all moved in the direction Caravan called us to. Caravan orients the direction home.

I found myself in Wicker Park, in the rain of course, thinking it would be nice to share what I was going through. It seemed unlikely. It was cold and wet and I felt a little disconnected from Caravan. Return-ing, I couldn't remember what I'd worked on there. I could remember Caravan. What I was working on just before returning felt fuzzy and distant.

Then I began to remember something about direction. In the endless, empty horizon of the absolute desert of Caravan, direction felt unclear, almost unavailable. I'd felt the need for a sense of direction to ground the work of Caravan. Watching the rain, I began to feel that a sense of direction would be a kind of order in the chaos of life in the horizontal world. I could use that, I thought. I felt close to something. We'd done a lot of work in Caravan since I'd first remembered Verity's call. Then, I had to ask myself whom I meant when I said "we." I could use a sense of "we" in Wicker Park, I thought. I could use a little "we" in terms of someone who knew about Caravan.

As I threw my keys on the drafting table entering the coach house, I remembered Kairos asking me to remember what I wanted. I wanted pizza and a date. For the first time in a long time, I wasn't caught up in the work of Caravan. I had illustrations due in a few days, my partner had left a message about work we had quoted, and we had a meeting to set up with our prospective new partner. We were still in dialogue with this possible third partner about creating a studio with an actual location and a "direction," and I had more doubts than ever that I even wanted to continue.

The messy chaotic possibilities of life in the horizontal world loomed on the horizon of any near future. I was tired, wet and lonely, and I wanted more than anything else to call someone. I wondered what that could lead to, feeling all that, so I took a shower and made myself dinner. I chose not to watch a movie or read a magazine or book. I allowed myself to eat quietly and relax into the chaos I'd returned to.

After eating, I cleared my mind and focused on my breath. Realizing that my Caravan self would help me sort things out, I finally felt like looking at my notes for the illustrations. Even with the sense of calm, knowing I could do the illustrations, I felt I didn't want to do this work anymore. I'd known that when I'd taken my mini-holiday to research life mission a few weeks earlier. And now I knew this with certainty. An inspiration came from somewhere, a kind of ordering principle and message. Behind even the answer to this illustration assignment, was a clear signal that it was time to change. I wanted something else.

"There you go, Kairos," I said. "I am clear. I want something else." As soon as I said that, I realized this wasn't new. When I was a child, upon reflection, I'd always told myself there was something I wanted more. I did imagine I could enjoy it for a while though, and that's exactly how it had turned out. It felt like a confirmation of the power of our thoughts to manifest, and a witness to the absence of my life mission.

I felt some relief when I said I wanted something else, and decided to work since I wasn't going to sleep. It helped to remember that when I'd imagined my work as a child, I knew I'd enjoy illustration. I remembered that was what I wanted when I majored in fine art.

As I worked, I thought about order and chaos. My life in Chicago felt chaotic and it would have been easy to blame that feeling on Caravan. I wanted to say I was distracted by Verity's assignment. In fact Verity, Kairos, Savitri, Bede, and Amar Nen felt closer to me than anyone in my life in the horizontal world, including my studio partner. I wanted to say Caravan and my assignment were too much. As easy as that would be, I had walked enough nights in Caravan to know the assignment was the answer, not the problem.

I was tempted to think anytime chaos showed up in my life, I was moving away from my life mission. Was chaos a signal? Was a sense of order a sign of congruence or alignment with my life mission? I played with these thoughts as I worked on the illustrations. I could hear Kairos in my head, saying "Again please." I went through my story with this in mind. Even though I couldn't identify my life mission exactly, I couldn't say the chaos in my life was the result of choosing something else.

With the little I knew already, I could think of situations in which things seemed to be moving in the direction of my life mission . . . and still there was chaos. I could also place times of order in my life when I was pretty sure I wasn't anywhere near my life mission. I knew there is a connection between order versus chaos and life mission. I felt there was an intrinsically ordering principle about our calling. If this is true, I wanted to know why chaos was still so present, even when one is on the path of one's life mission.

I was tempted to say that chaos is temporary. With enough time on the path of life mission, order eventually wins over chaos. Again I knew, that isn't the way it actually works. I thought about the people I imagined who spent most of their lifetimes deeply involved in the work of their life missions. Reading their biographies, I found chaos at regular intervals. Clearly life mission didn't mean a life of orderly progression of one inspiring project after another. Looking at the project on my table, I had to admit it wasn't inspiring, and the thought of the money it would make didn't help. The only hope of inspiration lay in the direction of life mission.

I worked through the night and inspiration did make an appearance. While making breakfast, I thought about that paradox. The inspiration for the work came from my turning it over to my Caravan self. I realized I was frustrated by the work waiting for me and feeling my life was in chaos wasn't because my work was intrinsically bad. I was frustrated because I had stayed too long at the fair, and I knew it. The work in Caravan got in the way, not because it took too much of my attention; it got in the way because it was the answer to my prayers. It got in the way because I wasn't happy, and it showed me why.

Inspiration came when I turned the work over to my Caravan self. I had no idea what that meant when I said it, yet something happened. The inspiration wasn't directly for the project. The inspiration was a knowing that brought a peace, and with that, a kind of order. I felt the answer to the project came from a part of myself that knew I needed to finish the project so I could get back to work on my life mission. It was like a friend helping to clean up a mess so I could get to work on the important stuff.

I knew my partner would be relieved. I'm sure she was thinking she'd have to push me to finish, so it was great to complete the project before the due date. Thinking about the other work lined up brought a new level of anxiety. I knew I'd have to let her know it wouldn't be long. There wouldn't be a third partner, with me, at least.

As I put the project in the portfolio and prepared to leave, I wondered how long it would be before I gave my notice. Walking to the El, approaching the park, I couldn't help stopping to watch the place of my return flights. A part of me wanted to go to Caravan and not come back. I knew that wasn't the answer however. Everything in Caravan was oriented to the work of helping us find our places in the horizontal world. That was the answer.

My partner was pleased that the illustrations were complete. In spite of not sleeping, this entitled me to join her in yet another last minute job, due of course end of day. This gave me the opportunity to see that she did love the work. It surprised and delighted me to watch her, thinking she was surely doing her life mission. It wasn't just that she was good at it. She really loved this work. She loved the whole crazy thing. She even loved the last minute rush part of it. It suited her nature in some essential way. I couldn't imagine anything else she'd be as happy doing. Unlike me, she was at home eating and breathing this work. Watching, I was profoundly happy for her.

"End of day" turned into after midnight before I stepped off the platform at Wicker Park. As tired as I was, I felt a deeper sense of peace. I didn't know how much longer I'd be in the illustration design business. I did know that my partner would be fine. We had momentum and contacts. This work was her life mission and it was perfect for her. She would be all right when it was time.

Like the first nights I remembered, Verity called me just as Caravan was preparing to leave. "Enjoy this moment," she told me. "You were feeling disconnected from both worlds. Take this moment into your heart. Everyone here is a part of you, and you are family to each pilgrim here. We will work together until we all go home together. Look, listen; breathe it in until you feel your place again."

In the horizontal world I would have guessed pilgrims had hours to pack, observing the pace of the packing. Invited to watch, Verity told me it wasn't a time for me to help. I noticed night campfires. Campfires were always for twilight-dawn morning and rest in Caravan. There were always at least two moons shining on Caravan, with more than enough light to move in the night. I had difficulty thinking of Caravan as a planet, which made thinking of them as moons strange. Still, there were always at least two and sometimes more moons in various phases providing light.

I liked the idea of night campfires. The horizontal world part of me felt more at home then. The lady dressed in deep blue offered Verity and me cups of tea, and we sat for a moment, watching as camels were slowly brought to the tents. There were few possessions in Caravan. They would just be extra things to pack and carry. Since everything would appear when it was needed, I was sure the packing was a kind of meditation. I was sure packing, like walking through the night, was part of the ritual, another way to contemplate the work of life mission.

I watched as Verity talked to several passers-by, occasionally pointing at something or someone. She occasionally held her hand to her heart and bowed slightly. Caravan was in the pause between in-breath and out-breath. The woman in the dark blue robe handed me my Caravan expedition journal as she poured more tea. Verity motioned to me and said, "You might begin with what Kairos left you with."

Caravan Expedition Journal:

I sit at the edge tonight as we are about to begin, thinking about the many things I have wanted over the course of my life, a question Kairos left us with.[47] *I could say they changed since I was young, and yet that isn't entirely true. Most of what I want now, I've wanted all my life.*

Kairos asked me what I believed.

He said to me, "If you believe you want something else now, the next question is why. Why do you want something you didn't want when you were a teenager? Is this because you have grown up, or is it because you stopped believing in your dreams? Did you believe anything was possible, and, if so, what happened to that belief? Whether your dreams have changed or not, it is important to take the moment given in Caravan to contact what you really want now. If you find that you do not remember what you wanted when you were young, call to your seven-year-old self. Call to your teenager within. See if you can get in touch with the part of you that had a dream for your life when you were young."

He asked me if I remembered a time when I considered anything possible.

He asked, "Do you remember a dream that you kept to yourself, even if you didn't really believe it would ever come true? What did you dream about just for fun, in your heart of hearts?

"As you tell your story tonight, remember what you wanted as you moved forward in your life. Both what changed and what didn't change about what you wanted are important. How did what you said you wanted change in relation to what you allowed yourself to dream? This will also point toward the direction of your life mission calling."

Note to self: I hadn't suggested anything out loud. I believe he was listening to my thoughts again. Was this absolutely necessary for the work of Caravan? Since it seems that someone is always listening to my thoughts in Caravan, it occurs to me as I watch Caravan prepare to leave that I will never be lonely in Caravan.

Verity reached for me as I paused in my writing. "Come, wanderer, worshiper, lover of leaving," she said, "we are leaving now." She handed the journal to the woman in blue and led me out toward the gate fires. Again we walked out through the space between the two fires with the rest of Caravan moving toward the endless horizon.

Again the breath slowed and thoughts moved out and across the sands. My thoughts did not return to me. All awareness was my family of pilgrims moving together toward a home on the other side of this endless horizon.

Thoughts and time returned when Verity guided me through pilgrims on foot to a group mostly seated on camels. Verity moved into synch with a woman I thought most likely to be American. She seemed completely at home riding, and in the horizontal world I would guess she was Middle Eastern, yet there was something that intuitively said North American.

Possibilities ran through my mind. In the horizontal world, this woman might be a European in Africa or Australia. She might be a European in the Middle East. In Caravan, a woman from a Muslim country in the horizontal world might wear a burka, and she might not. Her posture said she might be from a royal family in the Middle East, then again a royal family in Europe. Still without knowing why, I thought American.

She wore the flowing robes of the desert and felt very much of the desert. I couldn't see her hair or much of her face, yet I felt something. The feeling was similar to finding Alika and Lucio, only stronger. I was sure if Kairos were there he would say, "You have found each other and that is enough."

As we kept pace with my American, Verity spoke. "You were writing about what you wanted. You considered what you wanted over your life and what you want now. You considered what that meant by itself and in conjunction with the other work you remember doing in Caravan till now. You will have more time to integrate this with your high story myth work. You will be asked to go beyond all of these questions in terms of your childhood clues.

"All these considerations and the wants that come from them lead to the decisions you will need to make. Each moment in time calls you to decide. It is time to remember that you made decisions about your time in the horizontal world before you remember coming to Caravan. You will do more work with decisions now and that will help. You have caught up with your previous decisions and it is time for new decisions."

Verity then turned to my American. "Anni, it is almost time."

CHAPTER 8

⁺⋆⁺

Remembering Your Own Life Mission

As we walked through the night, we never moved away from Anni. The peace I usually felt walking in Caravan with thoughts moving out and away did not return. My thoughts stayed with Verity and Anni. Anni apparently knew me, and I didn't remember her. I wanted to see her better. I wanted to talk to her. I wanted to ask and I waited. In Caravan, when it was time, it happened.

As Verity walked with us, she reached often for Anni's camel. She wasn't leading her camel as much as connecting the three of us energetically, I thought. I already felt the connection and knew enough of the weaving of Caravan to know that was true. We moved with the flow of pilgrims, maintaining a place at the edge of pilgrims on foot and those on camels. Anni's camel was a dromedary (one humped camel) with an Egyptian saddle. Egyptian saddles are the ones with the higher saddle horns. Under the saddle was a kilim rug, the earth color of the robes the guides wear, with beadwork all along the border. She wore a long black robe often seen in the desert.

I remembered when Verity first called me to Caravan. Though I now remembered Caravan when I returned to the horizontal world, I was still waiting to remember my time before in Caravan. Remembering the previous time in Caravan was now tied to Anni, and I sensed Verity's assignment for me, and it felt suddenly like an assignment I might not be up to. Verity had said that even with all of the help provided in Caravan, sometimes we don't remember. I wondered if I was one of those cases.

How many times had I been to Caravan? How many times would I forget my agreement with the One that sent me? Verity said it was almost time. That seemed to mean that my forgetting was part of the plan. Perhaps forgetting, then remembering, was the usual plan for the horizontal world.

Verity turned to me. "You want to know what this means," she said. "You want to know what bringing you to Anni means, and what it meant when I told her it was almost time. While what something means often is everything, it does not always serve to know immediately. As we walk, allow these questions to sit in your heart for now. Allow the question of meaning itself to move with you."

I thought her questions where very much like a tuning Kairos would do. I thought everything in Caravan was a form of tuning. It was tuning for the work in the horizontal world, and a tuning of the heart to prepare us for what came next. It was eternal preparation for the work of our life mission, which in turn prepared us to return to the One that sent us.

I allowed the question of Anni to move back into my heart. I allowed it to be okay for the moment that I didn't know. I turned to the question of meaning. What meaning was in general seemed like answering a question with a question.

When Verity told me to allow the question of meaning to walk with me, I felt that could "mean" anything. I smiled at that. Since she always seemed to know what I was thinking, I looked to see if she was smiling now. She was looking at me. She wasn't smiling. Without the slightest trace of irony, she put her hand to her heart and said, "Again please."

So I went inward again. I went back to the high story of my childhood in the context of meaning. I thought meaning was the high or (hi) story. The myth I lived was a kind of structure or encoding container for this meaning. Meaning is life mission, I thought. That was not what Verity asked though. Verity wanted me to look at meaning in my life.

Then I heard her in my mind say, "Again please. " I went through my life story as if meaning were a character in the story. The character named meaning had traveled with me my whole life.[48] Verity wanted me to notice the part this character played in my story.

I thought about the guiding hand of Meaning always running somewhere in the creation of events. In my earliest years, I imagined the guiding hand was my parents' meaning. I looked for the earliest moments I remembered Meaning playing a part in the dialogue within me. I looked for the earliest decisions interacting with this character.

It didn't help to say life mission was meaning. If I wanted to remember my life mission, I needed to watch Meaning moving in my life. The question of life mission and meaning wasn't circular after all. The character in my story called Meaning left footprints as surely as walking the sands of Caravan.

Verity said I'd caught up with decisions already made, and it was time for new ones. I thought that meaning and decisions could always be found together. We decide based on meaning. Sometimes something outside tells us what something means. Sometimes it's the meaning we give that decides. Either way, meaning comes first. Then I thought we decide based on both meaning from our past experience and our best ability in the moment to respond to the meaning we find. I remembered times when I responded to the meaning my heart gave something, and other times when I responded to the meaning my fear or shadow gave.

To embody my agreement with the One, I needed to recognize when I had the ability to respond to the meaning my heart gave me. I needed to both know the meaning of my life mission and give meaning to living it. The paradox is that knowing meaning and living meaning is not circular. What I wanted needed to rise out of this interconnection, and the decisions I made would bring me closer or further from embodying my agreement with the One. Resolution could seem simple in Caravan. I knew it wasn't simple in the horizontal world.

As I thought about this time traveling with Verity and Anni, I thought about the others I had shared campfires with and everyone I had walked next to through the nights. We had all learned from each other. Already, helping each other with our life stories, we saw our own stories differently. Around the campfires, we learned from each other's responses to our guides. It is the way of Caravan. We learn together, we come to our life missions working together, and we all go home together.

I thought about all the people I traveled with in the horizontal world. I had only begun to think of our learning, working, and going home to the One together after my first few trips to Caravan. Our life in the horizontal world is a Caravan. It is, or can be, a sacred pilgrimage, yet it seems more like the Caravan of Forgetting. It occurred to me in that moment that this was the point of Caravan. The forgetting had its purpose. Then remembering was also important. Both forgetting and remembering had their place, and both had meaning in the plan. I began to find peace with forgetting and recognized it as a kind of beginning. Caravan calls us to transcend it.

Verity leaned in to whisper, "Welcome to the Caravan of Remembering."

I remembered more than I ever expected to remember. The work with my life, the high story, the myth and all of its stages, and turning points in the horizontal world moved through my mind. I felt grateful for all of it. I wanted to remember my calling. I also wanted to remember who Anni was to me and why we were traveling together now. I wondered when I would know the decision we would have to make.

We traveled together in silence then. Eventually my mind did quiet, thoughts moved out and away and did not return. Something in me surrendered to whatever the agreement between us was. I would know when I needed to. I decided the best thing to do then was to focus on my work in Caravan, finding my life mission. Even these thoughts trailed off and time slipped away. We walked silently with no destination except where the work could take us.

Verity leaned over. "While you contemplate Anni traveling with us and our time together, ask yourself who else you would like to walk the sands of Caravan with.[49] Who would you like to sit with in your next campfire? If you could pick twenty people with whom to do the work in Bede and Savitri's campfire, who would you gather? You can choose anyone, past or present, in the horizontal world. Take your time with this. Imagine this happening. What would you ask these people? What questions would you want them to ask you? What questions do you imagine would come from the perspectives of their life experiences?"

I began to imagine Savitri in a tailored Western suit with silver jewelry matching the sparkle of the silver of her hair dancing with the campfire. In my mind her olive complexion completed the elegant and Eastern feel, accenting her Western dress. In my imagination, Bede complemented Savitri's look with an elegant, though conservative three-piece suit of his own. Seeing them both in Western dress, I wondered if I would first call on people from my Western world to work around the campfire. As I had those thoughts, I knew I would eventually choose people from all over the world.

I thought about the kind of relationship I might like to have in Caravan by way of mentoring by someone of my choice.[50] Who I picked, the process they used to help me, and the questions they asked me would likely be tied to the context of their life and experience. That's the point, I thought. If I picked them for their expertise and life experience, then who I picked would tell me a great deal about what I was looking for before I asked them the first question.

I wanted to ask for help from people in the world that I respected. Then I thought about the timeless nature of Caravan and wondered who I would call on from all of time. Paradoxically, this was harder because there was an infinite number of people to choose from. It was also harder because they were all great in their own times. Not everything would translate. Still, some things are timeless even in the horizontal world. Sometimes it's an idea or a quality or a way of being in the world. To become great in any age calls for attunement and awareness.

I allowed my mind to begin sorting through possible mentors and guides. I called some of my favorite painters into my circle. I realized the painters I would pick now were not the ones I would have picked when I majored in art. I liked some of their work and sometimes later realized I didn't care for the person. What did this distinction between a painter and their work mean to the question of my life mission? When I thought about this, I realized it was true in all the visual and performing arts. I realized I wanted to talk to the artists I felt had contributed to uplifting us and adding beauty to our world. For me, it was more about what the art or artist inspired or catalyzed than the art itself.

I wanted to know about their process and what they thought about when they worked. How had they kept themselves inspired? What kept them working, even in the dry and down times? Where had Spirit entered in their work and in their life?

This led me to think about spiritual figures of our time. I wanted to meet the ones who changed us collectively, the leaders who seemed to have a connection to Spirit in the way they led and the way they seemed to care about humanity.

I wanted to meet scientists who had changed the world, the ones who led the wave. How had they continued when answers to their quest eluded them experiment after experiment? Suddenly I wanted to talk to anyone who had led the wave of growth and evolution for humanity, who kept themselves going, and helped the ones who came after them. I wanted to talk to them. Given the timeless nature of Caravan, I thought I might be able to meet all those great beings. I half expected Verity to make it possible for me. I began to look around for some of the people I'd chosen to work with.

Verity stepped closer again. "It won't be necessary just now for you to talk to them," she said. "What you have discovered is a good beginning. Continue to contemplate the group of your imaginal campfire. Allow them to speak to you there."

Verity moved off and away from us then. I continued to walk with Anni's group imagining the campfire of teachers I wanted to be with then. I watched them in my mind's eye sharing and integrating their experience and knowledge. I found myself especially interested in the way their experience created a synergy. I appreciated what each offered, and became most excited when I realized how to integrate the cross-discipline, cross-cultural inspiration.

Traveling in Caravan, I wasn't entirely sure this was theater of my mind. I wondered if it was possible it had really happened on some level.

It was night in Wicker Park when I returned. With no portfolios to pick up, I stood in the rain pondering Verity's questions. I asked myself who I would like to spend the next day with. Because Verity had asked me in Caravan who I would chose to do campfire work with, I now wanted to have a day with one of these exceptional people in the horizontal world.

Watching the rain, I asked myself who I would pick to meet the next day if it were my choice. I knew my day was scheduled for another round of work that held little to no fascination for me. I appreciated everyone I worked with, yet I did not share their enthusiasm. I wondered what was next. I dearly wanted to know the answers to the questions I walked timelessly in Caravan.

Who would I choose to spend the day with?[51] I thought about the "great ones" I knew who lived at least part-time in Chicago. I thought about the people who moved through Chicago. I thought there might be many great people I could include if I were aware of them. I thought there must be thousands of people I would love to spend the day with.

I began to think about the ones I knew personally, not limiting the list to those living in Chicago. That felt helpful. The question was about who I would choose and perhaps, more importantly, why. Why this person versus another? They could live anywhere.

Could they live anywhere? This added another question: Where would I choose to visit and spend the day with them? Why would I choose this? Was it the person, the place, or both? I walked slowly through the park, to consider the question of place, watching the rain. I always found the rain comforting after Caravan. I felt close to the gifts of both worlds in those moments.

I appreciated the luminous ozone green everywhere. I could see it even under the park lights at night. I enjoyed the feeling of grass under my feet, even with shoes on. I smiled at the birds moving between the trees through the rain. I even enjoyed the chill I felt as the night breeze moved over my rain-soaked clothes. Wicker Park was a good choice for departure and return, I thought. Then I had to ask why. At that moment, I realized I had chosen the park because it brought Caravan and all I loved there into my life.

I thought about places of significance in my life. I felt they were significant to me because of what happened in them. Many of the places I found beautiful had little to no attraction to me. Places that were not particularly beautiful were on my list of places to spend a day in as I thought of it then. Why did I want to go to those places? Was it because of a person or an event? I was surprised to discover I remembered a few places because of an *aha* moment that happened there. I wanted to spend the day there because I wanted to better understand that experience or realization of the process leading to the *aha!* I wanted to better understand what the people and the places came into my life to tell me.

Back at the coach house, I went through my list of people and places as I changed wet clothes for dry and prepared to eat. I picked at my salad and stared at my studio equipment. I wondered who would want to spend the day in my studio with me, and why. I didn't want to spend the day with me. I wasn't looking forward to the next day or place I had scheduled. As I thought about where my heart wanted to be, I let my mind wander.

I found myself thinking about what place in time my heart was attracted to, to spend a day. Renaissance periods emerged first. I thought about how many of these there were, even though they weren't all called Renaissance periods. It surprised me to find this calling in my heart wasn't tied to any one time or place in particular. Experiencing this creativity and inspiration felt important to me. The draw was the coming together of the call of Spirit and the needs of the time.

I wanted to spend the day with the people who led the changes. I wanted to spend the day with the ones who followed the call in their heart, even when it went against the conventions of the time. It was more about their life and placement in time than a specific type of work or way of living. If it was about a way of living, it was about the example of the call and answering it. I felt excitement growing as I went through the combination of the persons, places, and times of my choices, a web of clues. What could I make of this combination in terms of my life mission?

I asked myself how this helped me with Verity's assignment. I wanted to visit with any of those people who stepped to the front of the wave of growth and new possibilities, even when everyone else said *stop*. Spending the day with them in their time would help me understand how they arrived at their decisions. Verity had said it was time to decide. Something in me wanted to decide and step forward to make a difference in my time.

As I said this to myself, I was sure I'd heard this from nearly everyone I talked to, when the talk became serious and personal. When the talk moved past superficial, I would testify that nearly everyone in the horizontal world, in my time, wanted to make a difference. What I learned around the campfires of Caravan told me this was true in every time.

There was a way for me to make a difference that was personal and specific to my life mission.[52] When I knew the answer to the particular way I felt called to make a difference, I would have some answers. The places I wanted to visit held clues. The *who* and the *when* were also important.

The integration of the disciplines to create something new was the biggest draw. The people I wanted to spend the day with were the ones who had found ways to do that. They had found ways to manifest their dreams. I wanted to know how they did this and made it practical in their lives. How had they managed the politics and finances of their times and still followed their muses?

This seemed especially relevant in my time. As I considered what might come next in my life, I wanted to know how I could go for my life mission in a practical way. I longed to know that very moment. I couldn't imagine continuing my work with the studio. If Verity hadn't called, I might have spent years there before recognizing that I'd lost myself, before I found the courage to say I couldn't do it any more. I might have spent decades getting through the numbness, and died doing it.

I promised myself I would find my life mission, no matter what. Whatever the cost, I would stick with the search until I remembered it. Verity had said it was *almost time*, and I so hoped I would remember soon. I wanted the decision to be claiming my life mission.

I went to bed reviewing everything I'd been working on. I wasn't looking forward to another day in the studio, yet this work kept me going. I hoped as I fell asleep that it was really almost time for the decision Verity had spoken of. Was I ready? I wanted to be.

In addition to the reading I thought might help with Caravan homework, I took classes when I could fit them in on the weekends. I found these classes in the free papers. They were one evening, one day, and weekend classes. I used my intuition mostly. Why I took them didn't always make sense to my logical self. I knew I was looking for clues and wanted to follow my heart. I thought these classes would be a nice balance for the work in Caravan.

Also, I had the idea that agreements would be made in Caravan to help me. In the tuning with Kairos it was always clear that the weave set the cause in motion for the horizontal world. I felt that if I put myself out there, something would show up in the horizontal world to help me. I knew enough of Caravan and the campfire work to know that someone there would be talking about the possibilities to assist my search. Likely I had taken part in these dialogues around the campfire, if I could only remember it. As I thought about it, I could almost hear Kairos tuning the weave to set up our appointments in the horizontal world.

It was on an evening watching the leaves turning color outside that I got the call. I loved the way the sky looked in the fall. I loved watching the squirrels gathering food for winter. I loved the idea of walking in the cool, gray dusk, enjoying the chill in the breeze. The call was from a woman I had met through the seminar circles. She let me know about classes as they came up. It was almost a career for her, if she actually worked at anything. She seemed to find her connection to life in other people's responses. She never seemed to actually do the work or engage in any way herself. I always felt a little uneasy about her motives. Towering at least a foot or more over me in stocking feet (which we were at some seminars), weighing less than me still, she elicited a question in my heart. What did she really want?

"There's a gathering of some friends coming up for a kind of picnic," she said, "and I thought you might be interested. I told them about you, and they want to meet you. Also, there's someone I'd like you bring if you could. Her name is Anna and she could use a ride. We meet at the lighthouse beach, so bring her and bring some food."

I was going to say *no*. The word was halfway out of my mouth when she asked me to bring Anna. Instead, I found myself saying I would, and took down the instructions to pick her up. Again I had that feeling you have when you know something real is going to happen. I felt I would get the answer to something. I knew if nothing else made sense about that picnic, giving Anna a ride did. It was a feeling.

"Welcome to the Caravan of Remembering, wanderer, worshiper, lover of leaving."

I heard Verity calling long before I left, like an echo inside. It was still night in Caravan, only Caravan was a tent city again. Caravan wasn't getting ready to leave or travel anytime soon, unlike all of my other night visits. In every direction I looked, I saw tents and campfires. This was not twilight dawn in Caravan. I could plainly see the now-familiar stars, even with the two full moons.

Verity motioned for me to take the tea offered by the woman in the dark blue robe, then sat down next to the fire. Joining her, we were in the center of a pattern of oriental rugs laid out to tell a story, I thought. Each of the rugs was self-contained, and together formed a collection of stories. Verity ran her fingers along the lines of one Oriental rug, moving to another, and as often happened in Caravan, the lines she traced lit up and connected from one to another.

As she continued to trace lines and connect patterns, she asked, "How is your assignment coming?" I was sure she was giving me a clue, connecting the patterns of the rugs spread out under and around us. Like Caravan itself, every nation was represented in its patterns and colors. She wanted me to know something about connecting these patterns.

I was about to answer when something moved in my mind. In the moment I was searching the field to find what that was, Verity motioned to the woman in blue. As the woman handed me my expedition journal, Verity turned to look toward the door of the tent. "I asked Anni to join us tonight. Do you remember?"

I said *yes* without truly knowing what she meant. Anni came out from inside the tent carrying what I guessed was her own Caravan expedition journal. She sat just to the side of me. Kairos joined us, sitting just to the other side of Verity. I expected Verity to leave us with Kairos, and she continued to sit with us in silence. Anni was wearing the same earth-colored robe without any trace of the silver threads. I could see her hair was long under the hood and, I thought, light in color, even if I could barely see it. I could see almost nothing of her face, and yet I was sure I knew her, though I couldn't place where or how.

I half-expected Kairos to say, "You have found each other," and allow us to sit in silence. Instead he looked to me and said, "Many nights now, you have shared the weaving with me as Caravan tuned pilgrims and spun connections in the horizontal world. You have personally experienced the power of this. You felt a resonance with Alika and Lucio. I believe you know it is not an accident that you found your way to Savitri, Bede, and Jun. As I helped Alika and Lucio to find you, Verity has helped you to find Anni. That is all I will say about that for now."

He paused, then continued. "I want you to think about what you remember of your life. I want to you to include the times you remember in Caravan. While we sit together, I want you to write in your journal. Write about the times you felt the most alive, the most confident, the strongest. [53] Write about when you felt most in tune with your nature."

Staring into the fire, I thought about each question he asked. As I began to write, I noticed Anni also beginning to write. I felt myself moving again into the long "now" of Caravan, leaving trails of words instead of tracks in the sand.

Caravan Expedition Journal:

I remember feeling alive with music and loved art of every kind growing up. I loved learning and felt alive whenever I discovered something magical about the world. I felt alive creating and surrendering my sense of self to the worlds of imagination. I loved the night sky, and felt alive walking under it. I felt alive spinning great, mythic stories of possibility.

I wonder why I don't feel that aliveness now doing the creative work of our studio. Does it feel like too much of the same thing for too long? Each assignment is a new world and each assignment is a creative discovery. Why do I feel so numb and frustrated? Why this growing feeling I have to leave the studio now?

I admit that the time I feel the most alive now is my time in Caravan, and the time in the horizontal world I spend working on Verity's assignment. Do I feel this way because I'm working on the question of my life mission? Or is there something intrinsic to this work in Caravan that wakes me up and gives me the feeling of being alive? I feel most alive in both worlds when I'm doing the work of Caravan. Is this important for more than the answer to these questions?

Kairos is looking at me now as if to say, "Don't get stuck on that just now." I can almost hear him saying, "Again please."

When have I felt most alive? In my college years it was working in music and art studios. I was experimenting, trying every approach to find what part of me aligned with each style, genre, and period I tried on, and what my own voice wanted to say. I wanted to know what my style was. That pursuit of my way felt very alive then.

I tried this same approach with spirituality. I had the experience of the religion of my family. I wanted to discover what was true of other religions or traditions I could find access to. I felt alive in that search. Every moment of discovery in the pursuit of the thread that tied religions together was heaven to me. I felt alive discovering what seemed common to them. I had a thirst to know where they agreed on goodness, compassion and love. Where I experienced spiritual truth, I felt alive.

I felt this same grace when I encountered the threads of truth that tied the many worlds of science together. I loved to learn about the cosmos in all of its macro and micro glory. From biophysics to astrophysics, I felt alive in the process of finding the interconnections.

Writing this now, I can see it's this discovery of connection and integration that I wanted to learn more about when I wanted to spent a day in any of the Renaissance periods. It was this same thing I wanted to be with when I wanted to spend the day with someone. It begins to come together.

Still, I'm not ready to say what exactly this means.

Before I go back to where I felt most alive, I want to go to some of the other questions. Each of the things I felt most alive doing will be in tune with my nature. Did I also feel the "most confident" when I was doing these things?

The times I felt the "most confident" were the times further down-line from the process of discovery and seeking. When my research and questioning led to a new way of seeing or knowing, this gave me the confidence to push my idea of what I thought possible. I felt "most confident" when I was following the call of my nature,

questioning what I knew, or questioning my place, which led to
something deeper and more complex.

All of these working together gave me the strength I found when
I needed it. I could say I felt "most confident" when I was playing
music or creating art or pursuing spirit or science. That isn't exactly
true. When I really felt "most confident" was when I used the seek-
ing in each of these areas to understand my nature and that of my
world together, to increase the possibility of what I could imagine
was possible. It was a kind of synergy of all of these things that gave
me confidence and strength, and which in turn gave me the feeling
of being alive and in tune with my nature.

I know that working with these questions is meant to give me
clues to my life mission. The clues are in this and I'll hold my focus
on them while I wait until the integration of them emerges.

The fire caught my attention, as the flames seemed to lean in our
direction. I looked over to watch Anni writing in her journal. As Kairos had said, I did feel the power of our connection, and now had yet
another mystery to live with. I wanted to know who she was and why
she was suddenly in my Caravan life. I wondered what agreement we
made together in the time before I remember being here. Why did she
remember and I didn't?

From the first night I remembered being in Caravan, I've had almost nothing but questions. Being told I'd been in Caravan before was
something I had to trust. Strangely enough, I did. Now I had to take
their word for it that I had an agreement with this woman. In fact, all
of my time in Caravan since I'd met her again had been spent with her
and Verity. Now we were doing the work of Caravan together.

I felt nervous about what this might mean. It didn't put me at ease
that Verity told me the night she gave me her name and my assignment, that even with all of the help of Caravan, many choose not to
remember.

Back in the horizontal world, I stood for a moment watching the
leaves in the park. It was raining, as always happened when I returned,
only now it was the beginning of fall rain. The air was brisk and no
longer gentle. Still it did wake me a little. I was in no hurry. I wanted

answers, so I leaned in to the little shelter I could find under the remaining leaves, watched the rain, and wondered if answers would come any time soon. The longer I spent in Caravan, the longer my list of unanswered questions. The list of people both mysterious and unaccounted for also grew with each trip to Caravan.

As I thought of it, I realized that list also grew in the horizontal world. My investigation into the inner realms from the perspective of classes in the horizontal world brought yet another new world of people. Each of the classes I was now taking, and each teacher, brought a particular network of people. I kept to myself for the first classes, and still, in each case before long I was part of a new group of people seeking something. I wondered how many were taking these classes because they'd heard Caravan calling. I wondered how many of my fellow students had agreed to meet in these classes as a result of a campfire circle in Caravan. From what Verity and Kairos seemed to be saying, I had made an agreement with Anni. I now wondered how many of the people in these classes I had agreements with from Caravan.

It was an overcast Chicago fall day in the way Chicago does fall. It held the possibility of rain and snow over our heads as counterpoint to the hawk, the famous wind of the Windy City. I grumbled to myself about the idea of a fall picnic in that weather and wondered who would still show up under those conditions. Why didn't they cancel?

It surprised me to realize how much I was using my car. After very rarely driving for anything other than groceries, I was driving every week. Suddenly I was giving rides to strangers, to have a picnic on a dark, cold, and windy day, with strange strangers. That made me laugh. I was doing strange things, and was a stranger to myself in many ways since Verity called. I wondered if I'd said *yes* to this picnic, because I'd said *yes* to Verity's call. I would have to be more discerning, I thought. It would be so easy to make that association when it wasn't there. Then again, I said *yes* because of Anna.

That I actually found a place to park my car seemed auspicious. That in itself was a minor miracle, so I rounded the house in a good mood, letting go of my considerations. She had a basement apartment with the entrance in the back. She worked in what I was to learn later was her "Wonder Garden." It took her a moment to turn around, and when she did the world rippled. It was the woman from that rainy day at the coffee shop. We'd sat for hours reading books we'd both just purchased from the same used bookstore. We'd looked up at each other, smiled and almost connected, then let it go. We had nodded as I left, almost as if we'd known we would meet again. Of course we didn't know that. Yet in that first moment watching her in her garden, I guessed we had known, after all.

I half-expected we would both be whisked off to Caravan in the next moment. I listened for Verity's call, which didn't come. There was something else, something more than meeting at the coffee shop. I could almost hear Kairos saying, *You found each other, and that is enough for now.* My recent experience in Caravan led me to ask what we'd agreed to there. Was this yet another person I didn't remember making an agreement with that I now needed to make a decision about? What was going on with this woman?

The air continued to crackle as we introduced ourselves. We were both nervous and she didn't strike me as the type to be nervous about much. I wondered why I was so nervous. We talked as we drove, yet the conversation happened on another level. We bought two large bags of food, unlikely to be eaten because we were both somewhere else, together. By the time we arrived at the picnic, we both knew, whatever the reason for attending was, it wasn't about the picnic.

The whole time we sat in the cold not eating, half-listening, learning their names and stories, for the most part it was to understand who these people were that brought us together. Sitting together around a campfire so echoed Caravan that I couldn't miss it. I wanted to ask Anna if she recognized it. Did she remember setting this up in Caravan? If she had, then what had we agreed to?

Anna and I said goodnight to everyone, smiling at each other across the campfire. Then we came together to say goodbye to the woman who had brought us together. I thought I should be grateful to her for bringing us together, so I thanked her, even though I thought the group was going somewhere I wouldn't choose. I could tell Anna felt the same.

Driving her home, I turned to her and said, "I noticed you didn't seem all that enthusiastic about doing this again. I wasn't anxious to hang around any longer and thank you for picking up on that. I wonder, do you have to go right home?"

"No," she said. "Maybe . . . no, I could wait a little. Why?"

I turned into one of the pull-offs next to the lake, pointing the car toward the water. I stopped the car. "Have you seen the movie *Field of Dreams*?"

She looked puzzled. "What?"

"I was just wondering if you've given much thought to why you're here. On the planet, that is. You don't know me really, so I understand if it seems too personal, yet I was just wondering if you still believe in going for your dreams."

"I'll say yes, and I'll leave it at that for the moment." She smiled and turned to watch the lake. She seemed to relax a bit. I imagined then that she might have been wondering what this stranger was going to do by pulling off the road.

"I would like to hear more about your spiritual journey someday," I said. "I understand your reluctance; still I hope we get to the point where it's appropriate."

The subject had come up several times during the picnic. The group had a kind of spiritual sampling tendency, and I thought our hostess was a bit too interested in my leanings as well as Anna's. I learned spiritual interest was how she and Anna had met. When I asked she let it drop quickly.

"Someday." She turned as she said that, and watched me in silence.

I felt there was something I wanted to know. It felt just one question away. If only I could reach for that question. I thought, *Who are you, really? Why are you in my life now?* I asked her, watching hints of dusk, if she'd seen *The Navigator*. It was a movie about a group of people who go into a cave during the plague in Europe to do a vision quest to find the answer to heal their village. They traveled across time and space and find themselves in modern-day Los Angeles. They think they're in heaven because of what is to them an overwhelming abundance of light. Maybe I wanted Anna to say she traveled to other worlds, or at least would like to. I asked her about other movies, trying to tell her without telling her. I asked her about obscure things I discovered in my research for Verity's assignment. I looked for something I couldn't describe.

She seemed comfortable with me and a little nervous with my questions, so I stopped. We sat in silence, watching the night approach. It was a perfectly dramatic sky to complement our beginning.

We shared some fruit from the picnic; then she sat up to attention. "I have some things I have to do tomorrow, but we could try to get together the night after."

It was clear we were done for the night, and something had just begun.

It was still night camp in Caravan. Night had been for walking the sands, and the twilight morning had been for campfire work with the groups. It was general work about life mission. Now Caravan was at rest in the night. Walking in the night had been the most inward till then. Even as we moved there was space and silence. The movement created its own going within as we walked in deep time. Now the night work of Caravan at rest seemed to be personal, and so far, more deeply inner.

Verity was just taking her tea from the woman in the deep blue robe when I arrived. She looked out across the landscape to Caravan's tent city at night.

"Though you have failed in your vows a thousand times," she said, "come, come again." Turning her head a little, she motioned for me to have some tea as well. "Welcome to the Caravan of Remembering. Do you remember your vows?" She smiled then and motioned for me to join her as she sat among the oriental rugs. I thought the tent was the same and the woman who served us also the same. As Verity traced the patterns with her fingers, I noticed the rugs were different.

Anni walked out and sat with us. The feeling of connection was even stronger this time. This feeling of the connection between us allayed any questions about why we spent so much time together. Since Verity had introduced us, all of my time in Caravan was spent with Anni, and nearly all with Verity as well. The impending need to, as Verity put it, "decide," and the complete mystery of nearly everything made it all the more unsettling. The woman in blue handed each of us our expedition journals, then we sat together in silence watching the campfire.

Verity leaned toward us as if to share a confidence, then paused. [54] "How would you each describe yourself from the viewpoint of the other? David, you must know by now that you have traveled in Caravan with Anni long enough to do this. What would you know of your life mission if you could witness each other's description of each other?

"Think of the many people you met along the way," she continued. "You could include those you remember in Caravan. How would they describe you? What do they know about you that you miss in the confines of your own self-image? Do you think Kairos would describe you differently than Savitri? What do you imagine your design partner would say about you? What would your musician friends say? How would they describe you?

"Do you think Anni knows any of the same people in the horizontal world? If you imagined that you both had mutual friends, what would they say about the two of you, and what would that tell you about the connection of your life missions?"

I was taken a little off guard by these last questions. Verity had just come right out with questions of how our life missions connected. Not that I didn't already know that inside. I thought the decision Verity said I'd caught up to meant something like this.

I wondered how Anni would describe me. I thought it would be very helpful to hear. She might actually know me better than I knew myself. That thought made me excited about Verity's questions. I could at least imagine how the people I remembered would describe me.

Caravan Expedition Journal:

I'm a little surprised that Verity came right out and asked how someone who knew us both would describe us. How do I think Anni would describe me, or describe me from her perspective? Do I answer Verity's question, assuming that Anni does know me, and I just don't remember? Do I describe how she would describe me knowing only what she's seen since we met this time in Caravan? Maybe both? I think I'll let that percolate a little first.

How would my current friends in the horizontal world describe me? Distracted at the moment, I imagine. A little out of it, not too engaged, somewhere else. That would all be true. I've been in both worlds and not at all adept navigating yet. I don't think that's what Verity is asking.

They might also say creative, open, questioning, and driven in many ways. Seeking something, wanting to be different. They would say musician, artist, seeker, and even businessperson. I've actually felt good about most of these. Do I still? They might say restless for a long time, maybe always. They might note that uncharacteristically, I'd wanted to party a lot lately. How would they describe that and reconcile the seeker?

My business partner might remember some of those late night talks and describe me as a dreamer with big plans, to make a difference and save or change the world. Would my friends describe me as someone who has given up on those dreams, hence distracted, less driven, moving toward self-destruction? Did they see something beyond all of that, something that speaks to my reason for being here?

In describing me, what might anyone say that would give a clue to my life mission? What did people think I would do some day? What did they think I was designed for? My parents would have said I would be an artist because I went to college to study art. Earlier they might have said musician. Yet in the end, it was neither of these. I am skilled at both, enjoy them, and yet there is more. My high school counselor told me my best bet was the field of science. That made me chuckle even then. My test results showed "aptitude," never mind desire.

Looking back, I think the women in my life would have said I was looking for something. They might have said I was restless, that I was always reading, searching and researching, then searching some more. I wonder if everyone in my life would've said that I was looking. I was always seeking something.

Have I found what I was looking for? Caravan is certainly part of it. I looked for something like this. I certainly looked for Verity's assignment. I have looked for, longed for, the answer to that question for my whole life in the horizontal world.

I think this is how people would have described me. Anyone, anywhere in my whole life would have described me as someone seeking, longing for, looking for something.

As I wrote that I felt Verity's presence. As I looked up from my journal she held my gaze. She didn't smile or frown. She just looked. It wasn't a challenge. It wasn't anything wrong. In fact it was something right, I felt. I wondered what would come next. I felt she waited, as if she knew what I'd written, and this caused her to watch me. What was she waiting for? Anni must have felt it. She had looked up and waited. She didn't say a word. Was she in the same place as me, or Verity?

Verity leaned in to change a log in the fire, then stood up to signal for more tea. She seemed to grow taller as she surveyed Caravan. Our campfire would burn for eternity and not need tending, and surveying Caravan was either a message to us or she was weighing something. Maybe it was both. There were campfires as far as the eye could see, as endless as the horizon. For a moment I looked up toward the stars, great sun star fires dotting the night sky. Then I was up there, looking down at the galaxies of star fire campfires of Caravan lighting up the equally endless night desert. I loved them both in that moment.

Verity asked almost silently, just barely audible, "Yes, what do you love?"[55] She was still looking out across Caravan. "What do you find beautiful? In the horizontal world, what do you find beautiful? There are so many choices. When you find beauty, why do you find it beautiful? Why are you moved?"

Verity turned slowly as she asked these questions and was now looking directly at us.[56] "This will be connected to and mixed up with your motivation," she said as she turned to receive tea from our blue friend as if she felt her coming, then continued as we received refills. "For now I would like you to begin with your motivation. Asking what you want may help you, and you will need to look for what is behind and beyond that. What if you knew the motive behind your intentions? The question is *why*." Then, turning to me, she added, "What are you seeking? What do you long for in your intention?"

Verity slowed and repeated, *seeking . . . longing . . . why . . . seeking . . . longing . . . seeking . . . longing*, then silence. Then, she asked,

"What do you seek when you wait? What do you want the answer to? What does your heart long for? What does your mind long for? What does your soul long for? If the answers to these are different, then what do you hope the answer to each of these will lead you to?"

Verity touched our journals, a nonverbal signal to go inward, then asked, "What will give you rest? What is the bottom of the well of your longing? Why are you here? Why are you in the horizontal world? What moves you to go on? What is your motivation in Caravan? What is your motivation in the horizontal world?"

Caravan Expedition Journal:

When Verity asked, "What do you love?" she could have stopped there. I feel I might have written pages with no end. Before coming to Caravan, I would've had trouble saying what I loved. How would I have answered? I think I must have forgotten what I loved. I felt numb and disconnected from what I loved.

I feel so different now.

When I return from Caravan, everything in the horizontal world is more beautiful than I remembered in years. It is more than that, however. Everything is beautiful, and there are certain things I find especially beautiful. Beyond recognizing their beauty, these things call me. These particular things move me. Is moving me another way of saying they motivate me?

If I think about loving something, someone, an activity, a place, what moves in me? I could say as an artist or musician I'm motivated by the beauty of an arrangement of colors, or the harmony of notes. A scientist is motivated by a beautifully elegant equation. I feel all that. The beauty in all of these motivates me, and I also want to know how it works. What makes it so, and why do I care?

I want to know the profound Great Sacred Mystery. The sacred and the mystical motivate me. I seem to have forgotten that lately. All my life, I've felt that longing. I've wanted to discover, now I would say remember, how the Great Sacred Mystery works in our lives and why. I've been motivated to find the mystery and understand. It all seems like signs along the trail, to know and understand.

I longed to talk to God. In all of that I wanted to know my purpose, my life mission. I thought that if I understood life I would understand my place and our place collectively.

So there is the fundamental motive: I wanted to know God. I wanted to know why I'm here, why we're here. I lost touch with that. I was also motivated to inspire. I couldn't understand why anyone would want anything else. Along the way, I forgot that.

My motivation at times has been money. Also recognition, a partner, my own company, freedom, and (lately more than anything else) escape. When Verity came for me, I know I was motivated more than anything else to not remember. I know now that I've been unhappy for a very long time without admitting it to myself. Or anyone else.

Now I'm happy. I remember that I love to do things, to see things, to share, create, inspire, discover, remember, serve, and love. Which of these in particular calls me most? It's not a question of category. It's a question of specifically how-who-when-where, create what-where-why, inspire who-to what-why, and more for each of these loves I now feel. I can almost hear, "Again please."

I looked up and Verity nodded. "Again please."

I don't remember if I wrote anything else in my expedition journal. I felt the now-familiar sensation of seeing multiple exposures, feeling a sense of motion in no particular direction and anchoring to the sound of night rain in Wicker Park. I could still hear Verity saying, "Again please." Standing in the cold fall rain of Chicago, I asked myself if I was to go within now and ask myself what I love and why. I smiled as I shivered. Yes, I loved this world and my life and this park.

I loved my life? I felt like I should question that. That's what I was supposed to be doing. I was questioning everything, and that made something relax inside. Even the sensation of wet and cold was feeling something. I watched the way drops of water on my skin sparkled in the lights of the park. Everything in the park was luminous with a million diamonds reflecting life. Even with winter coming, life was everywhere.

I took my time walking back to the coach house. Why did I care about this life? Why was I attracted to the people walking in the park, to the sound of the rain, to the feel of the breeze and the possibility of tomorrow? Why? It wasn't anything at work. My life was different even if it was the same.

Then I remembered. My first kind-of-actual date with Anna was coming up. That was it, I thought as I stopped to watch a small group of what I assumed must be friends pushing and pulling each other across the park. I listened to what these feelings meant to me. I discovered it was Anna and something else. It was both. That surprised me the most.

Anna and what? I heard Verity's "Again please." What do I love? Why? What motivates me? Why do I want another date with Anna? Why do I want to know more? What do I want? I could ask why Anna suggested tomorrow. Verity's questions about love and motivation kept moving inside.

I was still asking myself why I wanted to see Anna, what I wanted, and my motivation when I picked her up for our date. It wasn't a romantic thing to focus on, and still, it seemed a better start than any of my other dates in a very long time. My life was a mess and questioning my intention going in gave me hope for a change. With this, Verity's assignment was foremost in my mind. It surprised me to find that Anna's implied preference to be friends felt good. I said to myself, "A good start." I remembered how lonely I'd felt in all the partying, and lately doing the work of Caravan alone in the horizontal world.

On the phone, Anna had said, "It's very strange. I don't know you, really, even if I do trust you. Maybe we could have dinner and a long talk. Then we could walk and see what happens."

We agreed on her favorite Thai restaurant. Food in Chicago is one of the benefits. Any kind of food is available, and each tradition has great representation. Anna's pick was one of the many obscure restaurants under the El tracks. You could walk by it a thousand times and not notice it was there unless you knew about it. They knew her and took us right to a table.

The coconut curry chicken soup was perfectly warm, sweet, and milky in a sterling silver three-level bowl meant for four. We had all night to talk, and Anna seemed perfectly at home. Pausing with spoons in hand, we looked at the other and said at the same time, "Tell me something about yourself." Then we laughed and relaxed.

Anna started. "I'm taking time off, even though I'm working. I need to get it this time. You'd think I would have learned something by now. By working, I mean I've figured out how to work four hours a day, five days a week, and pay the bills. The rest of the time, I'm looking for the answers to the questions. You know the questions."

I ladled more soup for myself and offered her some. She nodded as she continued. "For some reason, I have the feeling you might have some of the answers. That's why I suggested we get together tonight."

I laughed a little when she said that. "I don't know about that," I said. "I do think maybe we have some of the same questions, and I would welcome company in the search. I have people in my life. I'm making my living as a designer by the way. What I want to know isn't something I believe my colleagues would be interested in."

"Are you sure?"

"No, not for sure. I guess their focus is in a different direction though. That might have been fine for me before . . . my heart is looking for something I'm not going to find there. I know that much now. Only doing that for four hours a day would be a good start. Maybe you could teach me how to do that."

It didn't seem necessary to say what we were looking for. What we were seeking and the questions that called us felt like an environment, a world we both breathed. Our seeking was understood without saying it out loud, at least for the moment.

Looking back, I think we formed a pact and sealed the deal on some other level over that coconut curry soup. It was perfect in its way. We talked for hours and followed that with long walks divided by a changeover using the elevated. As we waited at the station I looked down the tracks and remembered that three a.m. visit by the woman I was now sure was Verity. A call that woke me to my new world. I turned from my vision of Verity to look at Anna and wondered.

CHAPTER 9

* * *

Creating Possibilities

I HEARD VERITY CALLING in my ears when Caravan came into focus. It was night still in Caravan. Our night tent not in sight, I stood with Verity and Anni in the midst of campfires as far as the eye could see. We seemed to be at some kind of high point looking out in every direction toward a far point that disappeared into night sky.

Coming in, I could inwardly hear Verity quoting Rumi. *Let yourself be drawn by the stronger pull of what you really love.* As I arrived in Caravan, she quoted Rumi to me. When I was firmly anchored in Caravan, Verity turned to me and inwardly still resumed with Rumi. *You that come to birth and bring the mysteries.* What she said next was just below what I could hear as we entered the tide of campfires. Then one more line as we moved through the tents and campfires of Caravan: *Roar, lion of the heart.*

For a long time, the three of us walked from tent to tent, campfire to campfire, culture to culture. It was a tour of the horizontal world's people. There were tents of many colors and no color. The rugs lying on the sand displayed every symbol and pattern, and many I'd never seen.

Occasionally, we stopped for a moment to be with a family or a small group to witness excitement over possibilities they might share in the horizontal world. Sometimes we stopped to sit and share silence. Other times we stopped to pray with a family or a group of pilgrims. They might be Buddhist, Hindu, Christian, Hebrew, or Muslim. Sometimes there were what we call indigenous North or South American,

165

African, Asian, or Australian peoples to share practices and possibilities with. We prayed in many languages and one. All one.

At times we danced.[57] This was a prayer certainly, and also communication. This was the wisdom of the body and movement of the soul. Afterward, the group gathered to talk about what they learned about themselves and those with whom they danced. They shared what the dances told them about their possible life missions. I was intrigued with how this might help me with my assignment, and what it could tell me about my agreement with Anni.

Nothing was said between us as the three of us walked. We said nothing in the circles we joined and they asked no questions of us. Verity's words were running through my mind: *Let yourself be drawn by the stronger pull of what you really love.*[58] What was it, I asked myself as we swam in the ocean of pilgrims, what do I really love?

As soon as I asked this question, Verity stopped and said, "Yes," and suddenly we were back at our tent. Our blue lady was there with a rich, creamy, warm chai tea in sterling silver cups. That got my attention. I stared at the chai, waiting to understand why it seemed important. I felt it and just couldn't place it then.

Verity motioned for Anni and me to sit. She traced the patterns of the rugs and we watched. As her hand danced and her fingers brought light to the patterns, she asked, "What were you drawn to? Who did you notice and why? What moved in you and what of love called to you?"

Verity looked outward then to the tents and campfires of Caravan we'd moved through only a moment ago. Her eyes still surveying Caravan, she asked, "As we moved through the ocean of possibility, why did we stop when and where we did? Did you think I was directing that, or could that have been you? Why are we here now and not still with Caravan's pilgrims?

"In the horizontal world, what takes you through your day? David, do you know the foundation that carries you through your day in the horizontal world, and what determines your time here? The question is, what do you truly love?"

With that our lady in blue brought our Caravan expedition journals. Propped against a pile of pillows, Anni and I began to write.

Caravan Expedition Journal:

Verity's questions have me spinning a bit. Her questions about the horizontal world are a bit unsettling. I expect to be questioned in Caravan. The events in Caravan have layers of meaning and call me to interpret them symbolically, metaphorically, and archetypically. I'm not used to thinking of my horizontal world life as though it was orchestrated to help me see something. That I would imagine it to be different seems to demonstrate how asleep in it I am most of the time. Yes, it is another pilgrimage. Perhaps the other end of a pole created with great love by the One.

Since Verity asked me to be aware of what I love, it was a cleansing rain to my heart to realize or remember that I do in fact love. I love beauty wherever I find it. I love the visual and performing arts, or at least most of them. I loved learning as I was growing up and still do. I love discovering, creating, and making connections. I'm happy to learn I love the horizontal world after all, and its people most of the time. I love things made with craft, with loving care and a sense of soul. What does this mean to me now?

Why the tour tonight? If Anni and I decided when we would stop, what determined that? Did what we love design our tour? What have I loved that determines my tour in the horizontal world so far? When I think of all that's happened in my life in the horizontal world, it's strange to think love designed it. Yes, some of what I loved seemed very much from my heart. What love created the rest of it?

Verity asked what we were drawn to. What we were drawn to was the praying and dancing. We were drawn to the talks of possibility. We were drawn, it seems, to every race, culture, and religion. It's true I'm drawn to all of that on any given night in the horizontal world. What does this tell me tonight in terms of Verity's questions?

What I noticed more than anything was how much alike all people are even in our differences and the beauty of those differences. I noticed the universal call. The One calls us universally, and we universally return that call with our longing. Everyone in Caravan longs to answer the call of the One. Each of us, in turn, calls our counterpart in the horizontal world to remember, to awaken, and remember.

What's moving in me is love, love for Caravan and all my fellow pilgrims. Also, gratitude for Caravan's carrying us for eternity until we remember our life mission, and all who help us with that remembering. What's moving is the longing to remember. Why am I here in this way? Why do I not remember Anni and being here with her before and what I agreed to?

I stopped writing then and scanned the ocean of Caravan campfires around us. Watching the subtle movements of people seated, engaged in the work of Caravan, and those moving about, gave me space to think before writing more.

What I loved, I noticed. Looking back, it was difficult to tell which came first. Maybe that was itself a key. Sometimes, I loved what I was drawn to, which was why I noticed. What drew me when I didn't love what I noticed? What was happening when something I noticed led later to a growing love for it?

I began to have a different relationship with the way I thought about what I loved. There is the love I felt for romantic, intimate, personal relationships. I saw relationship in a more expanded way. I saw relationship everywhere. What I chose to come into relationship with was tied into this sense of being drawn or magnetized. Why was I drawn? Why did I notice this versus that person, place, or thing? If the work of Caravan creates magnetism, attraction, or momentum toward agreements made in the direction of our life mission, then this is perhaps a signal from Caravan. I thought it might be wise to pay attention to these inklings of being drawn, to the impulses of my heart. I resolved to consciously pay attention to when and what I noticed.

I then looked at my life in the horizontal world and sifted through the days I remembered since Verity came for me. What did I notice? Where was I drawn? What did I love? I looked for any clue to life mission, vision, and purpose. I looked for any example that seemed to apply to my assignment.

Then I realized something else. Yes, that love drew me to the used bookstore where Anna was shopping. That passion to find the answer to Verity's assignment, to dig deeper, drew me to that coffee shop. My passion for answers would not let me wait until I got home. So I stopped for coffee next to the bookstore to read. Anna and I were sitting at tables next to each other for hours, both of us reading, not talking to each other, drawn together again after crossing paths in the bookstore. Then, when my passion to discover my life mission drew me to the network of people who produced the classes, we found each other again.

Out of the literally millions of people in the Chicago area, we were drawn together over and over again from different sources. How many times did Anna and I circle each other, pass each other and not notice, before the horizontal world put us together in a way that we had to actually talk to each other? Now we're spending time together. Why were we drawn together? I was sure we were both looking for the answer, even if we hadn't asked it that way yet. What are both Caravan and the horizontal world calling us to?

I looked up from my reverie. Verity was looking at me. I expected that. What surprised me was the realization that Anni had also stopped. Though I couldn't see her face under the hood, she was also looking at me. Did she feel it too? Did she also know my question and what I was thinking?

In that moment I made the connection. Although the passion to find my life mission seemed to draw Anna to my horizontal world life, it was Verity's assignment that had set it all in motion. She had animated my dormant passion to remember. Guessing that Verity knew my thoughts, I returned her stare quietly, waiting to see if she would respond to the question in my heart.

Without breaking our locked eyes, without the slightest trace of emotion or indication she'd heard my thoughts, she continued, "As you contemplate the movement of life mission and your pursuit of it in your life, I want you to notice where you feel you find it in the horizontal world.[59] I want you to also notice when you have the impression someone else is engaging his or her life mission. Look at why you believe this. Your impression is more important than your accuracy.

"Also be present to whose life mission attracts you most and where you find it. Ask yourself *why*. When this happens, ask yourself if it was the life mission you find manifesting that you noticed, or the person. Perhaps it was both. Discerning this distinction will help you in your search. Both will tell you something. Where you also recognize or intuit that a person is what drew you, ask yourself how their being in their life mission might coincide or support your life mission. What is who they are or the qualities they embody telling you about your life mission?"

I don't remember if I wrote anything in my Caravan expedition journal. I don't remember walking home from the park. What I remember is discovering myself thinking about life mission in the horizontal world, standing under a warm shower, home again in my coach house. I didn't remember anything in between.

As movies of people ran in my mind, I had no idea how long the shower lasted. Something in me was looking for impressions, examples of people doing their life mission. I didn't just look for people I knew personally who had been or were now in my life. Something in me looked for life mission wherever I could find it.

I took my time drying off. The sense of the beach-size, extra heavy towel running slowly over my skin grounded me. I felt an acute awareness of the people in my life personally and even in the greater cultural collective life I was a part of. The public lives portrayed in the media were part of my life. Now I looked for what that conveyed, symbolized, activated in me, in the search for my life mission.

Even knowing there was no deadline to meet, no pressure to figure this out quickly, I had a sense of overwhelm around the edges. Why? Caravan will travel for eternity while my fellow pilgrims and I figure it out. Why did I feel anxious? What was going to happen? I felt something was hanging in the balance. That something was in the horizontal world, the world of time. Time I felt was rushing toward something. I remembered Verity telling Anni it was almost time. Time for what? What did the question of others doing their life mission have to do with what I was feeling?

Warm and feeling a part of the horizontal world again, I checked my notes for the studio. I hoped my anxiety would recede into the background if I did some of the work I was no doubt behind on. I had both design and illustration work to do. In both cases it was early thumbnail work. I could allow my mind to wander over paper, leaving space for creativity to kick in, while some other part of me could process what I felt. I hoped letting go into my work, while holding space for anything, would allow whatever it was to sort itself out.

Ideas did surface and found their way onto paper. It didn't register within at first. I wasn't thinking about whether the sketches worked or not. As I drew, thinking on paper, in addition to my thumbnail sketches for the projects, a list of names emerged around the figures and designs. It took a few moments to realize it was a list of people I felt were doing their life mission. I didn't actually notice this until I returned to my drafting board after a short break. My first thought was, who did this?

I didn't remember whether or not I'd written in the Caravan expedition journal, nor did I remember returning to the park, walking home, what I did when I got home, getting into the shower, or how long I was in it. Now I didn't remember writing the names around my drawings, even if I did recognize what it was a list of.

I just stopped everything. I considered calling out to Verity, then I realized it was not going to help. I was back in the horizontal world to work with the very thing I was now afraid to work with. That impulse to call Verity translated into going to the phone. I did need to call someone. The walls of my coach house seemed to be closing in. I didn't want to stay another minute.

Pushing the button to retrieve my messages I felt a sense of foreboding that led to even more anxiety. I felt like my life was about to change, and the stakes were suddenly higher. For a moment, the thought of design and illustration seemed more inviting than it had in a very long time, and safe.

The first messages were from my business partner and our potential new partner. That made me smile and even relax a bit. The muscles in my stomach unclenched a little. Then there was a message from Anna with a voice that sounded concerned and a trace annoyed. We had tentatively agreed to go to an event planned by the woman who had put the picnic together. We were both concerned about this event without knowing why. Something was going to happen that didn't feel right, and neither of us knew why. We both wanted to decline, yet also felt we should go. We agreed to give it some time and get back to each other on it. I was definitely late in getting back to her.

In that moment everything went silent. Messages continued to play and all I could hear was Verity giving me my Caravan assignment. I remembered last night's meeting by the tent with Verity and Anni. Perhaps my need had called Verity that early morning in the subway and from that, the assignment animated my passion to remember. From that moment, everything else in the horizontal world had led me to Anna. She was the key. She was the key to my answering Verity's assignment. Anna was the key to the decision I needed to make, and that decision was immanent.

As Anna opened the door to her apartment, I felt a sense of relief without knowing why. I knew I didn't want to be home and anywhere else would just add to my anxiety. The only place to be in that moment was with Anna.

As she took my coat, I said, "Listen, I'm glad you were still up when I called and open for company. Thank you for inviting me over. I needed to get out and I also needed to talk to you. Sorry I didn't call earlier."

She motioned to have a seat in an alcove by the wall. I loved that her apartment defied convention. Her apartment was fiercely independent, I thought. Pouring tea for both of us she followed my eyes. "Everything here I found antiquing or junking. It's the adventure. It's holding an intention and not knowing where the treasure will show up."

I only partially heard her as she poured the tea. The perfume of Caravan was swirling around us. I could almost see Verity's tent and our lady in the deep desert blue. I couldn't imagine why I didn't come right out and ask Anna if she remembered Caravan. I didn't know whether or not it was allowed, and I just thought I should wait. I didn't ask.

Anna held her cup to breathe in the tea's aroma. "Are we going?"

"Yes, I think we have to, though I have absolutely no idea why. I don't think I knew that until just now."

"Yes." That was all she said, and waited. Then she went for cream from the kitchen.

Taking a chance, I said, "I don't know why, but I feel anxious about something. It might be about going to this, and it feels like there's something more."

I could feel the tension then. It wasn't the tension of being together, undecided or disagreeing. It was the tension of agreeing to something we both felt anxious about.

The last question Verity had given us was right next to my skin, so I just threw it out, hoping the surprise of it would break the tension.

"Who do you think is doing their life mission?"

"Are you really asking me that?"

"Yes, I'm really asking you that."

Anna laughed then, and for the moment the tension was broken. After a moment's reflection, she said, "First, I think I would like to have a better idea of what that means."

"I think the question of who might be doing their life mission might help us get to what we mean by that," I replied. "It will help lead us to ask better questions about what that means. As soon as I begin to scan for who might be living their life mission, all of my ideas about what life mission is are right on the surface."

I filled her in on my search and the book hunt that was part of it. It was what had brought us together before we were introduced. I decided as I told her this that she didn't have a conscious memory of Caravan. Still, we were brought together by everything that had happened, and I wanted to know why. I didn't tell her that part.

I did share a version of what I'd arrived at in my research into life mission, vision, and purpose. I told her I was open to other interpretations. I thought this looking in the world to answer Verity's assignment was tied to Anna now.

I returned to thoughts of who might be living their life mission. "I think Michael Jordon and Phil Jackson must be living theirs." This was early in the championship years of the Chicago Bulls.

Anna said, "Oprah must be living her life mission, don't you think? Also, I had a printer friend I'm sure was living his. He was never famous, but he touched a lot of lives. He touched mine profoundly. He was forced to watch people getting hanged in the South and barely made it out alive. He took in more then twenty kids and helped them all get through college. He was a wonder, and he changed my life . . . he lived his mission."

We talked about the famous people we both recognized, that we thought might be living their life mission: actors, musicians, writers, athletes, and spiritual teachers. Anna said, "Wouldn't it be nice if a delegation knocked on the door, tested you, and verified, 'Yes, you are the one for this mission. You incarnated to carry this one.' All my life I've prayed for an angel to knock on my door and say, 'This is your life mission, your destiny.' Maybe I'm still waiting."

Careful what you pray for, I thought. I might be just that. I had a hunch I was a messenger for her, and she for me, which wasn't that far from what she'd said. This didn't lessen the lingering feeling that I should be very nervous about this.

Anna poured more hot water for our tea. "I should let you know I'll be going away for about ten days or so after the weekend," she said. "I go every year to vision quest with my teacher and other students. I go early to support the work, and at the right time I'll go out myself. I guess there's some aspect of life mission for everyone there. For my teacher, it's life mission, I think. They have and continue to give their life to it. I hope it's their life mission, or there isn't much hope for the rest of us. When I committed to being a student of the Red Road, I felt the calling.

"Vision quest is itself a life mission ceremony. The saying is 'Cry for a vision, so the people may live.' This is asking Spirit, Great Sacred Mystery, 'What do I do with this life you gave me?' Then when you're given a vision, your work is to live it.

"Each of us committed to at least four years and we begin to prepare long before we go the first time. Between each vision quest we digest our last vision, while living our lives and preparing for the next.

"I had a deep longing to know why I'm here, and going directly to Spirit in this way is something I appreciate. Still, Spirit actually telling me my life mission is a little scary. My Native American teacher says, 'Pray, and then duck.' It might be time to duck."

I wanted to know this. Looking for the answer to my own quest was what sent me to the bookstore, then the coffee shop where we first met. Native Americans, as a culture, generally affirm the idea of life mission through vision quest, and honor its importance. I'd read a little about it and Anna was living it.

Anna continued, "My teachers say each person is born at a particular place on the Medicine Wheel, and recognizing the stewardship of this place will help them with the question of why they're here."

We talked for hours until I realized how late it was. I needed to present at least something of the thumbnails the next morning.

As it was time to go I returned to the subject of our shared anxiety. "Anna, I'm grateful you're coming with me. I don't know what we'll encounter, and it's nice to have someone covering my back. Even though we're just getting to know each other, I'm glad you'll be with me. I know neither of us wants to go to, and it feels connected to what we've been talking about. Not sure what that means exactly, and the clues there may be part of what brought us together. I think this 'seminar' qualifies as 'pray and then duck.'"

We gave each other a tentative hug, neither of us comfortable yet in our roles together. Anna was still a mystery, one of the many now in my life that I was fine with.

On the way out, I stopped for a moment to look at her terraced garden in the moonlight. It was filled to capacity with life. From what I knew of her so far, I imagined each plant was a companion planted to maximize the space and still be in harmony. I knew garden space in the city was a premium and thought her garden might be more. I wondered if her apparent urge to fill every inch of her garden was to balance her time in the absolute desert of Caravan. If we were both so actively asking for our life mission, she must also be working hard in Caravan. I felt I should know something about that, and felt something with that thought. I just couldn't get to it.

I let that go and walked out the gate and toward my car, shifting my thoughts between Caravan and my evening with Anna. Looking up, I soaked in the moonlight. I almost expected Verity to call for me. I was sure that if I were taking the El she would call as soon as I reached Wicker Park.

I could feel the crunch of sand as I walked the sidewalk to my car. As I drove the now surprisingly empty streets, I felt the pulse of Chicago at night. My return to my neighborhood was the return to my horizontal world's Caravan. Chicago, with its famous diversity of culture and race, is my horizontal-world Caravan.

As I parked my car, even at that hour people were sitting on the steps of their three flats. I felt the urge to sit with them, as if we were sitting by the campfire in Caravan instead of under the streetlights in

Wicker Park. Instead, I headed into my coach house. As we waved to each other and said hello and goodnight, I wondered how many of them I shared a circle in Caravan with, and if that's why we chose to be neighbors?

It was one of those mixed days when you couldn't trust anything. I looked out the window as I was getting dressed and knew even the weather couldn't be trusted. It was a multi-grey fall day, with the Hawk on the loose, like the beach picnic in the cold and rain, and again, I asked myself why I was going, why we were going.

I had a business partner, and having someone for this side of my life was new. Now Anna and I were co-conspirators in a plot that was a mystery adventure and had all the signs of a no-win ending. As I thought about it, I'd been a little uncomfortable about most events this woman had put together without knowing why. Searching for answers to Caravan's questions had brought me to the speakers she sponsored, and even when I enjoyed them, I had a kind of guard up about her. Anna and I had an even stronger feeling that this time, there would be something not quite right. I was still wary of the woman, and it was the speaker that had my antenna up. Why?

It was the speaker who had been asking about me. He'd asked her a lot of questions when he came to her to promote him. He'd told her to invite me and I was barely involved with her. That made me nervous.

On the way to the hotel where the man was speaking, I asked Anna, "Have you been thinking about who you thought was or is doing their life mission?"

"Yes, from time to time. Why?"

"It's a place to begin talking about what life mission means. You said you wanted to know. Maybe we can share the research. Also, it's something we can talk about other than where we're going now."

Anna looked over at me for a moment. She loosened her coat as the car warmed up. "All right," she said. "Let's talk about life mission. When we get there, we both feel we'll have something to confront, and hope it will have some clue for our search. We can decide what to do about that when we get there."

She ran her hands along the window, as if she were tracing people and buildings as we passed them on the street. "I had teachers in school, a few classmates in pre-med, my herb teacher, even a few of the people I met in business, who might have been living their life mission. Some of the lawyers and judges I meet at work now, and some of my family's friends . . . Of all the people I know even a little bit personally, I can't think of many. The percentage is very small.

"I feel some of the writers I love might be doing their life mission. There are people who fight for something that strike me as having found something. Life mission? I'm not so sure. I imagine doctors and nurses in Doctors Without Borders must feel they've found it. We talked about the visual and performing arts and the people who support them. I could go on. Though the people I know personally are small in number, there are enough to notice in the world. Maybe it's this small number who remember and live their life mission that keep it all going. They move us forward and create changes. Maybe they keep hope alive for us."

I smiled. "I think you might be right. I think there must be something about the very notion of life mission, which by its nature catalyzes, calling for something new. Maybe, for some, life mission calls one to fight to maintain or sustain something important. I wonder if someone in his or her life mission could sustain this calling without that also bringing change."

After a moment's quiet, I added, "Anna, after looking at everyone you could think of that might be doing his or her life mission, which of them were you personally drawn to? Consider even those you might never have thought had anything to with your life. Maybe they're a symbol or metaphor, like a dream where each person holds important information for you.

"I've been asking why, out of all the possible life missions I could notice, why this life mission, and why this person? Why did I even notice? I could have gone right past it. What chain of events or synchronicity brought this person and life mission to my life and awareness? I could chalk it up to the reticular activating system, and no doubt it is involved, and it's more than that. As my field scans billions of bytes of information in my world, in my environment, what brought this particular one to me and made sure it got my attention?"

Anna touched my arm and I stopped. "Intention is everything and the reticular activating system is what?"

"It's the mechanism that filters the scan of our senses, that determines what we consciously see or are aware of. The reticular activating system holds the idea of what fits our sense of self, which will send on information that is in alignment with our sense of self. What doesn't fit our picture of what makes up our world is filtered out, just as if we'd never seen it. It's like the natives who didn't see the ships in the Galapagos Islands or South America because they had nothing like them in their reality. They didn't have a context to process a sailing ship. The ships were not part of their world, so they literally didn't see them.

"The reticular activating system is also involved when anything becomes important to us. It alerts us to anything connected to what we have decided is important when it comes into our field of awareness. It animates or lights up for us. Out of everything we could notice, we notice particular things because our reticular activating system gets the message to alert us to it. It is like the search image in field research."

Glancing first to Anna's window tracings, then to her, I continued, "We're looking for examples of anyone living their life mission. That's become part of the search image of our reticular activating system. When we sense an example of someone living his or her life mission, our reticular activating system alerts us by drawing our attention to it. My question then, is why this person and not another?

"It may be," I continued, "that he or she is the only one in the area embodying life mission. My first question then, is how our reticular activating system knows that? It must have an internal blueprint of what life mission means to us. That itself is a sign of what our inner landscape describes to us as life mission."

Anna stopped me again. "My reticular activating system tells me that this afternoon has something to do with this question and embodying life mission."

The conference room at the Evanston Holiday Inn felt "off" to me. I knew from my little experience of helping our promoter friend do events there, the hotel normally carried a sense of neutrality and legitimacy. Entering the room now with Anna, I didn't feel either. The woman who had introduced Anna and me to each other was surprised to see us come in together. She didn't seem pleased. I couldn't imagine what she thought would happen after she asked me to bring Anna to the picnic, but it felt like she had plans that didn't include Anna and me being together.

I had to let Anna navigate on her own, as I had agreed to help with the event's logistics. I would be working the event and Anna would be scanning. Together we hoped to find clues as to why we were there.

Even working the event, I managed to avoid the speaker before he started. It turned out that he was a hypnotist, and was going to regress people to help them remember their past lives. This was, he said, going to help them know their reason for being born, and what to do with their present lives. A side bonus was his insight as to what had happened in their past lives that made them so screwed up in this life. They seemed to imply all this was in the name of a kind of life mission event, and I did my best to stay neutral. I wondered if his "I'm going to tell you what to do with your life" thing was why he wanted to talk to me. Even so, how did he know this was my interest and why would it matter to him? I wondered how Anna was reading him.

What happened next was foreign to everything I understood of life mission work in Caravan. Everything I experienced in Caravan was based on self-discovery—as long as it takes. I never once witnessed Kairos, Amar Nen, Savitri, Bede, or Jun tell someone what was true for their life mission. I didn't remember them telling anyone anything at all about why they were in the horizontal world, or what they were to do in it.

I was certain that in Caravan, Verity knew what our life missions were. She never told us, though she did her best to move us to remember. That is our assignment, I thought, to find this out for ourselves. I'd been told several times that I might not succeed in this. At no time was I ever led to believe I would be rescued in this.

I found it difficult to remain neutral, as I was part of the team for the event. I tried not to show my disapproval. Anna looked my way with a tilt of her head and eye that seemed both questioning and silent, as if to say, "This is wrong." For a moment I wondered if she remembered Caravan. Then I let it go.

The speaker called members of the audience up, one by one, and worked with each one for about ten minutes. Then he told each person about their past lives and what they meant. He then told them what to do with their present life. As near as I could tell, after having put them in a kind of hypnotic state, he did nothing to bring them out of it. It may have been a light state, and the people seemed mostly functional. Still, what he told them was mostly negative and a little scary. He made no effort to help them digest what he told them. There didn't even seem to be a connection between the past lives described, what he determined was their reason for being on earth, and what they were to do.

I smiled as I thought about what Anna might do if he tried his routine on her, and she didn't go up. He hadn't waited for people to raise their hands. He had just called on people, and they obediently went up. He didn't call on Anna. I guess he must have sensed that she was not a good idea.

Still, the speaker and Anna had an intense moment during the break. He walked up to her to talk one on one. It seemed controlled, if not friendly. I was working, so I just watched. I kept my conversation with him afterwards short with an excuse that I needed to leave shortly. He left abruptly, leaving an impression in the room that was not joyful. A number of the people who'd gone to the front of the room were sitting or mulling what had happened, looking a little dazed.

Anna turned to me. "They seem a little stunned. It has the feel of trauma and shock. At the least, they're confused and a little disoriented. I hope they aren't driving."

I was concerned that the people were being left in that state. "Maybe we should just check to see if there's something we can do to help them before they leave."

We spent time helping them to ground a little until they felt they were ready to leave on their own. We telephoned the mother of an older teenager and asked her to come and pick him up. He wasn't doing great, even when he left with her.

I turned to Anna. "He may have had problems before coming here. Regardless, this didn't help him."

At the door to the car, I turned to Anna again. "I don't feel like going home just yet. I'd like to unwind and do a little grounding myself. How would you feel about going to the beach?"

Walking the Evanston beach, Anna stooped down to run sand through her fingers. Without looking at me, looking out at Lake Michigan, she said, "Don't you think it's interesting that we talked about our being brought together for the quest of life mission? Then we're called to this event where the man takes it upon himself to just tell people what their life mission is. How do you feel about that?"

I moved next to her and followed her gaze out across the lake. "I know I wouldn't have gone up, working or not. What he did felt irresponsible to me and ultimately, not really helpful for anyone. Telling someone their life mission is x, y, or z probably has karmic implications of some kind. It would be a great responsibility, and take a pretty advanced being, who's done a lot of work spiritually, to know when someone is ready to hear their life mission, if ever. I can think of many reasons not to tell someone, and maybe they all come under the category of it's being so much better if you do the work to remember on your own."

As I said this, I sensed Caravan just outside the edge of my touch, nearly superimposed on the horizontal world. I could smell both the lake and the clear dry air of Caravan, surrounding and holding us close. The people walking the beach or spread out around us intermingled with the pilgrims of Caravan. Everywhere pilgrims were doing the work of remembering. All were doing the work to help their horizontal-world counterparts find their life missions and destinies. I could hear Savitri and Bede around the campfire. I could hear Jun and Kairos leading and tuning, and I half-expected Verity to call.

I wondered if this had been a test. Verity had given me the assignment to remember. Then she had guided me without giving me answers. Others helped when needed. I was expected to find my life mission on my own. Then this "opportunity" shows up and it seems so easy. All I had to do was to go to the front of the room, and this man would have told me my life mission. What would have happened if I'd done that? Something told me it was dangerous. I shivered thinking about it.

Anna watched the lake and ran her hands through the sand, silent, poised perhaps for something.

"Anna, I can't imagine you let him start with you. What happened when you talked during the break? You didn't look happy. For that matter, neither did he."

"He didn't get what he wanted, and got more than he bargained for. I hope we don't meet again, though I have the feeling we will. I was sad more than anything. I will tell you about it someday. Not now though. Okay?"

"Are you still sad about that, or something else?"

"Something else. The way those people were left brings out the warrior in me, more than it makes me sad. No, it is something more."

I could see the warrior in her. I must have sensed that when I'd asked her to come with me. Why did I think I needed that?

Anna reached for me. "David, let's walk."

The lake was quiet now, and the horizon way out and gray next to the sky. Sunlight came in beams through the break in the clouds. The air carried a heightened feel to me. Caravan felt even nearer. I saw ghostlike images of its pilgrims. We began walking among them.

Anna exchanged a laugh with a little girl on the beach who told her everything about what she was doing. Anna congratulated her on her masterpiece in the sand, and we moved on, leaving her to do her work.

Watching Anna and glancing back at the child, I said, "You and I found each other through the question of life mission. I wonder if that little girl knows why she's here. I wonder if she still remembers or has already been talked out of it. We come knowing, and then this world distracts and diverts us. It tells us everything, anything, to get us to do something else. Then at some point if we're lucky, someone or something calls us to remember, and whispers "now." Now it's time to do the work of remembering. Now you must make remembering more important than all the world's enticements and distractions. You must make remembering more important than the people like this man, who will tell you what your life mission is. Now, you must choose to remember."

Anna stopped to look back the girl at work in the sand. Watching her still, she asked, "David, do you think forgetting is necessary? Is part of the process to forget, and then have to work through years of what we're told and the pain of life, to get to the remembering? Does it have to be like that?"

"I wish I knew the answer. Perhaps it serves in the long run, though it seems a waste, and too much unnecessary pain. Mostly, I think no, it doesn't have to be like that. We could change this world. We could change the way it's not talked about. It may be time for that now. Maybe it doesn't have to continue."

Anna touched my arm and guided me toward the rocks at the edge of the trees that divided beach and park. We sat at the edge between worlds. We were quiet, watching the lake, looking out toward the horizon. Everything was still.

"We will find out together then." She turned to look at me, then, "Yes?"

"Yes."

"We are a kind of family now, you and I," she said. "More than partners on some kind of project. Our hearts have agreed to work together toward something important." She looked me in the eye and held my gaze. "On this we are family now . . . Yes?"

"Yes."

As we agreed to this, we were surrounded by white feathers falling like a gentle snow. A beam of light broke through the clouds. The air sparkled and I felt that at that moment we were the only ones in some world. I could find no source for what happened. Time stopped, and the feathers seemed for a moment to be almost suspended, they were falling so slowly. It was complete silence as we watched each other, and the raining of feathers all around us.

Anna smiled; she seemed to breathe into our miracle. Giving a quick scan in the first moment, and also not finding a source, she seemed more than happy to allow it to wash over her. There was nothing to do. I joined her in that, returning a smile that came from a place not touched in me for longer than I could remember.

As the feathers continued to fall, Anna said quietly to herself what I assumed was a prayer. She placed tobacco on the ground and collected some of the feathers into a book she pulled from her bag.

I thought her taking the feathers fit her Native American tradition and almost left it at that. Then I felt something calling me to witness this. I left a few strands of my hair and gathered a few of the feathers in my coat pocket, saying a prayer of my own.

We sat in silence, looking out toward the endless gray horizon, over beach and water; small white feathers rained slowly over us as day turned into night.

"Welcome to the Caravan of Remembering," Verity said. We were standing at the edge. In one direction the far horizon had nothing to meet my gaze except a line where stars began. In the other direction, an endless sea of pilgrims, tents, and the night campfires of my beloved Caravan.

Verity's silver flashed, lighting up the night on the edge. The earth colors of her robe faded into night while the silver threads became a web of reflecting light. The silver in her hair was a fire lighting her face, and the silver in her eyes, eternity flashing.

I thought of antique maps that showed the edge of the known world. Beyond these borders lie monsters and death. Here at this border's edge, I thought, lay magical, alchemical, sacred beings, and possibly the death of an old way of seeing myself. Here lay the death of the way I used to imagine myself.

Verity moved toward the edge of Caravan, and then turned to me. "The lines of family connect us in many ways. I believe you have found family to mean many things. The silver threads that connect our souls are many." Turning, sweeping her arm toward Caravan, she said, "Everyone here is your family, and there are families within families. Come. Your family is waiting."

Verity held out her hand to point the way, and we entered Caravan's family of pilgrims. As we walked, Verity scanned, seeming to look for something. Verity took in people and groups as we passed, taking her time. She seemed to weigh them slowly from within her. I thought Verity scanned long enough to decide something, and then moved on. I knew this was for me.

"As we walk," she said, "consider how you feel about each person or group we pass. You will not be able to figure this out with your mind. It is not an idea of who you think they are, based on a judgment of how they appear to your preferences or ideas of your culture. Can you recognize or remember them? Do you recognize your families of families? We form many families for the work over time. Sometimes they are biological for you in the horizontal world. You have a larger family. Your family extends beyond biology, even in the horizontal world. Can you feel the recognition beyond your idea of who you are, beyond your preferences, beyond you mind? Allow the possibility that they will light up for you."

Verity was quiet then and I stopped looking with my eyes. I didn't remember how to do what Verity was asking. I didn't remember how to see in that way yet. My effort was to get out of the way if possible. We said nothing more as we walked among the ocean of pilgrims.

I felt a new kind of tuning. Verity had spun something new in me, reminding me of something I'd forgotten. She reconnected my inner world. After timeless walking, Kairos, Savitri, Bede, Amar Nen, then Anni moved though my vision inwardly. Silver fire streamed from their robes, hair and eyes. Then, in my mind, Anni was sitting by our tent, her robes on fire with silver, and we were there.

Suddenly Verity and I arrived at our tent. Anni already sitting by the campfire waited for us. Verity turned to me, "She has been waiting. You have found your family and soon you will decide. The first steps have begun. Your family waits."

Verity motioned for our Blue Lady of the desert, then turned to me and held my eyes. "Join us, will you?" It was invitation and question. Implied was the necessity to choose. Like the first night I remembered in Caravan, I could have chosen not to go with everyone moving out then. What I would have done after they left made that not an option. Choosing not to join Verity and Anni was not really an option for me.

As we sat down I looked across the fire to Anni. I still felt how she had lit up in my inner vision. If she was family, what did that mean? Though I couldn't see her, Verity had already told me our destiny was connected. Anni was waiting for more than my arrival as we arrived. She was waiting for the decision Verity said was eminent.

Verity began, "Imagine who you would include in your life mission family.[60] In all the ways you hope your biological family could help in the best sense, this family would also be there for you. In all the ways your biological family can remind you of what needs work, this family may also serve. Imagine if you could choose from anyone, who would your life mission family be?"

Caravan Expedition Journal:

If I knew my life mission, who would I want in my life mission family? Anna said we were family by agreement of the heart and not like partners on a project. Sitting in Caravan now I thought Verity could have said that to me.

For my life mission family I would choose artists, musicians, writers, actors, dancers, architects, filmmakers, photographers, sculptors, and more in every domain of the visual and performing arts. Also scientists from every domain in the sciences would be included. I would choose spiritual mentors from every tradition.

That was easy. Who in particular would I choose? Why?

I would also choose people who knew how to do things in the world, and business people. Perhaps I would choose people in publishing. Did I want a politician or ambassador in my life mission family? A psychologist and philosopher? I might like an economist and sociologist and, the more I thought about it, why not an anthropologist and historian as well? Why not include the president of a university so I could have access to every branch of learning?

In my mind . . . what life mission needed all of these people? Did my choices mean anything, or was I just running off with my mind? I couldn't see the patterns yet. Maybe I wasn't serious enough. I looked up to see Verity smile and nod. She didn't say, "Again please," and I got the impression I was doing well enough, so I relaxed into it again.

I was feeling confident that if I could choose my life mission family, I really did want members in pretty much all of those categories. If I had to keep the number down, I might let go of some of the last categories. Still, I wanted all of them and more. I felt that I would call on all of them to help me navigate my life mission pilgrimage.

This was already a big family. I still needed to pick particular people and it was a start. Then who else? There was the question of my interest in navigating the inner worlds and the outer. There was the question of navigating the social context. There was the question of the practical challenges of manifesting dreams in the physical world.

I laughed silently to myself thinking about the family I would create from this list. Who from this list would be my life mission aunt or uncle, grandmother or grandfather? I got excited thinking about who might take the role of life mission father and mother. As significant as our biological mother and father are, I imagined my life mission mother and father would also play pivotal roles. What would these choices tell me about my about my life mission? Also included in what we call our nuclear family, who would I choose for my life mission brother or sister? What about a crazy cousin or two?

Verity then said, "Yes, it will begin to make more sense and provide more clues as you fill in your categories with specific people. You can easily see that including a domain like the arts could cover a vast spectrum of styles and attunements. Who in particular you choose for your family will tell you a great deal about both your life mission resonance, and also who you are. You can continue to hold this question and fill in the people as they emerge for you. Particular choices will come to you in many ways, now that you have this intention and hold this question in your heart."

Verity, rising to stand then, paused to study us for a moment, then said, "There are a few other questions to hold as you continue in Caravan. As you walk around Caravan, as you sit together, reflect on what you always just assumed would be part of your life. Another way to ask this would be, what would you never have imagined being without? What have you always assumed would be part of your life? What people, what things? When that comes up, ask why."

Looking out at Caravan, she said, "Past the attachment to a person, place, or thing, why were they so much a part of you? Why were they so close to your heart and nature that you assumed they would always be in your life?[61] Even if they have left your life in spite of your assumptions, why did you want them to always be in your life? Even if it was an organization, community, or idea, why was it so important that you couldn't imagine being without it?"

Returning her attention to us, she said, "All of this could be your lower self or compensatory ego-self or shadow. What I want you to consider is what if there is more to it? What if even with shadow and ego and attachment and lower self, there is also your wise soul working to give you clues? What if your Caravan self is giving you clues? What if these persons, places, things, activities, interests, subjects, and domains are not accidental? What does your soul want you to know in all of those things?

"With that I will leave you for now." She motioned for our Blue Lady to bring tea and walked off into Caravan's night. Anni nodded to me as she received her tea, then each went inward to contemplate Verity's questions.

* ★ *

CHAPTER 10

Creating the Container

I DON'T KNOW HOW long I sat in Wicker Park. It was one of those predawn moments when you feel something is imminent. You know the sun is going to come over that horizon because it always has. Experience told me that even when it seems it will be another day as usual, it won't be. My day would not be like other days. My days would never be the same.

After Verity had left us, Anni and I had reflected on what we had always assumed would be true for us.[62] We had considered what we couldn't imagine being without. Waiting for the sun to bring a new day in the horizontal world, I realized I couldn't imagine not having Anna to do the work with. We both wanted to remember, and we had been brought together to do so.

The only things I could remember being sure of, that I had always assumed, were that I wanted to make a difference. I wanted to do something creative, travel, have new experiences, inspire people, and move toward beauty in the world. I had always assumed I would find someone to share my journey with.

I still didn't know how to do these things in a way that meant something to me, to my heart. I didn't know why I had been sent or what I was in the horizontal world to do. I hoped I was creating more beauty in the world than pain. I had been creative and traveled. I couldn't be sure I made a difference or inspired anyone. What I did or embodied so far wasn't bringing me peace, only loneliness and longing.

Of all these assumptions, someone to share the journey with meant the most in the end. Watching the ambient light grow, listening to birds already singing and calling, I thought of Anna. We were not lovers or intimate partners. She said we were family of the heart, and that was enough. We were to share Verity's assignment, and Anna would make the journey with me. Even if she didn't remember Verity giving her the assignment, I was sure she had received it directly from Verity. Whatever our relationship was to be now, it was something I couldn't imagine being without.

Still, as I sat there, I realized Anna would be gone now. She would be on her way to vision quest. Maybe she would come back with her answer. Whatever that was, I now felt it included me. I thought I might take my place in that ceremony at some point in the future.

As the sun began to rise, as red and golden yellow began to stream up from the horizon, I watched without thought until the first visitors entered the park. I shared Anna's quest for a vision for my life and its purpose. It would be a new day when Anna returned. I wanted to hear her story and have something to add.

I couldn't remember Caravan moving to actual day, and predawn there was neither hot nor cold. This morning in Wicker Park I could see my breath in the frosted air. I loved the soft crunch of dried leaves and the light of crystal reflection everywhere.

I was vigilantly aware of everything that morning. I noticed the mother of the twins in the basement flat next door standing silent and still, watching as they left for school. She watched them all the way down the block. Then she turned to look at me. She didn't smile or wave. She just looked. Her dark eyes held mine unflinching. Her eyes were still alive. Mine teared a little. Then she nodded almost imperceptivity, and I returned the gesture. She went inside.

I watched the day emerge on my block. I sat on the walkup to my coach house and studied three flats, and two flats up the street from the "big house." In some ways it felt as if I were seeing it for the first time.

As I prepared to get ready for my day as a designer, I realized I had never designed this day, this life, at least not with intention. This was just where I had wound up. My life was great in so many ways, and I knew in my bones how blessed I was. It even had some elements of what

I had dreamed of in my earliest memories. When did it happen, that I forgot and slipped into what showed up?

What would I design by choice?[63] If I could start over, if I could choose my life now, how would I design it? This was the point of Verity's assignment, was it not? Yes, I would design my life around my life mission, if I knew what that was. I let that question sit, and walk with me as I left the coach house for the El and my day of design in Chicago.

I was vigilant, as if waiting for something to happen, or someone. I watched an elder black saxophone player dance with the flow of all us pilgrims moving through his platform at the station. I'd always liked his loose renditions of songs I knew. He played the crowd, and never went too far off the melody. I wondered how far off the melody I would allow myself to go.

I watched a "wild one" and a three-piece suit share a newspaper, just as if that were the most normal thing in the world. I watched a lime green and violet spike hold the laptop and coffee for Ms. Exec. East Indian, American Indian, Asian, Latin, Arab, street gang colors, commodities traders, artists, and uniforms—all traveling somewhere. Just another day for the pilgrims of Wicker Park.

I didn't choose this rainbow of people consciously. I thought I would, given the opportunity, knowing what I knew then. I felt in that moment the choice had something to do with my agreement with the One. Whatever my agreement was, I had found my way to a place very much like Caravan.

My first stop was the twenty-eighth floor of a building in the plaza just between Wabash and Michigan, off the canal. A beautiful view of the city, it was a great environment in which to work. River Plaza was high energy, clean, with a lot of life force moving through the building and the studio itself. People were big-city-in-a-hurry, and not so much they would avoid "hello." I knew Jim the doorman, and how his children were doing. He was often the first to ask if I was seeing someone. The cashiers at the convenience store on the first floor could tell you how your day was. I knew most of the servers in the restaurant. People from all over the building remembered each other. It was a community. It was its own community within the larger community of Wabash and Michigan, within the community of Chicago.

I liked the studio and the work I did that day. I kidded with our potential new partner as we worked. I even liked the two other studios I worked in that day. Each of them created their own world, with a culture of their own, and the appearance at least of a mission of their own—each of them kind and respectful, and invited me in.

In my only meeting of the day with my current business partner, I realized the paradox of our partnership. We were in business together and of course I'd chosen that. I did choose the partnership and now I wanted to remember why. We had agreed on a vision for the work, and that brought up the question, why this work? Why design and illustration? Both the partnership and the work itself had emerged from my music days and common friends. The paradox was that it had just happened without a conscious choice, and I had chosen it. One thing I knew for sure was that, on whatever level I had chosen it, whatever part of me had said yes to it, my life mission hadn't been part of the decision.

I noted so many things that day about the environment and community of this work. The financial rewards had created choices in so many areas of my life, when I had time to enjoy them. Those designer days should have been a wonder. This choice was close in so many ways.

As I walked down the stairs off the Elevated, back in Wicker Park again, another late night, after another not bad or inspiring day, I kept asking myself what I would choose consciously this time.

I sat at my drafting table and watched the milk swirl in my tea. There was something I wanted to register and couldn't bring it in. I couldn't lock the channel in and didn't know the channel, even if I could sense it. It was like the lines of sand moving over the dunes of the horizontal world. They etch waves in the sand of dunes that are themselves endlessly moving. Some dunes march great distances and others move within themselves. Who we think we are is both of these. I thought the manifestation of our life mission must, by the nature of our world, also be waves in constant motion. I began to wonder what it meant that the dunes of Caravan do not demonstrate this phenomenon. The absent winds of Caravan do not lift the sands. I could not as yet remember a sandstorm in Caravan. Then it occurred to me that anything could happen if it were part of the work. I realized how much I didn't know of Caravan.

I had design work to do for the studio, and the only design I had the heart for was this life, my new life now in the horizontal world. I realized it was more a chain of events that had swept me to the place I found myself, than any conscious choice. In the moment of deciding I must have thought I was choosing. It was only in retrospect that I could see I'd been carried by a current created elsewhere. I wanted to choose consciously and with my heart. This was the design assignment I was interested in now.

How would I choose to design my life? I had a large pad of newsprint on the drafting table. I began to half-draw and half-write images that emerged. I actually liked the day I'd just had, but only if I didn't have to continue living it. I began to wonder if I ever needed to do design and illustration at all, or if it was just where I found myself. Whatever the case, I knew I was done. This had not been my ideal day.

I asked myself, what would my ideal day be? Before Verity called I wouldn't have known where to begin. I didn't have the answer yet, and it was closer. Maybe I knew when I was very young and forgot, like I forgot Caravan. I felt there was something I was close to remembering in both worlds. That, I thought, was the point of Verity's calling me. It was the point of my assignment.

I knew from the work in Caravan some of what I wanted in my heart. Since Verity had called, Kairos, Savitri, Bede, Jun, and Amar Nen had all provided tuning in this direction. Lately with Anni and me, Verity was doing the work personally, instead of turning us over to one of the guides after calling us. Perhaps it was time to bring the work home, to a stage of completion. Maybe this was the decision she referred to talking to Anni. I wished I were in Caravan in that moment. I wanted someone to tell me if it was time to begin putting it together. I wanted to know if I would just go off on a tangent created by my need to "figure it out." Maybe I was looking for permission to go where my heart called me.

As I sat with my reservations and considerations, I noticed a few of the white feathers from the beach placed on the taboret next to my drafting table. I wanted them there so I wouldn't forget while I worked.

It was perfect. They did remind me. I wished Anna were with me. I wanted to stay up all night and ask her what she thought. She was with me, I realized. I picked up one of the feathers and held it in my left hand as I wrote with my right. It was like I was telling her my ideal designer day, while listening for hers.

It occurred to me then, that I could not just design my day. Days sat within the context of weeks, which sat within the context of months, within a year. [64] Over the average week how would I design a day, and how then, was a week built? How do I create my ideal? How did weeks create months, within a year of my heart's ideal? How would my ideal accommodate the ebb and flow of life, of active and going inward times? I smiled as this led me to think of the larger potential cycles of five to twenty years.

Thinking in terms of decades evoked a kind of resignation. Wasn't that out of my hands? This brought me back to the work already done in Caravan. I remembered the work with the hi-story of our lives. The story we tell ourselves about what has happened, and what we want to happen, largely determine the direction of our life. Then there is the question of intention. The work we were doing in Caravan called our horizontal world selves toward our life mission in each moment. It also called us to our life mission over a lifetime. This is a cause in motion of many decades.

I was not setting a long-term goal. In fact, I was not goal-setting at all. At least not yet, or in the way we usually think about it. What I wanted was what I would choose from my heart. What would my heart design for my life? What is my heart of heart's ideal life for me?

Looking at the highest story of my life so far, I felt blessed. I felt everything that had happened, even the mistakes (if they even were mistakes to my soul), could be used. What would I choose for the design that would create my future?

I now wanted a larger context in which to see my ideal life. I remembered a movie called *The Year of Living Dangerously*. [65] This title always stirred something in me. What I wanted to know was what a year of living dangerously meant to me. It had the perfume of a romantic notion when it drifted though my mind usually. That night I wanted to know if it carried the possibility of a year of really living. What would this year require for something real to happen? I asked Anna wherever she was that night doing vision quest.

I realized that in my life, I'd taken chances and started over several times. I'd put it all on the line and staked my future so to speak, with bands and even design as a way of living. There had been moments on the road when I'd risked my life, something I usually found out only in retrospect. There was risk involved and yet I couldn't decide if I'd lived dangerously in the way I was thinking about it then. What would a year of consciously living dangerously mean to me?

If I lived my assignment, holding nothing back and living unafraid, would I be willing to live what I discovered? My life living dangerously would be the real life and might turn out the safest after all. My living safely was neither safe nor living.

As I looked around my coach house I thought about what I might choose for my ideal life in terms of where I lived. I began to envision what I might choose if money were not an issue.[66] I thought about how this would affect questions of health, relationship, vocation, travel, community, and service. I wanted to allow any possibilities to surface without limiting them to what sounded practical.

It hadn't been practical to choose music when I'd decided to do that. When I'd decided to major in art, that wasn't the most practical of career choices. I hadn't bought into the starving artist myth partially because the money question wasn't in the equation at that point. My decision to do design, while lucrative, wasn't based on practical considerations. I hadn't limited what I could imagine as possible at any other time in my life. After my time in Caravan, "practical" was the last thing I wanted then for my life.

What would I choose if money and life force in general were not challenges? I realized that my reasons for the first choices to surface would be as important as what I choose now. With this in mind, I knew I needed not to censor what came up. There were clues for me in choices I had already made, in first thoughts about my ideal life. The more considered answers would come later.

Holding the white feather in one hand, I began to pace around the coach house. I felt something moving in me and needed to move. I thought of going to the park, then thought I should stay. I paced some more, started to leave and again stayed, telling myself I should stay in case I wanted to write. Then I decided I could bring the expedition journal. The journal's tangible connection to the momentum building in both worlds reminded me of the help given, so I relaxed as I grabbed it and walked out the door.

The moon was out and the park quiet. I tried to sit and needed to move. The feather was still in my hand. I wondered what Anna was doing just then. She was likely praying even at that hour. "Crying for a vision" was a way she described it. I felt the need of that. I was seeking a vision for my life. This stopped me, and I was still, maybe for the first time in days. Wherever Anna was, I joined her in praying. I asked for help. The words came more simply and directly than ever in my life. I asked the One that sent me to help design my life. I realized I was asking myself this question in a way I never had before.

I wanted help, I wanted guidance, and I wanted answers. I relaxed and let go a bit. I didn't have to decide in that moment. I didn't have to arrive at the realization of God's will for me before going to bed. I could start from where I was, acknowledge whatever impulse showed up, and listen. I could allow that to sit with my heart and soul and feel out how Great Sacred Mystery responded. I invited Great Sacred Mystery to whisper or shout as needed. In the meantime, I could begin where I was.

I found a bench to sit on. I pulled out the expedition journal and tucked the feather between pages in the back. It relaxed into the pages.

Expedition Journal:

All day, I've been asking myself, how will I design my life consciously? I design and illustrate for a living. What is it I want to illustrate or make visible with this life I've been given? What do I want to create and design? These questions would not let me go today. Tonight, walking here in Wicker Park, I remembered that somewhere out in nature Anna was sitting on a vision blanket asking these same questions of Great Sacred Mystery. That stopped me in my tracks.

Now as I write, I wonder: If I stood before the One that sent me, how would I feel about what I've designed for my life? [67] *How would I account for what I've done with the design given to me?*

Until Verity called me to Caravan, had I ever thought about the design I was given? Had I ever thought in terms of what co-design is possible?

What if the Angel of Death were with me, here, now? [68] *What if I were writing my last thoughts on this life? How would I have to have lived so that I could feel I had nothing to fear in this moment about what comes next? Who would I have to become to walk calmly toward what is next? If this were my moment, how would I feel?*

I admit that my life feels full. I took chances to follow my heart. I've had adventures and I've seen many wonders. Overall I feel blessed, I've enjoyed my life. I experienced it, enjoyed it, and maybe even changed a few lives. The question now is what is to come of it? What have I left? Is this world better in any way for my having been here? What is my legacy? I could be indulging in overly self-involved, whining self-pity. It could be a shadow, ego-maniac, stupid, crazy, carrying-on thing to ask . . . if it weren't my assignment from Verity.

Sitting here, I realize this could be vanity. This could be my ego wanting to feel it will live on. From my time in Caravan I know better. I know we're sent, and that there is meaning to our lives. We don't have to create a company or institution. To live the life we're sent to live will create a ripple in our world. If we choose that, we create a legacy; our legacy is our purpose. Our legacy will be the legacy of the One that sent us. If I can surrender to "Thy will be done," I'll have no worries about legacy.

A character in a movie I saw talked about the effect of being part of something great. He said all it takes is a moment, being part of something great, and nothing in your world will ever be the same. What if something great was being part of the movement of the divine plan? What if it's to do what I can remember?

If I can remember what I was sent to the horizontal world to do, if I embody the intention to live the reason I'm here, that will be part of something great, whatever that turns out to be. It will be part of something great because it's bigger than my idea of who I am, and will be part of more than I can know. It will reveal itself as it unfolds, as the Great Sacred Mystery unfolds in our life and in the world. "The Lord works in mysterious ways." If I remember in each moment my reason for being here, then the legacy will belong to the One that sent me.

Rumi said, "It is as if a king sent you to a foreign land, and you did a thousand things, but not the one thing you were sent to do." I've been sent on a mission and I feel I've done the thousand things. What is the one thing I was sent to do?

In the moment of my death, though I love that I have done so many of the things that were in my heart and will have few regrets over untried things, will I regret that I did not remember the One thing? Yes, I remember enough now to know that will be the one thing I care about.

If I'm to be unafraid in the moment of my death, I will be answering to my king and queen, "Yes, I have done the thing you sent me to do. I was part of the something great, the story I was sent to embody, the adventure I was sent to take part in and the legacy of the One who sent me."

I heard Verity calling and put the journal down, knowing it would be there when I returned. Verity stood again at the edge of Caravan. Since nothing is accidental and everything means something in Caravan, I registered that she wanted me to understand or remember something.

Verity looked back toward Caravan. "Come, come again," she said, then she turned to look directly at me. "You have put yourself in quite a state, have you not? You are on the right track and asking good questions. You can relax a little. It is serious, and there is room for humor and perhaps even joy.

"You were right to notice that you could design a beautiful life, a caring and giving life even, and still not embody your reason for being in the horizontal world.[69] Yes, the ten thousand things. It is also helpful to begin with that. You know from your campfire work here, your fascinations, motivations, passions, and interests are not an accident. Even your compensatory self, shadow, and ego attractions have a connection to your unique self. What you are drawn to create will have both sides of your nature. It will reflect your nature. As long as you do not limit your inquiry to this darker side, you can use it. It will have useful information if you treat it lightly and with respect."

Verity gave me a moment to consider the multiple sides of my nature. Still inward from our place at the edge, I watched Caravan. I contemplated the endless horizon of pilgrims engaged in the question of life mission. I wasn't sure what to think about what the generations in the horizontal world have done with the multiple sides of our nature. The question returned to what I have done. What will I do with these questions?

Verity used this thread. "Yes, stay with that," she said. "What will you do, and what will you leave? Your compensatory self has a legacy in mind. Your shadow has a legacy intention. You have many selves with intentions for your legacy. Allow them to have their voices without identifying with their stories. They are not who you are. There will be something important there for you.

"Your impulses, wherever they come from for the design of your life, are worth noticing.[70] Allow your imagination to create from unlimited possibility. The question of life force makes your inquiry richer and more complex. It may be helpful to start with the question of money not being a challenge.

"What 'something great' does your ego think you deserve to be a part of? Maybe the problem is you think you do not deserve to be part of this 'something great' that would change your life from that moment on."

Verity turned then to look out and away from the edge of Caravan. She was silent for a moment. I couldn't tell if she was looking at something in the night or was looking within. Still looking into the night of Caravan she said, "You are right about the danger. When it becomes real, you will be living dangerously. Mostly dangerous to your ego. The mystics say 'die before death,' the danger your soul has always called you to. It is the safest place in the end.

"Go with that for now. Design your life, your ideal, from wherever it comes, for now.[71] You can go to deeper levels after you see where that takes you. Do not discount what comes. Do not judge it for now. All your answers are part of you, or, yes, part of 'who you think you are.' Your answers will also come from parts of yourself you did not think were you."

When she finished, we stood for a moment watching the nations of Caravan. It was night, so campfires were everywhere as far as the eye could see. Colors of every nation could be seen against the tents and in rugs on the sand. Pilgrims sat with drinks and journals in dialogue around campfires. I thought that in her pause, Verity was allowing her words to anchor. Then she touched my sleeve and we entered Caravan.

As we walked I watched a hundred different ways of living in the horizontal world represented. Visions of the life I could choose in the horizontal world ran through my mind like a film festival. Yes, my shadow made an appearance, as did vanity and fear. Self-pity and ego were also presented. It was difficult not to judge the vision they wanted me to claim.

In the park and at the drafting board I'd allowed my mind to wonder without this judgment at first. Then I imagined and judged what I would want in the design of my life. Verity said that could wait so I laughed to myself and let go as well as I could.

I could tell Verity felt this shift in me by the change in our gait. There was suddenly more space to walk. I forgot Caravan is always responding to changes in our work and within us. I allowed myself to daydream, if it could be called that in a land where day was yet to arrive. These dreams were gentle to my heart and felt lighter.

As soon as I felt lighter, Anni was walking with us. Though I couldn't see her face I could sense her. It occurred to me that we never greet each other when we meet here. I couldn't remember if I'd heard her voice yet. We did not dialogue. We walked, Verity a pace or two in front of us. Though Verity seemed to be leading us, experience had taught me she was more likely waiting for something in us.

As we walked among the pilgrims, I experienced the condensation of my dreams. The possibility to design a life in the million ways that can unfold in time streamed through my inner world. I felt touched in some way by each of these possible lives. It was as if I had actually lived a moment in each. It was exactly like the experience of a night dream made of a tapestry of parts, all of which seem real. Some were sweet and some were steeped in shadow and fear. Some of them seemed carefree and dangerously mindless, and others seemed serious beyond a sense of joy. Some felt filled with importance with no sense of heart in sight. Some were filled with love, some with family, and others, mostly friends.

I knew they connected to the pilgrims we passed. I felt that Anni must also be with them in the daydreams, and the connection to the pilgrims we passed. If she was walking with us, she must be there, I just couldn't find her clearly. I willed my intention then to what was still possible.

Standing on a precipice amid the stream of dreams, I asked what might I still choose for the design of my life, for my ideal? When this conscious effort of will affected the streams and eddies of the dreams, I realized I was at least partially responsible for what I could see as possible. Verity guided, tuned, and catalyzed. In the end as with all things in Caravan, it was my responsibility to call the possibility to my world. I smiled and entered inward.

As we moved through Caravan outwardly, inwardly I moved through streams and eddies of possible lives. I couldn't decide if these were real lives, memories of lives, or fragments of mind creations like dramas of the dreamscape. Moments before this, I had realized I could choose which stream to move toward. I thought our lives in the horizontal world were very much like this. I wondered if I had called my life to me in this manner.

The Caravan tapestry of pilgrims demonstrated seemingly all possible ways of living in the horizontal world. My inner current of possible lives began to merge, without actually merging. The line between each was a fine membrane of consciousness. It was not an act of intention holding the boundary. I knew Caravan was a virtual world. The stream moving in my inner vision seemed potentially real. To my surprise, I realized my life in the horizontal world was the same—dreams within dreams, within visions within visions, within streams within streams. Without the time already in Caravan, I thought, I would be momentarily frozen with fear. Perhaps if Verity and Anni had not been there, I would have been more afraid that I would lose myself in this inner flow.

Verity spoke to us then. I couldn't really tell if she was talking in my head or outwardly, if you could call Caravan an outward place.

"Think of lucid dreaming.[72] You wake up in your dream and realize you are not what you were dreaming in that moment. You recognize you were lost in a dream, recognizing that within the dream everything seemed real to you and you were a part of it. You thought you were part of it. Then you woke up, only you were still in the dream, watching the dream, while you were still sleeping. Perhaps within the same dream you were lost in, now you are not in it, you are consciously witnessing it.

"From this vantage point you quickly discover you can decide what will happen, what to dream. You can choose within this subtle world landscape. You can direct the subtle landscape, the cast and crew, and the direction of the action.

"As you watched the streams of possibility within, you did in fact move from watching to calling. You had a starting advantage of knowing you weren't in these streams you were watching. You watched the vision or waking dreams and recognized you were not part of them. This recognition helped you move quickly to choosing which current to tune toward, and what you could eventually create or call the stream itself.

"This process is very close to your lucid dreaming in that you experience these visions. You sense an actuality in these possibilities. You enter them yet remain outside of them. You hold both simultaneously. You are briefly both witness and experiencer. Your experience of them, brief though it is, does touch you. Yet always, you remember you are outside of them. You find you are able to simultaneously experience several visions at once. You are able to be in any number of visions or dreams and outside of them at once, and consciously choose all of it.

"Now," she said, "choose consciously. You asked yourself how you would design your life if you could choose all of it, holding nothing back, all out, everything possible. Lucid dream now, if that is a helpful way to think of it.

"Choose or design your lives now.[73] Try as many variations as your creativity can imagine. You will find you can try them on in this way. You can be in any number of possible lives, experiencing each of them, touched by each of them, linking the tapestries and moving simultaneously through each, conscious of all that happens. Everything is possible in this subtle world."

Going in then I experienced entire worlds created from the desire to look good, or to be okay, or to show someone they were wrong or had underestimated me. I created streams within worlds in order to be noticed in certain ways by particular people, or to be special. I experienced worlds created to feel alive, life on the edge adventure, and exotic.

I experienced worlds, lifetimes created by shadow, denied parts of myself. These were the denied parts of the self I thought of as the current collection of ideas of who I was. Similar to lucid dreaming, I chose, and every part of me had access to the part of creative director.

Verity allowed these visions to run as we walked, until the moment I experienced enough to begin to rise above them. I had the opportunity then to create and stand outside of enough dreams, with distance, and with enough compassion and interest to have the first impulse to look for what was next.

Attuned to the moment we rose above the flow as Verity directed. "Yes, there is the possibility to choose your dream from a different place. I said to design your scenarios of possible horizontal world lives, allowing all of your selves to participate. You were to witness without identifying yourself with any of it. I asked you to let go of the question of your life mission and allow everything within to have its voice. I know your experience has given you vital insights into movement within you. There are important clues there and it also is not who you are."

My vision had settled for the moment while Verity talked. My awareness returned to Caravan, Anni, and Verity. I looked at Verity and asked, "And now do we bring life mission to this?"

"Yes, now life mission. You witnessed the creation of worlds and infinite possibility, and how parts of you, that you never even knew existed, were involved in creating them. You did this consciously. You can imagine how this is done in the horizontal world with little to no conscious recognition of being a part of it. You witnessed how effortless all of this is, without any thought to purpose, meaning, or mission."

Verity looked from me to Anni to the pilgrims around us, giving us a moment to digest the experience of creating worlds and the implications for life mission. Surveying Caravan, she said, "You know from the time you remember in Caravan that no one in the horizontal world is really left completely to sink in this. Always, they come to Caravan to remember who they really are and why they dream a life in the horizontal world. The creation of the dream within the context of your life mission is not more difficult than creating a world without your life mission in mind. Who you really are creates either with equal facility. Caravan is here to help you remember to wake up in the dream and remember why you choose that dream.

"Remember while you create your lucid horizontal world life, that within that dream you have an inner and outer life mission. In the dream the inner life mission is to wake up in the dream, to become lucid. Remember the One that sent you, the One which is all, and from which nothing is excluded. Remember in your lucid dreaming that you chose the dream, and yet witnessed it from outside. Who you really are is beyond the witness, and you and the One have never been separate."

Verity was silent then, giving us a moment to take this in. Having just experienced the lucid creation of my inner landscape, my inner life mission landed gently. The Caravan of Remembering became a different being for me.

Verity gestured toward our fellow pilgrims from the horizontal life. "The outer life mission is also the work of Caravan, as you know. You join the campfires to do the work of returning over and over again, as long as it takes to remember why the One sent you to the horizontal world. What are your vision, purpose, and mission?

"You have just experienced creating worlds without a conscious 'why,' or at least not one consciously focused on life mission. You experienced in this dreaming the ability to create your world just because, or for no reason. You have always been, will always be free to do that inwardly. While not this simple or immediate, you know much of the horizontal world is the result of this unconscious creation.

"Your time in Caravan has been to work with why the dream was created, and why you create the dream you do. It is not 'just because.' You also experienced, witnessed, how many selves are involved in these dreams you play in. Consider lucidly creating the simultaneous lives now all within the context of the inner and outer life mission. Embrace the same experience now within this context and intention. Allow, again, that anything is possible.

"There is a particular version of you required for the life mission you said yes to.[74] Within the dream you choose is a leading role. You are the 'One' for this, and only you can play that part. Others take supporting roles in this dream. We will address them later. For now what are you the 'One' for, in your dream for the horizontal world? An entire life can lead to a few pivotal moments when you are the only 'One' who can make the choice needed. Who will you need to be, and what will you need experience, to have the ability to say *yes* in that crucial moment?"

Verity touched Anni and me on the arm. She looked into our eyes, and something met in the space between us. Something in my forehead reached out to meet something from hers . . . and something began. Verity turned and began walking. Anni and I joined her, walking a pace or two behind, a triangle moving through waves of Caravan's pilgrims.

I remained aware of walking within Caravan's world and simultaneously moving into the streams within streams of possible horizontal world lives. I was aware of the impression of possible lives and consciously calling possible lives in the horizontal world.

Quickly this time, I moved to a place of lucid witness, calling, creating the streams I could move in. From this vertical place outside I remembered Kairos tuning and weaving as we walked the timeless dunes of Caravan. I remember weaving, calling, sorting, finding and agreeing to possibilities in the horizontal world with the pilgrims of Caravan.

I remembered the campfires with Savitri and Bede sharing what life mission, vision, and purpose could be, and how they moved in the horizontal world over time. We'd talked about the great beings that came to remind us there.

I remembered Amar Nen's impeccable guidance and support and the seamless way he'd always been there for me. I remembered how Jun's campfires began the deepening and brought the process to the personal. I began then to ask about my life mission within the larger pilgrimage of our collective life mission.

I remembered the beginning of the mosaic of clues to my personal life mission. Then Verity brought me to Anni and we began the work together. This is when Anna entered my life in the horizontal world and we began to explore the question of life mission together.

In that moment everything came together. It came together in the remembering, in the vision in my heart, in every level of my being. I became lucid. I remembered everything. I remembered choosing this dream and agreeing.

Anna and Anni came together. They were and always had been one. As with all remembering, once you remember you can't conceive of how you could have not seen it. How could I not remember something so obvious? Each of the clues and hints had pointed to their oneness. Verity had also said it in ways that as much as said it, and yet I didn't hear it. She had waited for me to remember and decide.

I remembered that there is a Way of living both inner and outer life mission in the horizontal world. There's a call to live these even in Caravan. In the movement inside me of Anna and Anni returning to one, outwardly the pilgrims of Caravan seemed to fade slightly and the three of us began to light up. Anni-Anna turned to me even as we continued to walk. Our eyes met and we went deeper into the streams moving within us.

I saw the "ten thousand things," code for choices without number. I felt the clues from the campfires moving in and through the eddies, moving now toward a choice. I felt the pieces, the threads of the weave, and their hints of possibility. Art, science, spirit, and life mission wove themselves together with all the other passions of my life. I felt the draw toward renaissance and living in the horizontal world integrating all the possible pursuits and interests of my soul. I felt the threads coming together.

Everything I dreamed of, each and every facet of my nature, each interest, fascination, and motivation was an important and necessary thread in this weave. Each of them pointed to this moment, and wove a vision, spinning at light speed toward this eternal now.

Then I remembered Verity and a moment of choosing. That moment, Verity, Anni, and I were together, as we were now in Caravan, and I said, "Yes," and Anni said, "Yes," and Verity said, "Yes." We all agreed to this, *yes*.

Everything on every level began to line up. It was the moment, a moment for the call to again open in a new way. The choice was not guaranteed. There was a risk I would not remember enough in the horizontal world to hear Verity's call to return consciously. There was no guarantee that arriving consciously in Caravan, I would remember my agreement, my promise.

Together Anni and I had agreed to enter the horizontal world, to live the life of the horizontal world, and to wake up within the dream, to remember both worlds in both worlds.

We had agreed to do this to be able to help others begin to remember. We had agreed to remember both worlds so we could join Verity in calling from the edge. Caravan has held us for eternity, moving in the direction home. The time to remember home and consciously turn is near in the horizontal world. I remember waking up in the dream of Caravan, to see this great being traveling for eternity and turning finally toward the Orient, the Sun behind the sun.

We are going home.

It was time to join Verity. We agreed with Kairos, Amar Nen, Savitri, Bede, and Jun to take the risk. Together, we had agreed to this. We would take the chance we might forget and not make it, and something of their places in Caravan were also risked as they invested to help us. I believe Anni and I were spared knowing what it would cost them, to lighten our hearts as we prepared.

To remember in both places we had to first forget in both places, and this was the risk. Having forgotten in both places we might not achieve remembering in Caravan and the horizontal world. Our guides could not reveal any of this outright, while they held the promise of our success.

I entered the horizontal world first, and Anni followed a short distance later. Soon Anna would need to remember. She would need to remember enough to hear Verity's call, and she would need to choose. The moment to choose had arrived. All streams in the movement within had led to this nexus, bringing consciously the agreement to enter the horizontal world, my life mission, and remembering both inner and outer life missions.

Now I needed the choice, the risk, and every moment in horizontal world, and remembering hearing Verity's call, and every moment in Caravan since, to remember the moment of choosing to undergo the pilgrimage that led to this.

Now, I needed to choose to join Verity on the edge of Caravan. I needed to enter consciously back into the horizontal world, to remember in both places and call my fellow pilgrims, my family to remember. I needed to choose to stand in the world and call to remember and stand in Caravan as well and call to remember.

Just as Anni had held the promise while I could not remember, without being able to tell me, I now needed to hold this same promise for her, in faith that she would remember. It was time to recommit. Soon Anna would need to remember enough to hear Verity calling consciously without forgetting her horizontal world self. She would not remember herself as Anni then when she arrived. She would be given the same assignment I had received on arriving. I would hold the promise for Anna then as she'd held it for me, until she remembered Anni.

We all needed to recommit to the last leg of preparation. There was still a risk that Anna would not remember, and I was certain that would not happen. Without being told what our teachers risked, knowing fully what it would cost us, we knew we didn't want a precious opportunity to be lost.

When Anna remembered Anni, when she reached this moment, it would be time to face the choice, to be willing to pay the price, to risk it all for the final turning. We would then together begin the work of calling the horizontal world to remember consciously in both worlds. We would, together with Verity, call in both worlds.

I knew in that moment the price we could pay for not remembering, and what we risked when Anna remembered Anni. I had only a hint when I'd said *yes* before. Having made it through, I knew so much more of what might be lost for each of our fellowship, not remembering or saying *yes*. I needed to choose again, knowing what I now knew. We would choose again when Anni was in this same place. Then we would both know all the risks. Knowing what might be asked of us to stand at the edge and call in both worlds, I also knew that in final turning I would need to choose again. Just as I had the last time, surrounded by Kairos, Savitri, Bede, Jun, Verity and Anni, I chose.

I said, "Yes."

CHAPTER 11

* ⋆ *

Moving into the World

I sat in Wicker Park watching people move through, wondering about their stories. I wondered if their Caravan selves were happy with their progress. I asked my heart to tell me if they remembered anything of their mission. My heart was silent. My heart reminded me it was time to see Anna.

I pictured Anni in my mind. We'd had only moments together after I remembered. She had held faith for me, and now it was my turn to hold faith for her. When we looked into each other's eyes, I thought we could have known each other for hundreds of years, and perhaps we had. What that could mean in a place outside of time, I didn't care in that moment.

When I saw Anni now, she would not remember. Verity had informed me that I would no longer see Anni when Anna came to Caravan. That meant I would not see Anni, who remembered me, until Anna remembered. I could not tell Anna in the horizontal world. I would be with her there and she would not remember Caravan yet.

After only moments of remembering together, Anni would now forget. It was the way it had to be. We had all agreed. It would take all of us in Caravan to help her remember, as all of them were there for me. Hearing Verity say, "There is no guarantee," made it bittersweet watching her walking away in my mind, as it was then in Caravan.

Across town, seeing Anna again, I thought her more alive than at any moment since we'd met. Vision quest had been hard, and hard work. She was deeper in as we gave each other a hug, and life force was singing in her. We stood back to look at each other. It was difficult to register her story. Watching her, I kept remembering and seeing Anni sitting across the campfire and her eyes as we parted.

"While on the blanket at Vision Quest, your face showed up, and I told you to go away," Anna laughed. "I said I'm busy now, I'm praying. You know, crying for a vision so the people may live. If I hear anything you'll hear about it. I know you're looking for your life mission too and you'll have to wait till I get home. You're not supposed to be here."

That brought me back. I laughed with her and thought, if you only knew the half of it. Out loud I said, "And how do you know I wasn't supposed to be there?"

"I don't, and you probably weren't there anyway. It was likely symbolic. Still, your face was pretty cute stuck on those animals' bodies."

"I won't ask which ones. What if I was there?"

"Just to be feisty?"

"Apparently. You said I'd have to wait till you came back and still I wait to hear what happened. So what happened?"

"I think it was more in terms of what I released inside. It was hard and miraculous. Miracles are everywhere now, and letting go is not the least of them. I left three tons on that mountain, and I may be willing to stay now. I've been angry for longer than I want to remember, and I wasn't entirely pleased when you showed up. I knew you would tell me I needed to stay, to live, just when I was ready to go. Just when I was at peace with going, you came along with a vision and a question. Actually, to be fair, I was looking for either a reason to stay or the peace to go. I didn't get a vision of what to do with the rest of this life. I did get a vision to live this life. That is enough for now."

I smiled. "Yes." I let it go at that. We sat in silence, nothing more needed. When it was time, I said, "Congratulations. We should celebrate the new beginning."

We walked to the corner for pizza by the slice, bought a bottle of wine, and talked for hours at her apartment. She told me the day-by-day of her pilgrimage to Spirit, and we decided together that she would support me in my commitment to do vision quest in the future. I felt the blessing of the chance to do vision in the traditional way with her teachers.

In Anna's presence, there were moments when I forgot Anni. Then I would see her or feel her presence as if two stations were broadcasting simultaneously. Just as Caravan and the horizontal world still were superimposed in my consciousness, Anna and Anni were both present for me. I wondered if that would be true until Anna remembered.

Verity was a welcome sight and everything was different now. We were co-conspirators of sorts. "Welcome to the Caravan of Remembering," she said, "wanderer, worshipper, lover of leaving. A new beginning, and perhaps it is not different in many ways. Now that you remember, what is next? You are here. Where do you wish to go?"

I hoped she would tell me. "What am I to do with remembering?" I asked her. "I know I agreed to help Anna remember as Anni helped me. As all of you helped me. How do I, how do we do that? How do I help her? Where do I start?"

As she turned and moved into the flow of Caravan, Verity motioned for me to follow. It was only then that I realized it was once again pre-dawn twilight morning camp in Caravan. I wasn't sure what that meant then. Because it was a change, I knew something new was going to happen. It wasn't till much later that I realized that change was always the result of something that happened inside me that changed my experience of Caravan.

As we walked, I noticed that the campfire circles were larger again. I saw few personal campfires. I didn't even notice when Amar Nen joined us. When he asked if I could help him I jumped, then smiled and nodded. I had no idea how I could help or what he was really asking. Apparently saying *yes* was enough in that moment, as he put his hand to his heart and disappeared back among the pilgrims and camels of Caravan.

Then I heard the familiar voice of Savitri speaking to a group of pilgrims around a campfire. "When you ask yourself in the horizontal world why you are there, what do you tell yourself?" Savitri looked up and smiled as Verity and I sat down with the rest. She was now wearing the earth-colored robe with silver woven through it. Even without them, I remembered knowing she was among those who called in Caravan. Her eyes were fierce with flashing silver in the pre-dawn light. She showed me something while she worked with the circle. As

I listened and occasionally joined in, I watched the new pilgrims from the perspective of horizontal world eyes. I began to see us having these conversations in the horizontal world and equivalent horizontal world versions of Caravan campfires. It wasn't all at once like a bolt of lightning. It came gradually, like waves coming in.

Bede began talking, sharing, then circling opposite Savitri with the fire between them. I saw Anna and me dancing like this in the horizontal world. When I looked up, Verity was watching me. It was as if she were waiting for the inevitable. I felt it. Having remembered, it was inevitable. With my promise to call from both worlds, I would remember Caravan's work deep in my essence. This was the work I would do, Anna and I would do, in the horizontal world. It was then that I remembered the promise, and some of my previous life. I realized I didn't remember the time out of time I must have spent in Caravan doing Caravan's work, before the agreement to remember in both worlds.

Verity stood then to leave. I knew to follow. "You will remember what's needed for your work here and in the horizontal world as needed. Your working to remember here continues to support your work in the horizontal world. Your not remembering before this, created innocent, truthful, common ground with Anna. Your need matched hers. You still have much to remember, again common ground. Your need to remember, and the consequence of not remembering was real for you, and still fresh. It is just as real for Anna. Your need to remember and piece together what you learned in Caravan will help you remember that she has to remember all of this as well.

"You recognized that the campfire circle with Savitri and Bede would be part of your work in the horizontal world, and Jun's contribution as well. You will be called to remember campfires where the work was done, as Caravan meets the needs of the work of life mission as it appears in the horizontal world. What else does this tell you?"

I allowed Verity's question to move through me as we walked. I watched pilgrims of all races and horizontal world ethnicities mix in the circles. Around the campfires, everyone was the same in the work. Even the rugs laid around the campfires moved energy between them, designed with every country's weave and sharing energy as the patterns connected.

Then my mind moved to the vision of my first nights in Caravan. What I saw in my inner vision was everyone moving together across the night sands of Caravan. Although collectively, we all moved together and there were streams of affiliations. Families traveled together. Nations moved together. I saw myself walking with Kairos and listening to his questions. I felt my tuning as well and watched the children weaving as they walked, calling pilgrims to the patterns of connections. I watched as a bird flying above as patterns of connection drew pilgrims away from their groups and out into the flow of other families, races, and nations, then back again. I watched as agreements were made that crisscrossed fine webs of connections across any perceived boundaries of the horizontal world.

I noted that Alika and Lucio found me long before I noticed them. I would have thought this was the beginning if I hadn't already remembered the many times we cycle through each of the stations of Caravan.

I looked at Verity then. She stopped with me. I hadn't realized I stopped. She watched and waited. I knew enough to guess she was listening to my thoughts. I began to think out loud then as she was likely listening to my thoughts anyway. "Everyone, since hearing you call me to Caravan after I had agreed to forget, has a piece of the work I'm called to do now, right?"

"Yes," was all she said, as if waiting.

"Even Alika and Lucio?"

"Yes."

"Then this too is a clue, this work with me. You are a clue. You are my work too. Or rather something in this I need to remember for my work in the horizontal world?"

"Continue to hold that question."

"And now you will say, 'You could hold that as your question in Caravan today'"?

"Yes."

Smiling, I said, "That was clever of you. And, yes, I did notice you didn't answer my question. Which of course is an answer."

"What else?"

"Anni is also an answer or a question. Both. I need to remember what we did in Caravan. Will I remember that as I work with Anna in the horizontal world?"

"That like Anna, remembering Anni is not guaranteed."

"When I returned this morning," I said, "you asked me what is next. Our walking and seeing Savitri and Bede leading the circle have helped and given me more questions. How do I bring my life mission to the horizontal world? I barely remember my life mission. How do I do that? I sense how doing that is woven with my agreement with Anna-Anni. I sense how it's woven with my agreement with all of you and Caravan. I'm not clear about how. If you say it's best to begin at the beginning, I'll call for Amar Nen."

Verity ignored my attempt at humor. I surprised myself with that. She did look away for a moment though I sensed there was no admonishment in it.

Then she turned back to me. "You could begin with Kairos and Amar Nen. What do you sense Caravan is suggesting?" As she asked this she began to scan the horizon. Her direction, relaxed and direct, told me everything I needed to know.

"It's twilight dawn morning in Caravan," I said, "and twilight dawn morning in Caravan is when a certain kind of work is done in Caravan. Everything in Caravan has a reason and is perfectly suited to the task at hand. What is next lies in the work of twilight dawn?"

Verity stepped into my field then, that personal space we hold, the first few feet around us. "When preparing a meal in the horizontal field, you gather the ingredients you need before you begin the alchemy.[75] Gather your ingredients with intention. What ingredients will be required for the alchemy you are committed . . . we are committed to? You must know we are still in this and I cannot lay it out for you now, even as you cannot for Anna. Gather your ingredients."

With that she returned to the ocean of Caravan.

As I watched Verity join the pilgrims of Caravan and disappear, I thought of the others. Kairos, Amar Nen, Savitri, Bede, Jun, and Anni along with Verity were ingredients in my life mission. Lucio and Alika were apparently also key ingredients, yet to reveal where in the recipe they belonged.

Twilight dawn in Caravan had been for the work of understanding life mission, Caravan's work, and how it moves in the horizontal world. We sat together, all races, nations and traditions, and talked about how life mission has moved in the horizontal world, and how it still needs to move and take form. Together, we worked out what might be possible now, and in the future, if there was to be a future.

Now this very work was needed in the horizontal world. Now the campfires needed to move to the horizontal world and into time. We could no longer wait. We could no longer wait for our horizontal world selves to work into our lives there the work we were doing in Caravan. It was time for more people to remember in the horizontal world. The Caravan of Remembering needed to be remembered. It was time to deepen the work. Perhaps we could all go home together soon. I wondered what *soon* could mean in a world outside of time. Even in a world outside of time, there are moments of great change.

I wondered if this was the restlessness I'd felt in Caravan during some of those first nights when everyone was so inward. I had felt the currents of something moving through Caravan as if there was something to be collectively decided in the horizontal world.

I considered the commitment we had made together—Verity, Kairos, and the rest, with Anni and me to take this risk. What was it really? Verity had said everyone I'd met since returning after our agreement was part of the work. What happened, and when, like everything else in Caravan, was a key.

Verity led me first back to Savitri and Bede, to the twilight dawn campfires. That is where I had been when I'd returned. Then she suggested perhaps Kairos and Amar Nen. Other than Verity, they were first and it was night and everyone was traveling. Then we met again, when it was time to do the work on my life mission.

This was a possible way to begin in the horizontal world. We all travel together across different landscapes with the illusion of a destination, though most of us have forgotten that we don't remember the destination. How do we get people in the horizontal world to begin as I did, to sit by the campfire and enter into the dialogue of the work of Caravan? Then we can do the work together on remembering.

As I thought about the journey after returning, I counted each of the steps taken as ingredients. My pilgrim fellowship in our commitment to the work, my team, my colleagues and the steps I could remember. Verity said I would remember the work we did together before the agreement as the need called it forth.

"It is enough for now," I said to myself. The ingredients and the rough outline of a recipe were forming. There were likely many recipes and a broad range of ingredients for the process of remembering. If we have worked together as long as I felt we had, I thought the list might be as endless as the pilgrims moving with us homeward.

I sensed there might be four stages of work at that time and more might be possible. I looked for Kairos and Amar Nen, as Verity had suggested I start with them. Pilgrims began to move out and away from the campfires. Gradually, as if a long slow breath were being inhaled and now just beginning to be exhaled, the packing of Caravan began.

The camels were gathered and the rugs pulled and rolled or stacked. Though campfires continued, the pots and silver cups were gathered. It was all slow and considered, as if the work of packing were part of the process of Caravan's work.

Yes, something was ending, a phase in the work, and it was time to move. It was time to gather my remembering, such as it was, and pack to move. It was time for Caravan to move in the horizontal world as well.[76] It was time to check my bags for what to carry. What would my camel be in this pilgrimage? What would my "ship of the desert" be in the horizontal world? What should I pack and what would the vehicle be that would travel with me? I was left to decide.

It was beyond dawn in the horizontal world. When I returned, Wicker Park was teeming with life. The Caravan of pilgrims moving to their Chicago destinations was fully on the move. I watched the buses carrying full loads, and smiled as they seemed like giant camels overflowing, standing room only. On the platforms the trains filled, leaving some unable to climb aboard at each stop. It was another rush hour commute in Chicago, every race, nation, and tradition represented. I wondered how many of these people remembered and how many were lost in forgetting.

Now that I'd remembered my agreement to bring the work of Caravan to the horizontal world, how would I begin? I felt only a little ahead of those who had forgotten. From the place of beginning to remember, to the beginning of the work felt like a lot left to sort out.

I thought of Anna then. She would be joining these pilgrims on another side of town. Back from vision quest, she would be going to work soon. We would meet later to begin the work. I myself needed to negotiate my remembered life mission and the work of the design studio, still an obligation in my life in the horizontal world.

I watched my partner in the design studio assemble a team for a project. It reminded me of the first days when we had worked with our collective of designers. I'd felt plugged in then. I would be looking for a new team now. My partner included me in this project and I could tell she was covering the bases in case I went missing.

I appreciated both the wisdom and competence of this. I appreciated the space she gave me without saying anything to me. We were already in different worlds, and I could go gently it seemed, if I wanted. I thought about how many times the way is prepared for us long before we recognize it. I thought she probably knew me enough to know I was already on my way. As if reading my mind, she turned to me. Across the room we each smiled. She nodded, and I gave her a kind of wave. It was almost as if waving goodbye. It didn't feel sad for either of us. It was time.

I reflected again on Viola's wish in *Shakespeare in Love* to spend her whole life dreaming if she could do it in the company of players.[77] She meant fellow actors. When I set out to do design and illustration, these incredible beings were my company of players, and I had come to love them. Now, I was being called to a new company of players.

I thought each domain or life mission field must have its own stage, its own theater. Just as I had become aware of my company of players in Caravan, and Anna was to be first in my new horizontal world company, each of us in the horizontal world needed to find our place and our company of players.

How do we move our part of the play, our work, out into the world? Every one of us has that question. My question now was how to move my life mission into the horizontal world. With help from my teachers in Caravan, I began to have an inkling of how it could come into form. There was also the question of how to translate the work itself to this world of more than six billion stages.

As I watched the design team showing up over the morning and the assignments being delegated, I thought about the creativity needed to bring something into manifestation and completion. Bringing the work of Caravan to the horizontal world called for these same skills I had honed as fine artist, musician, graphic artist/designer, and even scientist. I had a sense of all the pieces of my life fitting together to support the embodiment of my life mission. Watching the meetings and early sketches beginning to surface, I began to see the horizontal world work of Caravan emerging.

These people had been my family for one life mission, and now I would find the new family for the rest of my life mission. Creativity and surrender would lead me to these people and opportunities, along with synchronicity, serendipity, intention, and will. All of these had been foundation for the process before, and now I would use these same pieces to embody Caravan's work. Colleagues and associates would come of the orbit of our common love and intention, I thought. I hoped. It was time to find my company of players, who played for the love of the game, and would choose a lifetime of dreaming the dream of their hearts.

As I parked my car, I noticed winter had come to Chicago. Anna's neighborhood had the look of resignation to the season. I wondered what that meant for our work together. I looked up noticing the squirrels no longer gathered. Time to go in.

Anna and I would hunker down in her warm basement apartment, looking up and out occasionally to watch the cold gray Chicago day, passing into ever cold and more "the Hawk is out" winter nights. We would talk about our dreams and possible life missions. Walking to her door, I hoped I would find a way to help her consciously remember enough to hear Verity calling her to Caravan.

I thought about not knowing and how hard life seems to us. How hard we fight this, thinking we will or won't remember this thing so important to us. That Anna and I wouldn't find it together felt possible, looking at the barren trees, early winter sunset and the pulling in of each and every sign of life. Chicago braced for a big one, and I could feel it in the air. I relaxed knowing I could take the El home if necessary. Anything was possible, I thought. It wasn't a comfort. I shivered and rang the bell.

Anna welcomed me with a warm tea already in hand, as if she knew when I would arrive. She pulled me in without preliminaries or hello. "I have something to show you," she said. "I wrote some notes on what jumped out from my journals of the last year, and what led up to you showing up. I went through a few journals from the last few years in a more general way, and wrote out some correspondences with what surfaced at vision. I've already shared some of vision with you, and there's more. This called me all day. I couldn't wait to get home and start. Have a look while I pull the pizza out."

Not a great food plan, and this was our mode of operation. We had pizza and tea or wine, and the two of us formed a plan, without really knowing we were forming a plan. It was the call. I could hear it consciously by then, yet I was still very much in her place of unknowing. We were both looking, scratching for . . . next?

"It helped in that it showed me I'd asked. It didn't just happen. It wasn't outside my choice. Maybe you would've shown up regardless. It was good to see or remember consciously that I asked."

Anna set the pizza between us and topped off my tea without missing a beat. "It's funny," she said. "You can forget you asked or that you're asking. In the midst of all the pain of being so sick, I asked, not just why me—why this? I wanted to know why I was here and what it had to do with all the suffering and confusion. I wanted to know in general for all of us, and I even demanded that God show me. I shook my fist at God and demanded to know personally, especially personally. I said, 'Show me what I'm to do with this, how it serves, or else I'm done. Show me a reason to live this life, my life, or take me now.'

"I thought I was ready to go," she continued. "I thought I'd surrendered to it. Now I know I was asking, demanding that someone show up, that something show up with the question and the work. What we're doing now is what I demanded then. I asked."

Anna's eyes, unfocused for a moment seemed back at that moment, of shaking her fist at God, asking, demanding to be shown. Then, breathing deeply, running her fingers along the edge of one of her journals, she returned to me.

She continued, "That book fell off the shelf and led me to the Sufis. The Red Road, my Native American path, showed up around the same time, bringing me another way to pray and call for my place on the wheel. It helped me claim back a missing piece of my ancestors. There have been many teachers from many traditions over my life, and especially in the last few years. Looking back, it almost seems coordinated by someone or something. Even with 'crying for a vision,' though, I was missing this question of life mission, in important ways."

One hand pulling her hair back and away from her face, Anna said, "What are we personally here for? I grew closer to Spirit, closer to a sense of peace with everything that happened, and still I had that vague sense of the missing piece. Doing everything you know to do. So much pain, for so long, and so tired, yes. I was asking. I needed to know, specifically and personally, or I was out of here.

"What I know is, I'm staying for now. At least long enough to know what all this is for. I'm still looking for my life mission, I know I asked, and now here you are."

Listening to Anna, I felt at home for the first time in a long time in the horizontal world.[78] Caravan had quickly felt like home while I felt more removed from our world. Now, Anna and the question of life mission were home. Doing the work of Caravan with one of my company of players felt like home.

I wondered if this would help us bring Caravan's work into the horizontal world. It was a good question for the life mission work, for anyone to find the work that was home to him or her. How could Anna and I use this question to bring the work of Caravan to this world? Perhaps it would be an awareness, feeling it with people we met. Perhaps it would be a filter to bring to the strategies we created. Did this feel like home? Was this my life mission work?

Anna stopped to run her fingers over her notes during the few seconds I went inward. She traced her notes as if there were a code behind the words. I waited, breathing with her, present to her without thinking.

"I felt the vision for my life was there as I prayed on the mountain," she said. "I asked to be shown how I could serve the world. I asked for myself, for this world, for this life. Show me the vision of my life mission and purpose, and I felt it was there. I asked and I received an answer. It's just that the answer will be some time unfolding."

We sat back then, taking our time with the pizza, and I reheated the water for our tea while she let her thoughts sink in. When I returned, I filled our cups, and brought my cup to hers. "We have a warm place and many winter months to call the unfolding," I said. "I have some specifics of my own to unfold."

She didn't comment on my volunteering her apartment for the winter, inviting myself. She looked through her notes.

"You shared with me Jung's injunction to find the myth you're living," she said. "He said it was some of the most important work we can do. You said it would help us also to define our life mission, even if that myth didn't say it outright. Vision quest and the Red Road have been so much a part of the myth I'm living. The Red Road is part of the myth of one set of my ancestors that I reclaim. This vision quest was asking what part of this is my place. Where is my place on the wheel, in the Hoop of Life?"

Anna turned to look at the circle of Persian and Oriental rugs, North and South American blankets, and European tapestries. Crossing these to a collection of personal treasures on the other side of the room, she said, "The myth I'm living includes several paths or traditions, each with a myth of their own. The myth I'm living feels like the call to be part of the creation of a new myth. So now I'm looking for my life mission and the new myth so I have a reason to stay, so I can live."

"Yes, to all of that," I said. "Count me in. Joseph Campbell felt it was now our task collectively to do just that. He recognized the movement of so many of our time to search everywhere, in each of the traditions, for our feeling of home. Maintaining that the old myths still hold vital blueprints of what it means to be a whole and healthy human being, he seemed to feel they wouldn't carry us through to where we must go now. He said it was our collective task to create the myth that would carry us through the birth pains to the next age of humanity, or something like that."

I watched as Anna traced the pattern of a Chief Seattle blanket, elsewhere, it seemed. A bite of pizza, and a sip of tea, silence then . . . to leave room for thought.

Then to test the waters I said, "I think the collective mission to create the myth of our future is tied to our personal calling to do the same as individuals. How we bring the journey to find or create our myth, to our work in the world, could greatly affect how we articulate our life missions, most importantly to ourselves. It isn't an exact correspondence, yet the relationship between collective and individual myths is interdependent. I'm not sure if you can find one without the other. I might say, find the myth you came to live, and that will, of itself, reveal, unfold, and call much of your life mission to you."

Anna moved to the window, and looking up from her basement apartment she could see the street. "What does Great Sacred Mystery want out there, on the streets, in Chicago, in the world?"

I thought that was an interesting shift. We were in the underworld asking what myth we were living, what myth Great Sacred Mystery wanted us to live. Anna was lost in thought looking out.

"It's snowing," Anna said. She was out there in her thoughts. She was in that mode where we're present to something in the outer world, while inside the wheels are spinning and the mind is in search mode.

I joined her at the window, silently waiting for the question. We shared that. We both lived focused on the question. We lived the question. Our questions overlapped and only differed in degree. What question did we each need to act on? What question would empower us to move? What questions would help Anna to consciously hear Verity calling?

"Let's go out." Anna pulled my arms and moved toward the door. She tossed my coat at me and headed up to her garden without waiting for my reply. We walked into the storm Chicago had been bracing for.

Yes, I thought, that was required of us. We were braced for something and bringing the work of Caravan into the world was a lot like this. We needed to walk out into the storm. The sense of wonder and magic Anna brought to those crystal messengers of winter would help. We wouldn't find the questions staying out of the weather.

We sat in her backyard city garden, watching snow fall, large crystal ships moving across city lights and beams of the streetlights. Neighbors walking their dogs laughed and played winter sports with their pets in the alley. If Anna had had a dog, we would've joined them.

The snow came in heavy sheets, wave after wave, as the big ones always do. Half an hour of watching cars beginning to slip and slide in the alley moved us out into the streets. As the hours passed we became ambassadors of human good will. We moved along the street as snow rangers, patrolling, and helping strangers navigate what couldn't be seen behind windshields. It was our mission to help anyone keep moving, find a way to start moving, or find safe haven. We helped people into and out of parking spaces. We helped people carry packages through the snow. We helped people just get through an intersection.

The evening progressed into a storm no one should be driving in. Yet there were still people who needed to get somewhere. Some needed to get home. Each had a mission. Our mission was to help them with their missions. Our mission was to help them find a way to continue.

As we pushed and pulled cars, carried packages, and held arms for those just unprepared or elderly, I felt our questions were answered. It would unfold over time, and answers were given that night in the storm. Out there, the need was in our faces. It was the storm everyone knew was coming, yet so many were unprepared for. As we faced each person's unique call of the moment, community formed. Sometimes it felt as if from nowhere, from thin air community formed. From a doorway, a shop, a car, or a sidewalk, people came. Together we pulled and pushed and dug snow and laughed, cried, sang and cheered. Mission accomplished together. In the end, with each person's need, it was mission accomplished together. We were a team of strangers, all pilgrims on their way to somewhere.

There's a big storm coming in our world. Many of us feel it, have felt it coming for a long time. The experts all tell us the world as it is now is unsustainable. It's why Anna and I said yes. It's why so many have said yes to their personal agreements with the One. It's why we agreed together in Caravan. We hoped to prepare ourselves and as many people as we could.

I wondered if enough of us could do Caravan's work in the horizontal world in time to make a difference. If enough of us said yes, could we avert the storm that's coming? Whatever happens, I thought, we'll do what needs to be done. We will move out into the storms of this world. We will make ourselves available to do Caravan's work here, trusting that we will find the stuck vehicles and the people in them. We'll show up, remembering our unity and intention to help people remember their vehicles, and help them get to those vehicles. We'll do our best to help dig them out, and push, pull and cheer when they move out and into the world. Moving out and into the world. I smiled at that, ducking a snowball lobbed by Anna.

We found ourselves part of several improvised communities throughout the night. We were communities as long as there was something to do together. When all the cars were moving and free, and pedestrians were on their way, people in our improvised communities went on their way. Anna and I went to search for the next group to join in service to the help needed in the moment.

Sometimes I paused to consider the Navigator that brought us together in what I knew was not random collections of souls. Who decided who would experience these demonstrations of our need for each other, and the answers that came over and over? Who recognized the ones who needed those demonstrations of our caring more than anything else that night? Who created the life situations that put them out there in the storm?

I knew the same Great Sacred Mystery, the Navigator, would navigate our passage into the horizontal world with Caravan's work. I knew it was the same Great Sacred Mystery that watched over all life missions, which were all agreements with the One. The question of what to navigate, our life mission, called us to the Navigator. Holding this question called us to show up, to say yes, and to go out into the unknown. If we go out into the storm of our world, the Navigator will call the others from shops, and sidewalks, and unforeseen places. The Navigator will call others to help and assist us. Together, and with the Navigator's help, the work will be done.

Watching the Navigator move people together in that song of nature, I was reminded of Caravan's perfect flow. What was needed always matched the pilgrims' places in Caravan. What moved inside always matched their outward placement in Caravan.

I've heard it said in Caravan and I've heard it in the words of Hazrat Inayat Khan that we have inner life missions and we have outer life missions. Great Sacred Mystery showed us firsthand how they moved together.

What happened on the streets of Chicago that night outwardly touched each of us inside deeply, which in turn fed our commitment to continue long after we could have justified stopping. What happened outwardly fed something inside that led us to search for what else we could do to serve. We experienced the call of the circle of life and life mission, inner and outer, in the Great Sacred Mystery's movement in our world.

I felt both my inner and outer life missions harmonizing with the greater song, as it would need to do in the time ahead. I smiled, looking up into the night sky of the storm, half-dollar snowflakes melting on my face. I smiled, watching Anna and thinking of Anni.

Night in Caravan, with all pilgrims on the move, no one is stuck physically. There we work with our stuck missions. The weaving brings fellow pilgrims meant to help us find our life mission vehicle, and move our horizontal world counterpart out and into our missions.

Watching us in our storm I thought, here, like the very nature of our horizontal world, we were physically demonstrating what was the inner work of Caravan. Inner and outer are always together, worlds within worlds within worlds, dramas within dramas within dreams within dreams, like the ones unfolding before us on these Chicago streets.

Watching Anna digging, pushing, and pulling, I could see her also relaxing into a knowing that would unfold later. We were held and greatly helped. The questions were held lovingly by our storm. The question and the answers together were provided in the language of life.

We smiled at each other across trunks of cars. Anna was remembering, and I could see Anni's eyes looking through hers.

I was exhausted from our snow adventure. It was early morning when I returned to Wicker Park on the El. I planned to go back for my car in a few days when the streets would be clear enough to drive.

I enjoyed the lights with falling snow. Everything felt and looked clean in the new snow. I loved that fresh look when the snow is new. In a few hours it would turn gray, as the soot from traffic would lay over sidewalks and streets. For a few hours everything was sparkling. I chose to enjoy the sparkle before going to bed.

It was again time for Caravan to pack and begin the walk through the night. It was reassuring to hear Verity calling.

It occurred to me that the absolute desert had something in common with an absolute snow cover. In Caravan, the sand was fresh, pristine, and sparkling in its own way. I imagined Chicago's vast snow wonderland laying over the rich earth colors of Caravan, and felt a deep peace in their connection.

In the heart of this I wasn't sure if I'd called Verity or if she had called me.

Verity and I were once again at Caravan's edge. "It was a little of both this time," she said, answering my unasked question. "We called each other. The veil between us is thin now, and the connection clear. You will not always need me in order to move between Caravan and the horizontal world."

As soon as I noticed it was night in Caravan, I looked to see if Kairos was with us. Verity smiled and nodded. He was standing behind me.

"Come." Kairos pointed in the direction pilgrims were already moving. Then he moved out, and as on the first night, following him seemed the thing to do.

I turned to Verity and said "Thank you" on my breath, barely audible. She nodded and smiled. We both knew in that moment, I was thanking her for being there every time I needed her, for risking everything with us, and for things I knew I had yet to remember. I was only beginning to know what she meant to me. In an eternal world, on the journey home, how do you understand what someone like Verity can mean to the possibility of getting home and fulfilling the destiny of your soul?

I walked with Kairos for timeless time, thoughts moving out and away, not returning as they had the first nights I remembered returning to Caravan. It felt healing to release all thoughts and sink into the

Ocean of Caravan. An ocean of pilgrims moved together across the absolute desert of Caravan's embrace. There, as always, was the empty, endless landscape with nothing to catch our thoughts, except thoughts of each other.

Waves of pilgrims rolled out across the ocean of Caravan. From a certain viewpoint, the unleashing of pilgrims across the sands could be seen as a storm rolling across the landscape of Caravan. In the inward state we were then in, it could be seen as a gentle storm. The perfume of the desert swirled, stirred up by our passing, saturating our presence with the call of the work.

As if hearing thoughts returning to me, Kairos responded, "Your snowstorm called you toward your work, and its tuning brought you to the ones you helped. The storm was an embodiment of the movement of the great call home. Wake up from your sleep; help each other lighten the load of your things, and come. It is time to go home." As he said that, his voice boomed over Caravan and his arms rose up. He seemed the embodiment of an old world prophet.

"You were right," he said, "when you sensed the storm was an instruction for you, an answer to your question. Do you remember those first nights walking like this, flowing into and with pilgrims of all races and nations of your world? Your mind did not tell you where to be and what to do. You were open enough to find your place in the weave. You allowed Alika and Lucio to find you and said yes to them. Bringing the work of Caravan to the horizontal world will be very much the same."

Kairos slowed and turned to me. "Anna has a vision still to unfold. With great faith, Anni risked a great deal for that. You are there to help her. You both said yes to the unfolding of the vision of Caravan's work in the horizontal world.

"You both said yes, that you would help in the storm of life, in the horizontal world of everyday, and help your everyday world prepare for the storm that is coming. You have remembered enough to know life missions are never just for us. We all go home together. Life will show you how to help people embody and share the vision they brought with them.

"In your world of time a new year is coming, and yes, a new way and a new time, as is often said there. This is the time you chose to be born, a moment of collectively deciding, calling for a greater remembering."

I'd felt less present to the end-of-year concerns of the horizontal world. This was a good reminder of intimate connection Caravan holds with everything in our world.

"The tradition of creating resolutions for the New Year and a new life can be helpful," Kairos said. "It is powerful if you bring your self fully to it. There is a new breath of life moving in you and Anna. You remembered your assignment in Caravan and committed to the next step. Anni consciously entered into forgetting. You demonstrated resolve in more ways and on more levels than you remember. You have barely begun to remember.

"Use this tradition of making resolutions.[79] Bring what you remember of your assignment to create a resolution for the coming year, for the life that is coming, for the resolve needed for each and every day you have in the horizontal world. Be clear as you can consciously on how you will use the time you have in the horizontal world."

As if anticipating Caravan's change of direction, Kairos reached for my arm, guiding me into a new stream of pilgrims. "Include Anna in this exercise of creating a New Year's resolution if she responds to your invitation. You have work to do together. This will help to remind her of the tuning and weaving of Caravan's night work. It will help her to build a foundation, and this will help to thin the veil so she will consciously hear Verity calling.

"It takes a great amount of life force to have the will to embody resolve," he said. "You noticed that Anna has more life force moving through her now than at any time since you have known her. That is true on more levels than you know. She has gone through many initiations and painful events to prepare her for her part.

"Sometimes the container cracks or explodes in the fire of the kiln. Still, she chooses life and chooses to remember, in spite of everything. You are both already in the first waves of the storm. Already, it is coming. You were right to sense the premonition, the hint of the snowstorm. You will be guided and help will come."

My mind returned to the times Anna had told me about the darker moments of her illness, and that moment in her apartment when she shared her decision to stay in our world.

Kairos continued. "Anna's body will continue to sustain her. She will live, as you already know. Her remembering was never assured and that has not changed. You know that as well. It is her choice what she will do with the life force moving through her now. She has experienced lesser versions of this before. She was sometimes able to use it for life and sometimes it moved her toward self-destruction. All has led to this moment, all was preparation for this time in the horizontal world. She had no way of knowing this consciously, though it will be crucial for her to remember Anni and her life in Caravan in time to hold this expanded life force and use it."

Kairos felt closer in that moment, less detached, speaking to something deeply personal to me, in a way that hinted a length of connection I was yet to remember.

As if sensing my awareness of this, Kairos held my gaze as he said, "You went to the horizontal world first for a reason. Your resolve will be important to her now, even though she was not always happy you showed up. She will find other times when she will not be so grateful for the reminder your presence brings of her promise. If it goes well, she will rely on it. Bringing Caravan's work into the horizontal world relies on her holding this life force moving through her.

"If you hold the vision now, she holds the empowerment for it. She is the embodiment. She is the womb and the creatrix, the divine feminine birthing the container into form. It is time for Caravan's work to birth into form in your world. If you are the father, then she will be the mother of this child. This is a being of life mission being born into the horizontal world."

It was the way he said this that astonished me more than the idea of it.

"This life force moving through her," he said, "is the life force that can lift your vision, our vision, the one we all agreed to, into form. We will have to wait to see if she can hold it. We believe she will. She has paid a great price in horizontal world terms to prepare herself, even if she did not consciously know why. She did agree to it before birth. Life mission is already moving you in the horizontal world."

I stopped walking and the pilgrims of Caravan moved out and around us. Kairos stopped with me. Our family, I thought. Anni chose to go to help them, to forget, to take a chance she would remember in time. My team, the fellowship of my life-mission family in Caravan, all said yes to bring this to our pilgrim family, and to their counterpart selves in the horizontal world. As the pilgrims moved out and around us, I saw their counterpart selves in the horizontal world moving in their day. I felt both worlds moving through me.

"Kairos, how do I do this? What else can you show me? There must be something else. I want to be ready. I want to hold my resolve, my commitment. I don't want to let Anni down. Or you and Verity, or the rest of the team."

Kairos leaned in, putting a hand on my arm. "One more thing for now." With that he turned me toward the rush of Caravan's pilgrims. From the midst of them Amar Nen emerged. He emerged, as always, seemingly from thin air. He was among them, I thought, and yet I hadn't seen him.

Kairos leaned in again, "Amar Nen will help you to remember the mastery that was yours for moving among the pilgrims of the Caravan, the mastery you will use in the horizontal world. Perhaps most importantly, he will help you remember what you used to know about mastery itself."

Amar Nen stepped close to me then. "Breathe with me now. Allow yourself to breathe into resonance with the attunement of Caravan's pulse, its rhythm. Listen with your heart of hearts. Listen with the heart behind your heart, deep within. There is a wave moving underneath supporting every rhythm of pilgrims on the move with us now. There is a harmony with each that invites you to join."

With that we walked into the ocean of Caravan. There were moments when I felt exactly like being immersed in the currents moving around and through us. I had the sense I understood all languages. I understood every expression of every nation and race. I walked among every element and was at home with each. I laughed with joy. Tears moved in me for my family of Caravan. I felt as if I were simultaneously with them in Caravan and with their counterpart selves in the horizontal world.

There were moments I was certain we were invisible to both worlds. It felt as if we were moving among them, unseen, as Amar Nen had so often appeared and disappeared to me. When we appeared, it was always just right, like the people in the storm, pouring out of doorways, out of shops, from sidewalks and cars to help when needed. Just like Verity on the El platform that early morning in Chicago and her voice calling to me in Wicker Park.

Just like those moments Verity appeared in the middle of Caravan, with "Come wanderer, worshiper, lover of leaving."

CHAPTER 12

⋆_⋆⋆

The Way of the Heart
and What's Next

THE HAWK WAS OUT. The winds of Chicago screeched through the canyons of Michigan Avenue, and followed me all day as I made my way around the Loop. I did my duty to my partner in design with only one thing on my mind, and it wasn't our studio. Trundling portfolios, having meetings, pulling boots on to take them off to put them on again, I thought of one thing. Standing in snow and sinking in slush that topped my boots, bracing for each gust of the Hawk's test of my many layers of clothing and resolve, I had one thing on my mind. Rushing to the El at day's end, only one destination called.

Finally with Anna in her underworld, pizza and wine, warmth, and the work of Caravan, I was in the one place that made sense to me. It was the one thing and the one place that made everything else all right to do, until what came next was in place.

Anna seemed genuinely happy and the life force hummed through her in a way she seemed destined for. Doing the work kept us balanced and flowing. I could see Kairos in my mind's eye, hearing his warning to help Anna hold the energy that would continue to move through her. It was Caravan's work that helped, it seemed to me. That felt just as true for me in those days.

Anna, of course, could not be told we were doing the work of Caravan. She could not be told she already knew this work. I could not tell her she already had a wealth of experience with the question of life

233

mission. Still, we had made the connection, we were engaged in the work, and for the moment she seemed at peace.

Anna jumped into the work without knowing how we would do it. She knew only that we had to do it, and could wait no longer. She knew and felt, I hoped, that my stated commitment to the question of our life mission was real for me. We were co-conspirators, committed to this work together.

Anna was covered in notebooks and notes, sitting on the cross-section where three Persian rugs met. She had pages of notes on each knee, three notebooks stacked between her legs, and others open to a particular page over her legs. Journals lay in a half circle around her, an assortment of colored pens and highlighters in front of her, a pen tucked behind one ear, and one absentmindedly in her mouth.

"I did each of the biographies you suggested," she said, "and a few I thought of.[80] I created several versions of my story and possibly my ancestors' stories. I sifted each through the filter of what the story prepared me for, and why I might choose all of that if my soul were wise. I looked for the clues to my life mission and set the tendency toward therapy aside. I asked myself what in those terms kept me from finding why and what it served. It feels like this could be endless. I'm very creative, as you know. I could create hundreds of versions, looking for the high story of my life. How do I know when I have the life mission story?"

I thought about the campfires I'd shared with Savitri and the others. I could still hear them telling their stories, over and over. Each time they told their stories, something dropped away that was not part of the high story of their life missions. Sometimes something would be added. That adding would be in the first stages of their life mission stories. As they got closer, usually it was something dropped that brought them closer to the highest version of their stories.

I didn't know how many times they told and retold their stories before I arrived at their campfires, nor did I remember how many times I heard them tell the stories, sitting with them around the campfire. We had all looked for the highest version of each story, theirs and mine. It wasn't important how many times each pilgrim told his or her story. What was important was getting to the life mission story that empowered them, the high story, the life mission story that ran deep in their bones, in the truth they felt.

When their story found resonance, when it felt just right, we could begin to add other clues, and the story would have foundation. As far as I could remember, the work of Caravan started there. Our story was the foundation. It was important that the foundation was solid, complete, and true with nothing that was not our own.

"I'm still working on mine," I said to Anna. "I think we'll know when we tell the high story that's *it*. I don't think it's something set once you get it. I think it might grow as we grow. There's a point where there is enough truth accumulating in the story to empower our search. I think that's why it might be important to keep retelling your story until you know you're there, until you feel that empowerment."

"We're figuring this out as we go, you're telling me?"

"I say . . . try it again."

She again went through her stories and biographies from many angles and categories, each time looking for the highest story from the highest point of view, and the filter of what it might say about why she was in the horizontal world. Each time she retold her story I could see Caravan's campfire circles, and thought we enacted another version of those campfires in the twilight and night.

Anna had her own collection of rugs, which she moved around according to her mood. I thought this was unconsciously symbolic of the work to be done. Had she been feeling Anni and Caravan when she bought them and moved them into her underworld in the horizontal world? The interconnections of cultures and patterns felt just like Caravan. I often expected the lines of energy to begin moving the way they did in Caravan.

This was the work of Caravan we did together. The work now was to be present to this for the horizontal world.

"Thank you for this," I said, "For being so willing to try this—our, my crazy ideas of how you or I, or someone might find their life mission."

Anna looked over at me. "We're in this together, right? Besides, I appreciate having a place to start. It feels good to try something that seems tangible and reasonable, grounded and possibly practical. That's important for me at least, especially now. I've encountered enough magical thinking for a lifetime. I really want to know why I'm here. I also want to remember, as you say, the real deal and not something that's wishful thinking."

"It has to be tangible, practical and . . . " I repeated. "What did you say?"

"Grounded and reasonable. Though I think I mean, what would make sense to an intelligent, open-minded person. 'Reasonable' people have sometimes already made up their minds. I know a few who think what we're doing now is wishful thinking. And anything but reasonable."

We laughed, and I said, "That's the point of this, isn't it? I see two questions looming over this. The first is the 'how' question: how do we live the question of why we're here? The other is the 'what' question, the 'what' being, what is my life mission? As you said, how do we make that central in our life here in a way that's grounded, tangible, practical, common open-minded sense, and intelligent, and real?"

"That's a mouthful," she said. "And it's an important question for me. What is the 'what'? That's it exactly."

"And we both agreed," I said, "that clarifying our life mission is for more than just the two of us. What we're doing is looking for 'what' we're called to do, and to create the structure to remember our what. We're doing this for ourselves now, because it's up for each of us, and we're doing this to develop how anyone could work this out, right?"

Anna put her notes down, and began to trace the lines of the patterns of her Persian rugs with her fingers. Anni was clearly present for me when Anna did that. It made the hair on my arms stand up. She tilted her head and looked away, as if the two of them might be talking it over somewhere.

Anna returned with a smile of reserve. "Yes, we agreed, it's not just for us. And I want that. It's a qualified *yes*, in that I want my life mission to be delivered, you know, like the UPS angel we joke about that brings it to the door. I reserve the right to decide what we do about what we come up with. I reserve the right to decide what I, or we, will do when I'm clear about my life mission."

Reflecting, I thought that was not a problem, since I already knew our agreement, when, and if, she remembered. I smiled and let the silence carry the moment.

I said, "That brings me to the second question. How do we live our life mission in the world? Once we remember our agreement with the One that sent us, how do we live it? How do we actually bring life mission into form? How do we make it real and tangible and practical as you just said? If 'why' we're doing it is the meaning that is foundation for the 'what,' then 'why' is foundation for the 'how.' 'How' is the question that follows 'what.' How do we live our life mission, manifest it, embody it, and bring it into form in our world?"

Anna smiled. "That sounds a little like Abbot and Costello doing 'Who's on first.'"

I had to smile, too. "Funny. So . . . you're primarily concerned now with the 'what' question. 'What does your life mission call you to do?' That's the work we're doing together now. It's the 'what' you hope to find, the clues you're looking for in telling and retelling your story through all the different biographies. I have many ideas for other ways of getting to the 'what.' We've talked about some of them. I can see now, that the first work is the 'what' question. To think about 'how' while still asking 'what' could prevent us from considering something that seemed too daunting. I'm looking forward to tossing our ideas back and forth as we work this out."

Anne leaned in now. "And what about the 'why' with the 'what'?"

"In some ways," I said, "the process for that is still unclear. What I think now is that we should hunt for clues to the 'what' while we're also holding the 'why' question of meaning and values.[81] Then, as the sense of the possible 'what' begins to emerge, another question would be, 'In service to what?' That would be the reason 'why' behind the 'what.' This thing we think might be what we came to do and be . . . what is the purpose of it? What is it in service to? Why would we do it? Why would we make that agreement with the One that sent us? It still needs some refining."

"Okay," she said, "so how does the 'why,' the question of the meaning or why we're here, work with the 'how' we bring our life mission into being?"

As I was still sorting this out myself, I thought about it for a moment, then said, "Motivation, I think. When we piece together what we came to do and why we want to do it, that emotional connection is one of the clues. A clue is that the 'why' is also the emotional connection that will move you to act. Napoleon Hill said singleness of purpose was one of the most important of the laws of success. Purpose is that 'reason why' meeting the 'who' you will need to become to manifest your life mission."

"Abbott and Costello, 'Who's on first.' I knew we would find *who*."

It was good to lighten things a bit, so I laughed with her. Then I said, "The 'reason why' is the reason that underlies everything else. Even though it's the foundation to saying *yes* to the 'what' of life mission and be moved to act on the 'how,' it doesn't seem to me that you could start there. We could experiment with it, though. It feels like it will emerge almost of itself, however, when we have the 'what' clearly in mind."

Maybe it was the "Who's on first" bit coming up, and Anna was done working. She moved into prankster mode. Any possibility of doing serious work went out the window. There was only one thing to do . . . move. We put music on and danced.

We moved outside to play in the snow and allow everything to find its place. It was perfect timing. I knew later, looking back, that we were at the end of talking for that night. In a calm moment, just before leaving for the night, leaning against my car, which was buried deep in the snow, I said, "You know the hints are strong. My life mission is this, this work we're doing together. You must have sensed I'm done with design. And there is no way I'll go back to music. Sharing my biography and high story versions with you, there was always something else I really wanted. I love this. I love this life mission work we did tonight, what we committed to help each other with. You noticed too, right?"

"Yes," was all she said, and left it hanging.

I didn't know if continuing would be pushing, so I left it at that. I thought it might be too soon to ask her if she was getting the idea this work was her life mission too. First she needed to notice on her own how into the question of life mission she was, how animated and juiced she became as we explored it. It was more than just excitement about finding her own life mission. She needed to see how lit up she got as she talked about the importance of these questions, and the need and longing people in the world had to know their life missions. I knew we would arrive at the point where this would grab her and call her to feel that for herself.

I gave my car a few taps and said to her, "Think about it." I could tell she was not sure exactly what I meant by that. She nodded and waved goodnight. I left my car, still buried in the snow, and headed for the El for my ride to Wicker Park.

Sitting on my bench in the park, I let the night's work with Anna wash though my thoughts. The snow was fresh and still sparkled under the park lights. The park itself was completely empty except for me. I called the bench mine because it had almost become the office for my Caravan work when alone. Before going to the studio in the morning or late at night or after work, I would sit there and listen inside. Not surprisingly, the bench was always empty when I needed it. Caravan provides. At work doing its mission, I thought. Lately, the bench was the place from which I usually left for Caravan. If someone was in the park, I thought, I would be back before they noticed I'd left.

I wasn't surprised to hear Verity calling. I turned toward her.

"Welcome to the Caravan of Remembering," she said.

I looked at her for a moment, waiting, then said, "You haven't said that in a long time." Funny, I thought, how we so often talked about time, even though time never touched Caravan. Verity just waited.

"That was much like my first nights in Caravan after forgetting," I said. "Or consciously hearing you calling me again."

"Yes."

"That was the beginning of my needing to remember."

"Yes."

"The Caravan of Remembering," I said. As the words sank in, I noticed, like those first nights, that it was night in Caravan. Only now Caravan was in night camp. We were once again at the site of the tent where Anni and I had done our personal work with Verity. I looked to see if Anni was there, knowing she would not be.

"I need to remember something else, something that hasn't come up yet. We're here because it's personal. It's personal and yet necessary for Anna and me to do the next step of our work in the horizontal world. Is that right?"

"Yes." Verity extended her hand toward the rugs laid out around the campfire. "Would you like some tea?" A rhetorical question, as she had already called our blue lady of the tent to bring some. Taking a seat was also understood. Our rugs were now Southwestern Native American Indian blankets. When I looked at them, I felt something personal in my response to them. That was all. Something stirred and nothing surfaced, or at least nothing I could describe.

Verity affirmed that I needed to find my next step in the horizontal world. Those Native American blankets were symbols of my horizontal world, from my country there. They could have been rugs from any other country and they weren't. Everything in Caravan has a very specific reason. Southwestern Native American blankets, why?

"Verity, as nothing is an accident in Caravan, I know it's important to remember why these Native American blankets are significant. They're a link or clue to my next step to our work, right? In the horizontal world? In Caravan? Both?"

"Yes."

Silence followed. She didn't help with an explanation. I had to remember on my own, and I thought then she likely couldn't help me. I wondered why that mattered so much. Although that answer was for a later time, I suspected it was the way of Caravan's work, and necessary to finding life mission.

"It is true," I said, "the Red Road has entered my life now through Anna. I felt called to that and Anna has agreed to support me. She has blankets like these in her apartment, though she has others out and on the floor at the moment. What they might mean to me now seems to have to do with her. Is that it?"

From behind me came a question. "Is this the first time these blankets have been in your life?"

Jun stepped into the light of the campfire and sat down next to me and across from Verity. Now each of my teachers—it seemed co-conspirators, since consciously hearing Verity's call to me—had come to help prepare me to help Anna remember. Each had a part to play in our gamble, and each now came to offer something for the next step.

Jun laid his dragon cane on the Southwestern Native American blankets in front of us. As he did this, I remembered I was born in the year of the Dragon. Watching it in the light of the campfire, I thought the dragon comes to the West. The dragon from the East meets the West, the American Southwest. Which is what actually happened. The dragon came to the Southwest of America. It's where I entered the horizontal world through my birth. Then I remembered the first blankets in my childhood were Southwestern Native American blankets. They were my first container in the horizontal world. They held me and protected me. Seeing Verity now watching me, I thought perhaps they surrounded me in a pattern of something I was to grow into.

I remembered them around me when I was very young, on the floor, on the walls, on my bed. Then I remembered I'd had a special blanket. Though I slept under it on a few rare occasions, I usually kept it folded up. At that moment everything moved into still and complete silence. Even the campfire quieted to silence in front of me. I looked across the fire and remembered Verity bringing me that special blanket there in the Southwest of my childhood world, years ago in the horizontal world. I watched her wrap the blanket around me as if it had happened only moments ago. I remembered her wrapping it around me every time she came to visit while I was very young. I watched as she showed me how to fold it and where to put it away. I had always known she was coming. I must have heard her calling then. When I knew she was coming, I would unfold the blanket, and she would wrap it around me. My Caravan self felt that my younger self would have found that comforting, would have found some sense of safety in the blanket Verity had brought.

Sitting across from her in Caravan that night, I knew it was a Caravan blanket she had brought to me when I was young. I thought this memory had to be more than a nod to my being born in the Southwestern United States, and for more than quieting the potential fear of a child. Why a Native American blanket? Then I flashed back to Anna and my commitment to do vision quest and her commitment in turn to support me.

I turned to Verity, saying, "The blanket then was for now?"

"Yes, it was a kind of seed planted for now. It was also for that moment. There were many currents to be set in motion. It was connected to other seed moments for other intentions and promises as well."

Jun leaned forward then to shift the dragon so that its front faced me. In its mouth I saw a world that moved as he moved the dragon. Again, the silence surrounded me . . . and I was a child, back in my room with Verity. Verity and I were not alone there. This time Jun and Kairos were there with us. In that moment, I remembered all three of them visiting many times. Sometimes it was only Verity, and other times either Jun or Kairos, or both would come with her.

Looking at Jun and Verity now, I asked, "Did you tell me then why I was in horizontal world?"

Verity answered. "Then, as now, we could not tell you. We could only guide you, ask you questions, and be there to point to certain things. Help you not to forget."

Jun moved the dragon again. With Jun, moving his dragon cane always meant something. I was again mesmerized by the dragon's mouth and the world spinning and flying in it. Again, I was returned to my childhood and could see Jun there with Kairos and Verity. I could see the dragon cane, and even then I had been fascinated by the world in the dragon's mouth. Even then, the world of my child self went completely silent and all my attention went to the world alight in the void.

I saw this world alight in the void of space as like a great pearl of light in the Ocean's mouth. As my attention zoomed in and toward this world in the dragon's mouth, great sparks of light moved in long and streaming trails around the surface and within. Then these same streams of light began to rise from one place on the surface of the world in the dragon's mouth, and moved up and into the ocean of space, orbiting just above it. There they formed balls of fire that continued to collect the light as they it moved into space, orbiting that world like beings with a purpose for the world below. Then I watched as the light that streamed to them seemed answered by light streaming back to the surface of that world. After a time, the streams of light connected to other places on the surface of that world, and the world in the dragon's mouth was alive with light streaming into orbit and back again. My contemporary self thought it could represent what happens with the World Wide Web. Perhaps I was attempting to anchor what I was seeing to something grounded, and safe. I could not remember what I thought or felt when I was a child, though he clearly was not thinking, caught up in the wonder.

From my place in Caravan, I watched myself watching the world in the mouth of the dragon of my childhood, and knowing it was also in front of me now in the Caravan of Remembering. It was not necessary for the world in the dragon's mouth to light up in Caravan. In remembering that moment, I knew I remembered the moment the seed was planted that anchored me to the horizontal world.

Jun now spoke. "It is not necessary that you understand what it means now. It is enough that you remembered. It will speak to you now."

I could still see that world, the light streaming around and through it, then out to space and back again. All of this while held in the mouth of the dragon. It was as if it were the breath of the dragon, its fire poised to stream forth. The breath itself on fire seemed a kind of creation. I asked myself somewhere deep within, what was given birth to then? What seed was planted, what intention, plan, or promise was anchored in the field of my very young, horizontal world self? On the level of symbol, metaphor and archetype, I thought I could contemplate those questions for weeks and let all of that go in a breath.

When my awareness was once again back in Caravan, I was sitting with Verity and Jun in silence. I listened to the night, and what had quickly felt like home since I'd returned. Now I knew that Caravan had come with me in many ways. This created as many questions as it answered, and I smiled as I thought that was likely Verity and Jun's intention.

Finally, I looked to them and asked, "What happened to the blanket and why was it missing from all my conscious memories?"

Verity was holding it in her hands then. "It served the purpose for which it was given," she said. "Then we brought it back to Caravan with us. We told you then we would return it to you some day. You were not concerned. There was a point past which this kind of help had to be more limited. We could not visit as often. The seeds had been planted: ideas, dreams, intentions, and possibility. It would be largely up to you.

The blueprint was in place in your heart and in your field. These seeds were going to grow into form. Or not. You would remember in time. Or not. Depending on what the horizontal world could hold and what you could hold within it. There were other blueprint-resonant objects that came to you directly. We could not help you understand them directly. Indirectly we helped where we could, and sent people to help you."

Running my hand over the blanket brought up more questions about my childhood. I looked from Jun to Verity and waited.

"This blanket will be here for you in Caravan as you call for it. Look for it and you will find it. You remembered it, so it will be available for you here. It may be useful to you as you unravel the rest."

Looking at the blanket, I asked, "The blanket and the horizontal world I just saw in the vision were not what I came to remember tonight, are they?"

"Yes, there is more, and as Jun told you, it is enough for now. You have remembered what we called you, hoping to help you remember. The rest has a greater chance of returning to you in your travels." Verity looked to Jun, then got up to talk to a pilgrim who was standing just outside of our campfire light.

Jun pulled the dragon cane into his folded arms. Staring into the fire, he began. "You will receive an invitation. It will be a woman calling you. She will explain that her teacher has asked her to help you. She will tell you things you have shared with no one in your life, then she will invite you, in that way of telling you, you will come. There will be three such journeys, then it will be time for you to begin. If you do your work and share what your heart tells you to share with Anna, she will also be ready. If you do your work, you will be able to help her hold the life force moving through her. If you can attain your place, she will be ready to begin together with you, and you will remember the rest of what was seeded that day in your childhood."

Verity moved next to me now with the man she'd been talking to. He could have been related to Amar Nen, or maybe he came from the same tribe or lineage, I thought. His presence held many of the qualities and the manner I felt in Amar Nen, if not as strong. I thought he might have been a student of Amar Nen. I also thought he would have some of the same ability to move among the pilgrims, appearing and disappearing as needed.

Verity spoke. "It is time. Our friend will help you prepare for your travels. We will be with you as always, even if we cannot help you directly." She leaned close to me then. "David, these three journeys are not without danger. As for each part of the journey, it is not a certainty you will complete them. Do not take them lightly or assume someone will rescue you. There will be a point at which help will be greatly limited. If you lose your way or become uncertain, listen for me. I will be calling. That much I can always do. If you can hear me calling, then you will find your way. Go now."

As I moved out into Caravan with the man who seemed of Amar Nen's lineage or training, with no name given, I surrendered to what was next.

This man, now my guide, turned to me. "Breathe as I breathe, attune to the pulse of Caravan, listen to your heart of hearts."

I was grateful for my night of practice with Amar Nen.

I received the call foretold by Jun. The woman said everything he'd told me she would. Then she invited me in the way he'd said she would. There were two additional invitations leading to three journeys, just as Jun had said there would be. As Verity had foretold, my return was not assured.

The first journey took me to a place that began in the horizontal world. I flew to a southern American city. What happened and where I was taken, even the direction we moved in after leaving the airport, I could not be sure of, for I wasn't sure which world I was in. When I arrived, I found myself in a place I now refer to as "the place of shifting sands." It was the kind of place that shifts when you look away. Sand was not always immediately obvious in the landscape. It was more that it was fluid in appearance and manifestation, much like the sand dunes of the horizontal world.

"The place of shifting sands" was a place of training. My time there was the beginning of what I think of as my retraining. I was sure I had moved in these ways before, on my own, between Caravan and the horizontal world. Now the shifting landscape was a reminder of the dance of the Navigator. This was training in remembering. Remembering could call a landscape. It could lock it into form, the field of possible probable end points. It was the beginning of my work in the fields of all life.

I learned to navigate the intersections of our worlds, which helped me more readily do Caravan's work in the horizontal world. I came to know some of the others who do Caravan's work.

Now we were to begin Caravan's work in the horizontal world, and I found this required a new level of skill with the fields and the manifest world. There were many tests, as Verity had predicted. The results and my success always seemed just on the far edge of my ability to complete. I wondered sometimes what failure would mean, a fear that stalked me, and seemed just a breath or an action away. As Verity had warned me, nothing was assured. I was grateful for the warning. This journey seemed to go on for many months, or even perhaps a year, and yet when I returned to Chicago, I found that I'd been gone only weeks.

The second journey also began with a flight south. Leaving the airport after landing, we traveled through what seemed an unbroken and endless flow of city landscapes. Although I knew the airport I flew into, I could not testify with any certainty as to the city where I eventually arrived. Then we traveled to the underworld of that city, where my second assignment, training, and tests began.

My assignment was to accompany a fellow pilgrim in the delivery of both her and a package in her charge. This was both test and assignment. It was training in moving between worlds and among the multiple worlds of our world, safe and unnoticed. It was further training in reading a field, a person, a situation, and working on the level of the unseen.

The practice moving in Caravan with Amar Nen and the man who seemed to have worked with him there was deepened and refined. We had to move through the many worlds of the horizontal world as invisibly as Amar Nen had in Caravan. I knew I had to at least minimally mimic this example for my charge and myself to survive the journey.

To add to my concentration and focus, I was informed that detection by the wrong group, at the wrong moment, could be "really not good." This was not a dress rehearsal. I wanted to believe I was told this for my benefit, for effect, and it was not literally true. It felt all too real and all too likely in some of the worlds we moved through.

I remembered Verity's injunction to listen for her if I found myself in trouble. I took to listening as often as I could steal the moment, hoping this would prevent me from just those kinds of close calls. Still, I had moments when I was lost and in trouble. We were in trouble and I could not find the way through. The resonance built to find Verity and hear her call guided us through close calls and the Way found us. In the end, we did arrive safely, person and package.

The third journey was an intense course in working in the fields of all life. My interest in all fields of science throughout my life began to make sense to me. I needed all that I had learned up until then to keep up. I felt like a slow learner in their company. I was thrilled to find each field of science integrating with the science of the unseen. Though research into field theory was well underway in the horizontal world, it was not generally shared with the general public, as it would soon be. I could have stayed years in that world of the fields, again on fire with the art, alchemy, and the spirit of what is not only possible, what we need from science.

Once again, I had no way of knowing where we were. Only later would I realize the months I thought had passed were only days out of my life in Chicago. Though we must have been in a place in Caravan or some other location of the vertical world, everything done in the laboratories I visited seemed to be part of the horizontal world. We could have been in the horizontal world were it not for the lack of time's movement. Science was still science, and everything experienced there would be verified in our world in time to come.

My three journeys became a kind of foundation and tangible, sensible, grounded understanding for the discussion of the movement of the unseen in our horizontal world and Caravan. This was foundation for the work with fields within the fields where the call to form and action begins. It would be important to know this for myself and to also incorporate with Caravan's work in the horizontal world. I would need that foundation to help others who answered the call to work in the fields, in order to help them manifest their life missions in the horizontal world.

The integration of all fields of science and their very real merging in field science would become important in the foundation of the work.

When it was more or less universally agreed that I was as complete as I could be in my training with them for the moment, I was sent to people who were beginning to teach a kind of fieldwork in the horizontal world. The first of these was for only days and before the return from my third journey. I would later return for more work and time away from my design work. This would become the rhythm of the last days of our new beginning.

While I felt as if I'd been in nearly two years of pilgrimage, training, and preparation, the time was at most a month out of my Chicago life. Anna kept busy with life mission work between my trips away. She worked with suggestions I shared based on my experience in Caravan, and those I guessed came from her experience there. Even if Anni was not conscious for Anna yet, I could feel her presence in those moments. Our life in Caravan echoed between us then and I could feel our co-conspirators near.

Always excited to share her progress, Anna was also full of questions about my travels and how they would help us in our quest. I shared what I could, what I felt I had permission to share. Returning from the last journey, I felt we could talk over some of the research I'd been a part of in a small way. I shared what I'd learned about working in the fields, and we talked long into the night about the potential to use it in our work together and in the horizontal world. We talked about how the fieldwork could help, when the very questions designed to reveal something of our life mission trigger wounds and we freeze. We looked at how the trigger activates personal and collective field information and would be a good place to work with these programs. Then we are free to act, move, and remember our life missions.

It was time to go on the road in the horizontal world to work with the group doing the fieldwork there. I gave Anna a copy of my notes to work with while I was away. I looked forward to what she would uncover as she used them. Meanwhile, I shared what I was learning as I worked with people on the road. I always looked forward to that part of coming home.

Another journey. This time it would take months in the horizontal world. The moment of truth was approaching with my partner in the studio. She agreed to run things while I was gone, and I conceded to her any income that might come of the work I missed. While she was left with all responsibility and the commitments that went with it, we left the door slightly open, both of us knowing I was all but gone at that point. Few questions and no judgment, she was a friend in my leaving.

Though I might have thought I was simply leaning toward a new life direction, I began to realize that I was in fact already into my new life. My life in Chicago seemed to belong to someone I used to know. I felt something was destined to change when I returned. Something was destined to change long before I returned this time.

"Welcome to the Caravan of Remembering," Verity said. "Join me."

She walked out into Caravan's night camp, and I followed. Although it was night camp and personal work was in progress, I found an unusual flow of pilgrims on the move. Caravan itself was stationary, and the flow between tents was something I had not yet witnessed. We moved in the flow of Caravan in harmony with the underlying pulse Amar Nen had first taught me. Tuning to the song that sustained the movement, I could feel and at times hear the questions washing through Caravan. I sensed the tides of work as we moved through them.

"This is how you will remember now in the horizontal world," Verity said without turning to me. She seemed to be almost gliding as she seamlessly found the way through Caravan for us. "You will have to find this place within you as you travel there. What you studied in your recent journeys will also help you transform learning into action. Use all you have learned here to continue discerning your own life mission. You still have more to remember to begin your work with Anna in the horizontal world. As you tour your country teaching people to work in the field, use the movement of your life to remember. Ask yourself who you are there. What else is there for you to remember? What have you learned in Caravan, in your life in the horizontal world, and to what end?"

This was the night in Caravan I remembered and carried on my breath as I traveled with my new teachers, teaching fieldwork as a

means of movement in the horizontal world. Although it was not specifically addressing life mission, I inserted the question of life mission,
and a few ideas about that where I could. I observed the movement in
people's lives using the fieldwork and grew in certainty that it could
help with the foundation for Caravan's life mission work in the horizontal world.

What traveled with me to each city in the horizontal world, puls-
ing just under the surface of each interaction with people, mile after
mile, was Verity's question: "What else?" I felt a growing certainty that
my life in Chicago was coming to an end. Traveling again reminded
me of the life I was designed for. Verity was exactly right that the work
and the remembering would largely emerge in the movement. "What
else?"

I kept going back to that night when we had walked in Caravan
at rest. I could see the personal work being done, and realized that was
true for those working alone, or in groups of two or three by campfires,
and also for those of us on the move between tents. Verity and I did our
personal work as we walked. Aware of that, I moved more deeply into
the Caravan work as we traveled mile after mile in the horizontal world,
a pilgrim in both worlds always. I sensed Verity's presence as she was
that night and heard, "What else?"

Touring with the group teaching fieldwork, I relaxed knowing it
was one of those days when our next city was only a few hours away.
This meant we had more time than usual before we needed to leave.
It was pleasantly cool and raining lightly. I loved days like that and
wanted to enjoy walking in the rain. I found a park and a bench that
reminded me of my "office" in Wicker Park.

As I watched the rain falling, in my mind I scrolled through aspects
of my life that were creating my journey in the horizontal world, that
led to that moment. I thought of all I loved in my pilgrimage. I thought
of the people who touched me, leaving something of themselves within
me. I thought of each of the loves that moved me, that fascinated me,
that called me to research and practice and to put all of myself into
them. Sometimes it was a person that called me. Sometimes it was an
idea or a possibility. There was, I felt, something missing, and it was this

sense of something missing and holding that question that helped me to hear Verity calling. It helped me to see her when she came, even before I heard her calling.

Verity had given me the assignment in my first days of consciously remembering. "Why are you in Caravan?" she had asked. "Why are you in the horizontal world?" Sitting on that bench in the rain, I remembered enough to know I would call to the Caravan in both worlds, and that assignment had seemed like everything when I first remembered. When Anni moved into her assignment and it was my turn to hold intention and remembering for her, it seemed complete. Yet even before Verity asked, "What else?" I felt something calling, further, something else. Even our promise together asked, "What else?"

As I sat on my new office bench and watched the rain, I felt the song of Caravan. The beautiful song of Verity calling brought the familiar sensation of the park moving into shifting multiple versions, until Verity was next to me again.

"Welcome to The Caravan of Remembering," she said. "Join us and we will see what you remember."

Once again Southwestern Native American blankets were laid out around the campfire. This time there were Persian rugs interspersed with them, united around the campfire as one pattern on the sand. Yes, I thought, each of these is a significant tide in my life. Especially now.

Jun sat next to me again. He laid his dragon cane across the rugs of both traditions. Once again the world in the mouth of the dragon began to light up for me. I could see the light of the campfire dancing across Jun's and Verity's faces in Caravan, and I could see them with me all those years ago in my childhood. Kairos was there then . . . and, is still, I thought. In that place in both worlds, I began to wonder if who we were in Caravan then had been present in what I thought of as my childhood. Had the doors of time been open back then? Were we literally in both worlds, even all those years ago?

Inwardly I could hear Verity then, saying, "What Else?" and I turned my focus, going inward. I returned to the world in the dragon's mouth of my childhood. Texas was the place of my birth and within a short time my family had moved to Colorado, Arizona, and New Mexico. I could

feel each of these states still present in some way. As Verity wrapped
the Native American blanket around me I felt each place had been
important. Then also it was dark night, and the light dancing across our
faces reflected fires in twin resonance. There in the horizontal world,
it was candles, and the light of the world in the dragon's mouth was
lighting our world.

Again, inwardly I heard Verity ask. "What else?"

Then I remembered the place in the world in the dragon's mouth
where the light had begun to stream into space and back to the world
that was the Heart. I knew it was the heart of something in the world.
I felt the blood of fire circulating a kind of life. I remember we called it
the Heart, in that circle.

The streams of light were moving in that world to the Heart, then
out into space, to something orbiting on fire with light, then back to
other places on the surface of the world in the dragon's mouth, then
back to the Heart. My Caravan self felt a kind of nervous system lighting up and coming to life within the body of the that world. The Heart
was on fire and lighting up the world.

I heard Amar Nen saying, "Attune to Caravan's pulse. Listen with
your heart of hearts."

I listened with my heart of hearts. I listened to the heart of that
world. From the heart of the world I heard, "The Way of the Heart,"
and as I listened, what had been missing was returned to me. What the
child had always known, I now remembered. The Way of the Heart was
the call I longed to remember. It was the call from the Heart within my
heart of hearts. It was the call that led me through each of the incar-
nations of art, science, and spirit of my horizontal world life. In each of
those pursuits it had called. The call to remember my life mission in
each of the worlds I knew and the call of the Heart were intervals together in a chord, creating the call. Together they were the foundation
for the melody, harmony, key, time signature, theme, counterpoint, and
form of the song, which is The Way of the Heart. All together this song,
this Way, was the call.

In each of my pursuits of beauty in the horizontal world, it had
been there. In each of the arts in which I had made my living, I now
heard, "Yes, further . . . what else?" In my search for answers in the

sciences of the horizontal world, and each of the spiritual traditions I had immersed myself in, I heard the call. "Yes, further . . . what else?" Even in Caravan, remembering my call to our commitment to the life mission work of Caravan's work in the horizontal world, I still heard the call. "Yes, and further . . . what else?" Holding what I knew, the certainty that each of the longings to know and express had to be included, I heard the call to my heart. "Yes, and further . . . what else?"

I remembered then Savitri's voice from the campfire. "How would you feel about living in a way where you had a felt sense that life was asking you to give freely and passionately everything you have, and will remind you when you are not? What if you felt so strongly about the high story that everything in your life was an ingredient in the story of the movement of Spirit in the world?"

Then a voice I could not place in time or place said, "The Way of the Heart is about making the decision to reach for the high story of your life. It begins with returning to the reason you are here. If you have forgotten or have not yet taken the time to search for that in your life, now is the time. The Way of the Heart begins with that inquiry into who you are. The exploration of your life mission is for many, an ongoing journey into the evolution of the self. For some, life mission will be expressed as the same vehicle for their whole life. That will be the exception now in the horizontal world. In most cases, life mission will be a series of growing, concentric circles, each transcending and including the gifts and lessons from what has come before.

"When we remember the 'what' of our life mission, then the Way asks us to begin the journey to bring our life mission into the world with conscious intention. The manner in which we travel the landscape of our mission is as important as arriving at the end point. This is the Way of the Heart."

The Way of the Heart. These words had moved through me in each and every place I remembered. It moved with everyone I remembered in each and every moment of my life in the horizontal world. These realizations streamed through my awareness like a near-death experience, the kind we face in our moment of transition. Caravan had cleared any remnant of fear of death, and I knew the transition was as much a birth as anything.

As the stream of my life cleared from my vision, I looked across the fire into Verity's eyes. Eternity smiled back to me. Jun and Kairos stood to each side of me. Jun touched the dragon to my shoulders as if he were knighting me, and left me with Verity. In my mind then I said, "Yes, I am your knight, and I serve the Lady of the Lake. I choose. I say yes."

Verity, more inside me than out loud, said, "If you are a knight, it is the One who sent you that you serve, and the One's Messenger, Caravan."

"And the Messenger's message I feel."

"Yes. And the Message."

Anna was radiant as I found her preparing her garden for the new season. It was spring and a time for beginnings in the horizontal world. Cycles within cycles within cycles, I thought. We didn't talk. I sat with her as she prepared for the new life, poised and waiting. It was perfect, even as I suspected that she knew she would not see this garden complete and surrender into winter's sleep. It was the way of life, and I wondered how many times we prepare the way for someone or something we will not be present for, when the season of blooming arrives.

I felt surrender in her field. Her time in Chicago with her beloved garden already belonged to someone she used to know. Her time of learning in the underworld of her basement apartment was nearly finished. Her time in the underworld was the completion of a cycle, and we would both return to it as needed. I was grateful for her invitation to join her there in the work we did together. The Way of the Heart was calling us to come out and into the world. Spring was coming.

Sitting with Anna in her magic garden, I told her what I knew of The Way of the Heart. I told her it was the integration of art, science, and spirituality. I told her that life mission was the foundation to the Way of living this integration. It's a renaissance kind of life for our times. I could not tell her how I'd been shown this, that I'd been helped to remember that we'd both known this before coming, so I shared it as if an inspiration I was working out, a new clarity about what we were moving towards.

"I call it the magical, mystical, mysterious, alchemical, archetypal, heroic, high story, adventure life," I said. "It's the integration of every piece and stream of our design. It's the last missing piece. It's the blueprint and container for the message and my vision of it."

I paused and waited. "Anna, anything new you found or tried? You seem to be in a great place. Any *aha* moments? Any life mission moment you want to tell me about? Any sense of how this fits for you?"

"The Way of the Heart," Anna said quietly to herself as she ran her fingers through the soil. I felt Anni's presence just at the edge. "Healing is art, science, and spirituality. Life mission includes every piece, and my life mission calls me there. Relationship, *Mitakuye Oyasin*—'all my relations.' It is art, science, and spirit. Life mission calls me there in part. The Red Road, Sufism, Christianity, and the other spiritual traditions are art and science in their calls to Spirit. Life mission calls me there. The work in the fields we can do together is science brought to art and spirit. Life mission calls me there. Each cycle and experience funnels into and seems designed for this calling. You've said all along that everything needs to be included for it to be my life mission, for anyone's life mission."

Anna stopped everything then. Looking first to the earth, to each direction, then to the sky, she put her hands to her heart, then breathed in and held silence. When she was done, she looked at me with light in her eyes and said, "Yes . . . The Way of the Heart . . . my life mission . . . Together . . . Yes." With that she stood up, and we came slowly together. We took each other's hand, almost as if we were going to shake on it. We held each other instead, heart to heart.

In the weeks that followed, I shared the news that the founder of the group with whom I was teaching fieldwork had invited me to customize the work, to work directly with the question of life mission with people. Anna was invited to join me in this. Anna and I would be able to use the work in the field to assist with Caravan's dialogue in the horizontal world.

Saying *yes* meant we would have to leave Chicago for the high desert of the Southwest. This would return me to the place my pilgrimage began. I knew I was going and hoped Anna would join me. She didn't yet remember Anni, and we were in this together. I began to believe that if Anna was going to remember, it would be there where it all began.

She did say *yes* to going west, as well as *yes* to The Way of the Heart. We began the preparation for leaving. She had a series of garage sales in which she surrendered treasures from her underworld. She held ceremony to "give away" other treasures of her world in a sacred way. I had a series of sales from my apartment on alternating weekends. Though I did not have a ceremony, I attuned to what I could also give away in a sacred way before leaving.

My partner in design wished us well, as did my other friends from that life. Even though they didn't understand what I was doing, I could tell they knew I would not be back. My partner had run the studio by herself long enough already that nothing would really change for her. Now it would be all hers. This too was perfect.

We had a series of going-away events to say goodbye to and complete our life in Chicago. We said goodbye to family and friends, to professions and places, and to the part of us that had lived that life.

We headed west one morning in spring, southwest, moving in what Anna's Native American tradition called the direction for going inward, in order to move out and into the world and our life mission in The Way of the Heart.

This, like everything in our mission together, was a risk, and the outcome far from assured. We moved toward the mystery, toward the Great Sacred Mystery, toward the Call of the Caravan of Remembering in both worlds.

"Yes, Yes, Yes, Yes."

Epilogue

"WELCOME TO THE CARAVAN of Remembering. Wanderer, worshiper, lover of leaving . . . Come. Come, whoever you are . . . Ours is not a Caravan of despair . . . Though you have broken your vows a thousand times . . . Come. Come again."

Verity's smile was deep and unreserved, and the Ocean in her eyes sent streams of silver and light dancing in every direction.

It was dawn in Caravan. On the horizon were two magnificent suns, one behind the other, just beginning to rise. Twilight morning had surrendered to the beginning of day.

Watching the horizon, Verity put a hand to my shoulder. "Two suns to answer the call of the two moons of our night. Two by two . . . do you understand?"

Standing there with her hand on my shoulder, at the edge of Caravan, looking out over our beloved Caravan at work, understanding did come to me. It was a new day. It was a time for beginning and returning to remembering.

Still looking out and toward the horizon, she said, "Yes," and we breathed together in silence for a timeless time. The sun and the sun behind the sun remained where they were on the horizon, timelessly in place.

Eventually, I came to understand this as well. Dawn had come to Caravan, twilight morning giving way to morning. There was still a long pilgrimage ahead, with much to do and remember before day came to Caravan. There were still many travels between our worlds before Caravan's suns would be high overhead, and, I thought, completely in my heart. Anna and I, the container, had need of refining and tempering, to hold everything Caravan and the One who sent us offered. There was so much yet to remember between us and going home. Still, morning had come to Caravan.

Verity turned to me. "Now we will call together from the edge of Caravan. I will join you in both worlds, calling, though not all will hear me in the horizontal world. For most in the horizontal world, my call will be just behind conscious hearing for now. You will call with Anna in the horizontal world, and she will be heard by many. You will both be heard in ways you have yet to understand.

"Though life in the horizontal world is precarious, we of course believe that Anna will consciously hear me calling, and come soon to work in Caravan. She may wonder if you know about Caravan, recognizing from your work together in the horizontal world Caravan's influence. She will wonder if you remember the work here consciously. She may attempt to test you and find ways to get you to tell her that you remember Caravan. She will not be able to ask you directly as you know, and you cannot tell her.

"She will remember Anni, and in that moment it will all be clear to her, and she will join us at the edge."

And so it was and so it is. If you are reading this, then you have heard us calling, even if you do not yet remember it consciously. I have remembered my life mission and my place standing at the edge of the Caravan of Remembering, calling You.

"Come . . . come . . . wanderer, worshiper, lover of leaving. Though you have broken your vows a thousand times . . . ours is not a Caravan of despair . . . Come, come again."

Yes, come, fellow pilgrims. I will greet you from my heart of hearts. "Welcome to the Caravan of Remembering." Verity and I will be there for you in your hour of need, when you call without knowing that you are calling, though the answer will not necessarily mean you know we have returned your call and have come for you. Savitri, Bede, Jun,

Kairos, Amar Nen, and soon Anni will join us there. There are so many others to help, though if you heard Verity or me calling, then this is the fellowship to which you said *yes*.

I invite you to Caravan's work even now and before you remember. I invite you to work in Caravan and the horizontal world even now. I invite you to the campfires. Imagine yourself there and do the work I shared with you here. Imagine you are there with all of us. Imagine walking with us to the campfire you need to join, then do join in the work. Create you own Caravan expedition journal to record the work. You can do this work anywhere you are. You can do it in your heart and mind wherever you are. You can do the work in your journal as you read and do the work of Caravan.

As you do this work, you will build resonance and connection to Caravan and your life mission. You will move toward The Way of the Heart, the way of your heart's heart. Your life will move toward remembering, toward the embodiment of your life mission, vision, and purpose in the horizontal world.

Listen Beloved, in the night, in the rain, on the El platform, and park bench. Listen Beloved in the high-rise and airport, in the farm field and meadow, in the office and schoolroom. Listen in the ballpark and between movies, in your car, or shopping. Listen Beloved, in quiet and silence, on the move or still, anywhere in your life. Verity and I will be calling you.

Come . . . Come . . . whoever you are.

Welcome to the Caravan of Remembering.

$$\cdot_{\star}^{\star}$$

Questions and Exercises

Chapter 1: My Call

1. From page 14:
Why do you think you are in the horizontal world?
Who are you meant to move with in the horizontal world?
How long are you meant to weave your life together?
What is your purpose in the horizontal world?

This early in the process, you may feel unclear about how to answer these questions. The answers will come into focus as you work in Caravan. However you answer these questions now, it will be helpful to refer back to your answers as you move through the book.

2. From page 18:
Survey your home as if it belonged to a stranger. Ask yourself who this person is that owns these things and why. What can you tell about this person's intention or lack of intention for their life? What might this person's priority for their life be? What kind of life does this person who owns these things have? What is his or her life about?

What might your things tell you about who you are and what is important to you? Is this true? Do these things indicate who you are? Do they reflect what is important to you?

3. From page 19:

A *"permanent" address becomes a kind of identity.* How would you define your identity? Describe this in as many ways as you can. What does your home say about your identity?

Looking at your home and your possessions, what would you say they're in service to? When accumulating the treasures of your life, do you believe they serve your reason for being here? What clues do you find in your home about what might be your life mission? What might not fit in with that?

4. From page 19:

I looked through my books with the question, "Who would have this collection and why?" What would be important to someone who owns these things? Why is he living this kind of life? Does this make him happy or fulfilled?

Answer these questions in regard to your home and life.

Chapter 2: Life Mission, Vision, and Purpose – Assignments and Agreements

5. From page 31:

"There is a saying among shamans," he said, his voice softer, *"you become what you hunt. Anything you dwell on becomes something you hunt. If you don't ask what your life is for, what its purpose is, then you hunt something else. If it's true you become what you hunt, then what are you becoming?"*

What are you hunting in your life?

6. From page 32:

What do we know now? Where are we now in our calling? Beginning the pilgrimage, consider how you would like it to end. How do you want your life to go? What do you want your life to be about? Why are you here?

Again, you may feel unclear about your answer to these questions as you read Chapter 2. Answer as best you can. What can you identify now? This will be informative to you when you look back later. Also, you can return to these questions later in the process and add to your answers as often as you work in Caravan.

When we ask what was packed for your journey, your provisions were arranged before you even began. Everything needed for this journey was sent with you. What you can do is take a moment to see what you were sent with. Even in the abundance of gifts packed, nothing was wasted. In nature everything is used and nothing is without purpose. Every thing you have in the way of gifts is meant for something you agreed to do during your journey.

What was packed in your bag and what might that tell you about your life mission?

7. From page 34:

"The Poet Saadi wrote about a warrior who would not put down his sword, and a statesman who would not put down his words," Savitri continued. "It strikes me that he is saying they recognized the essence of these things for themselves. They recognized there was something essential in this. To give them up, or 'put them down' would change who they were. They would cease to be the very person they had come to be."

What would you not put down?

From page 34:
What would you die for? What would you be willing to really live for?

8. From page 35:
What is your essential self? What is your life calling you to? Why you were born is a twin question to what is your essence.

9. From page 44:
Savitri said, "It is true that dharma means duty. It also means nature. Our duty arises out of our nature. It is not imposed upon us. This is duty that arises form the blueprint of your being and essence. It is the nature of seeds to grow according to their destiny. An acorn will grow into an oak tree and not a fig tree, a call it is designed to answer."

What is your nature? Observe in your day to day life that which calls and feels aligned to your nature.

Chapter 3: Life Mission, Spiritual Agreement

10. From page 50:
If being a human being isn't something that is automatic, if the status of human being is something we're called to and must earn, reflect on how the recognition of your life mission would help you recognize the qualities of a human being. Reflect on how seeking to embody your life mission would help you to embody what makes a person a human being.

11. From pages 50-51:
If your life mission were a being calling you, watching over you, taking care of you, reflect and write down places in your life when this being might have been the guardian angel that kept you out of trouble, or inspired the just right insight for your next step.

12. From page 52:
What were you designed to express?

13. From page 54:
Contemplate your call and what it would mean if you were following your heart. What is the call of your heart for your life? What does it call you to inwardly? Outwardly?

14. From page 57:
Can you remember "moments of epiphany" in your life, *aha* moments where some insight about life called you or inspired you, moments that might hold clues to your life mission?

15. From page 62:
If your life mission is a sacred trust given to you to steward moment by moment in your life, how do you think you're doing with it? Would thinking of life mission as a sacred trust given to you by spirit change the way you live your life or the question of life mission?

Chapter 4: Committing to the Process of Life Mission

16. From page 67:
Reminder: have you created your own Caravan expedition journal for this work?

From page 68:
17. Reminder: Company of Players. (Whom do you include in your company of players?)

18. From page 69:
What is your life mission logo? Does someone else's logo describe, characterize, or speak to your life mission? If you were to design a logo of your life mission, what would it look like? What qualities would it represent? What would it include? What would it symbolize? It is possible that your symbol may emerge before the exact words to describe your life mission.

19. From page 70:
What is the central ideal or idea you feel called to stand for, to embody? Is there an idea you can see yourself giving your life for or to? What are some reoccurring themes in your life about what you commit to?

20. From page 71:
Do you know when your inner beings are on the move? Who is it that rebels when you are inspired and say yes to something? When you commit and believe, do you watch for the part of you that says no? One force in you wants to help you, another one wants to stop you.

As you hold the question of your life mission, what, who, and where in you wants to stop or resist the process? (Consider your comfort zone, shadow self, resistance, compensatory self, and one or more of your inner beings.)

21. From page 73:

What's important, however, is that "they've been part of something great." He said that once you've been part of something great, even for a moment, that stays with you for the rest of your life.

What is the something great you would choose to be part of?

22. From page 73:

There's a story that when you go to heaven, there's someone you'll meet who wasn't talked about much in your family tradition. That person is the person you were meant to become. How would it feel to become that person now while still living?

What would have to happen to become that person? How would your life have to change? What would you have to pursue?

23. From page 73:

When I think about why I'm here and how I would bring this to work in the world, the love of the game begins to breathe in me. I long for the passion and joy the "love of the game" symbolizes to me. I want that radiating and informing my way in both worlds. The being of my life mission deserves this. We deserve to have this love affair in our life.

What would you do "for the love of the game"?

24. From page 75:

Sufi master Pir Vilayat Inayat Khan wrote that what we take with us when leave this world would be the "quintessence of our experience." If we've been a carpenter all of our life, what we take with us will not so much be the knowledge of how to build a cabinet as knowledge of the essential nature of creating form. The quintessence of the experience we're called to suggests a place to look for clues to our life mission.

What does the quintessence of what you've done so far in your life tell you? What does the quintessence of what draws you tell you about your life mission?

25. From page 77:

Savitri also said, "Our life mission may be born from our wounds." It certainly seems to be true for many people. It may be true even when it doesn't seem so in the moment, in an ashes place. When we find inspiration for our life mission, maybe we find it in the wounds of our past.

"Down and through the wounds, the shadow, and the ashes lies a path we have to go. In that way lies chaos certainly. The promise is there is something in our underworld worth finding. There is our golden shadow of redemption."

What hints about your life mission can you find in the wounds of your past? Sometimes a life mission is birthed by what we want never to happen to another human being. Sometimes it is something we want to stop. Sometimes it is about redemption.

26. From page 78:

When you arrive at the crossroads, or turning points in your life, how do you decide? When it is time to decide if you will say yes to an opportunity, leave or stay with someone or situation, have an operation, give something, take a risk that could change your whole life, or allow someone his or her choice, how do you decide? What are your criteria for making these decisions?

How would it change your decision-making process to filter it through an awareness of your life mission? How would it create the intention for your life? How would your life mission or intention create your decisions?

27. From page 79:

Our mission simply cannot be done without the influence, inspiration and support of the right people. The question of whether or not we manifest our mission will come down to the environment we create for our life. Who is in that environment with us will be the most important question to ask about that environment. Did the challenging environment itself create the motive to succeed in the dream?

What is crucial about the environment that would support your life mission? What do you feel or sense about that already? What do you already feel or sense is important to recognize about the people in the environment that would support your life mission?

Chapter 5: Life Mission Across Cultures and Over Time

28. This chapter gives some examples of how the question of life mission has been addressed over time by people such as Plato, Sigmund Freud, Viktor Frankl, Erik Erikson, James Hillman, and Joseph Campbell; traditions such as Sufi, Muslim, Buddhist, Hindu, Christian, and Jewish; and disciplines, including medical studies, science, spiritual, and intelligence research.

What was your experience of the question of life mission with the traditions surrounding you as you grew up? After reading the chapter, imagine you are still in Caravan with your own Caravan journal, and write out your response to this dialogue around the campfire about life mission across time. What would you add to the discussion?

29. From page 86:

Write about what you know now about your "essential nature." What hints do you have about this from your life experiences? You can always return to this question and add more insights about your essential nature as you move through the process. What does this tell you about the way you might be of most service to the world?

30. From page 87:

What would an extraordinary life be for you? What examples of extraordinary lives can you give? How would you recognize your extraordinary life?

31. From page 87:

Rumi said, "Let the beauty you love be what you do." If you let the beauty you love be what you do, what would that mean for you and your life? What would you be doing? What would you be doing differently? What would you stop doing?

32. From page 91:

What would "an environment for life, according to your gift or bent" be for you?

33. From page 96:
What is the archetypal myth of your life?

34. From page 96:
How is the cultural context of your life affecting how you think about the question of life mission, and what you think is possible for you?

Chapter 6: Life Mission - Individual

35. From pages 103-104:
As I considered this, the guide said, "Listen for the highest story of your life. If we were sent to the horizontal world to embody a particular mission, what in the story of our life tells of that? Listen for the clues the teller of this tale is missing about his or her life. We create our life in the sharing of it.

"In the telling we find the pattern in the tapestry of our life in the horizontal world. We see a thread moving through an event, and see for the first time, perhaps, why we made the choice we did. Witness the context of the larger weave of your life used to create the story of a life mission lived and embodied. Even if you do not remember this work we do together when you return to the horizontal world, perfume of the highest version of your story will be with you. You may feel a sense of peace or the rightness of a direction. Watch for this as we listen or tell our story. Each time, feel your way through. Help each other and watch for your part in the story."

Caravan asks what our highest story is. Caravan asks us to imagine what it could be, and to see it as better than we remember it. Caravan asks us to seek the life mission the story is calling to. One of the campfire guides asked people in her circle to remember it as a greater possibility. "Now go inward and remember what is possible for your story in the inner world of your imagination."

The guide continued, "Tell and retell your story with the resonance of the imaginal realm. Find the place of the mythic, magical, alchemical, mystic, and heroic qualities you wish to embody in your life."

Tell and retell your story until it is the highest version of the story of your life you can imagine telling. Then tell it again, imagining it from an even higher perspective. How do the turning points serve the highest story? If your soul had been infinitely wise to choose this life, what would it have had in mind to prepare you for when it set it this way? What is the largest and most inspiring context for your story?

36. From pages 104-105:
Look deeply, listen deeply, feel deeply, as you consider the neighborhood you live in and your home. Contemplate the series of neighborhoods and homes you've had in your life. What do these tell you about you? What clues do you find about the high story of your life? What kind of person has this story?

37. From pages 107-108:
Jun asked the group, "When you told yourself the story of 'how it came to be this way,' whose story did you tell? How many stories make up the story of your people? Who exactly are 'your people'? As we shared the campfires in Caravan, was there someone there you thought was not 'your people'? In the horizontal world, each culture has its version of how it came to be or how it should be. As we told the stories of our lives, our place within the stories of our culture was nearly invisible. With help around the campfire, this surfaced to some degree."

Jun continued, "Now I want you to tell the story of 'how it came to be this way' and 'how it should be' from your cultures and traditions. As we tell these stories, the life mission of our cultures and traditions step forward from the background. What is the myth of your culture and tradition in the horizontal world?

"If the tradition you entered in the horizontal world is purposeful, then what is essential about your nature that called you to it? When all the stories we tell ourselves about how it is and how it came to be are gone, essence is what remains. What is the essential nature or dharma of your culture? What were the agreements? What is the great myth of your culture and your part in it?"

In the great stories of the horizontal world, what are the great mythic qualities carried in the blueprint of your culture? If the story of all people added together creates the 'great story,' what is the role your culture was meant to play? If all parts are valuable and necessary, what is the life mission part of your culture? What is your individual part?

What is the high story of the traditions and cultures you are surrounded by, have moved through, or have called your own? What are their myths? What are their collective life missions? What is your place within these collective high stories, myths, and life missions? How is your personal life mission connected to them? What is the myth you were meant to live? Are you called to take a place within the myth of collective life mission of a culture outside your birth culture? What tells you that? Do you feel you were never meant to take part in the collective life mission of the culture you were born into? Are you called to change the myth of that culture?

38. From page 114:
The highest story you can embody and the highest mythic blueprint together form a container for your agreement with the One that sent you.

What does the container formed by your high story and the myth you were meant to live tell you about your life mission? Working through the exercises and questions solidifies this container.

39. From page 115:
Our work in Caravan assists our horizontal world selves in the work of embodying life mission. Together with the One that sent us we create a container for the work in the horizontal world. There is another kind of miracle that happens with this.

Something is created in this that is a kind of life. We co-create the being of our life mission. Like your self, your life mission is a being that lives in both worlds and moves with you. Your relationship with this being is as ancient as your relationship with Caravan and the One that sent you. Your work here requires your conscious participation in this relationship, at least here in Caravan.

The being of your life mission travels with you for the entire journey. It can be your closest friend and greatest protector in times of danger. In fact, the safest place in the horizontal world is traveling with your life mission.

Dialogue with the being of your life mission. One of the ways to do this is to ask it a question, writing with your dominant hand. Use your non-dominant hand to answer.

40. From page 116:
The being of your life mission is on intimate terms with the Divine Spirit of Guidance. It is close to the Spirit of Guidance because it is your life mission.

How do you best recognize guidance from the Divine Spirit of Guidance? Ask now for guidance around your life mission. What does the Divine Spirit of Guidance want you to know about your life mission? Where does it call you to explore?

41. From page 117:
Yes, the being of your life mission is with you here in Caravan. It is part of you, has been with you from the beginning, and does this work with you. You can ask its help here as you can in the horizontal world.

Ask the being of your life mission to help you remember, and ask it for guidance.

Chapter 7: Considering Your Own Life Mission

42. From pages 122-131:
It was time for my high story. I realized all the different ways I told my story, even to myself. It was time for my life mission. I began to see . . . As David tells his story, as Kairos directs "again please," again and again, what does this trigger for you about your story? Invite yourself to tell your high story. Return again and again to your story for hints of your life mission. Listen for the clues.

43. From page 128:
If you look for it you will find the rites of passage in all areas of your growing up in the horizontal world. When you tell your story, what determines the kind of initiation and rites of passage you experience? What

determines the direction in which they take you? If your life mission is a resonant attractor calling your life in a particular way, why this turning point versus another? Why this initiation? Why this rite of passage?

What clues do you find about your life mission in the nature of the particular initiations and rites of passage of your life?

44. From page 129:

What did your experience with the unique combination of firsts in your life tell you about your life mission?

45. From page 129:

In the work of identifying my life mission, I looked for the footprints or fingerprints of the guide. I looked for the impressions of the invisible hand.

What has the invisible hand been directing you toward?

46. From page 131:

If you think of your life mission as a direction you are called to move toward, what does this direction tell you about your life mission?

47. From page 136:

I sit at the edge tonight, as we are about to begin, thinking about the many things I wanted over the course of my life, a question Kairos left us. Kairos said to me, "If you want something else now, the next question is why. Why do you want something you didn't want when you were a teenager? Is this because you have grown up or is it because you stopped believing in your dreams? Did you believe anything was possible, and if so what happened to that?"

It is important to contact what you really want. If you find that you don't remember what you wanted when you were young, call to your seven-year-old. Call to your teenager within. Remember what you wanted as you moved forward in your life.

Chapter 8: Remembering Your Own Life Mission

48. From page 141:

If "meaning" were a character in the story of your life, a character traveling with you for your whole life, describe the part this character would play.

49. From page 142:

Who would you like to share a Caravan campfire circle with? Who would you like to spend a day with? Why? (You can pick anyone alive or dead, real or fictional.) What would you ask them? What questions would they ask you?

50. From page 143:

Who would you choose to mentor you? Why? Who you pick will tell you a lot about your life mission. (You can pick any person alive or dead, real or fictional.) What do you want them to help you with? Why? What is significant to your life mission about their process? What is significant to your life mission about their style? What fascinates them and is important to them?

You might go to an imaginary campfire circle in Caravan and ask them questions and work with them there on the question of your life mission. Ask them why they think you believe they can help you with this.

51. From page 145:

Who would you choose to spend a day with? You can pick any person alive or dead, real or fictional. Where would you choose to spend a day if it could be anywhere real or imaginary? Why? Then, what place in time would you like to visit? Why? Again it could be a time before time, outside of time, or once upon a time. Why do you choose this particular place in real or make-believe time?

52. From page 147:

How in particular would you like to make a difference in the world? Why? What are the qualities needed to make the difference you want to make? Why this difference in the world versus another? What is unique to this difference you want to make? What is unique about the particular way you would create this change? What does this tell you about your life mission?

53. From page 150:

Write about the times in your life when you felt most alive. Write about the times in your life when you felt most confident. Write about the times in your life when you felt strongest. Write about the times in your life when you felt most in tune with your nature. Write about the times in your life that felt in perfect harmony with your personal style.

54. From pages 157-158:

Become someone else and describe yourself. What can you see about your life mission from their viewpoint? Become one of your family members and describe yourself. Become a friend and describe yourself. Become a co-worker and describe yourself. Become someone who has only encountered you briefly or who has just met you, and describe yourself.

55. From pages 159-160:

What do you love? What do you love doing? Where do you love going? What do you love listening to, feeling, watching, breathing in, discovering, exploring? Why?

What do you find beautiful? Why?

56. From page 159:

What motivates you? What is the motive behind your intentions? What is your reason why? What are you seeking? Why? What do you long for? Why? What are you seeking the answer to? What do you hope these answer will lead to? Why is that important to you?

Chapter 9: Creating Possibilities

57. From page 166:

At times we danced. This was a prayer certainly, and also communication. This was the wisdom of the body and movement of the soul. Afterwards, the group gathered to talk about what they learned of themselves and those with whom they danced. They shared what the dances told them about their possible life missions.

Pick music that speaks to you and allow yourself to move with it as a conversation with the wisdom of the body. Feel, listen, and watch for what your body can tell you about your life mission. Call it your life-mission dance and make notes of clues to your life mission that you receive from the dance.

58. From page 166:
"Let yourself be drawn by the stronger pull of what you really love."

What do you really love? What were you drawn to? Who did you notice and why? What becomes "magnetized" for you and why? Why did you notice that person, place or thing? The exercise is to be present to and note in your life mission journal what you notice that you notice in your day. What are you drawn to and why?

59. From page 169:
Who in the world do you believe is doing their life mission? Why do you believe this? What does this tell you about your impressions of life mission? What does this tell you about your life mission?

Whose life mission attracts you most, and why? Is it the life mission that attracts you or the person? Perhaps it is both. Both will tell you something.

60. From page 185:
If you could have an additional family, specifically a life-mission family, that you could choose, who would you pick? Who would you pick for your life-mission mother and father? Grandmother and grandfather? Brother and sister, aunt and uncle? In all the ways your biological family can help (in the best sense), this family will be there for you with experience and knowledge around your life mission. Imagine a life-mission family picnic, and the talk around the picnic table. Why did you pick these people and what will you ask them? What does this tell you about your life mission?

61. From page 187:
What did you always assume would be in your life? Why? What does this tell you about your life mission? What did you never imagine being without? Why? What does this tell you about your life mission?

Chapter 10: Creating the Container

62. From page 189:
Continue to contemplate what you always thought would be part of your life, and what you couldn't imagine being without (from chapter 9), and write about what you always assumed would be true for you. What does this tell you about your life mission?

63. From page 191:
How would you choose to design your life? If your life were a design assignment, what design considerations would you include in your decisions? Your might do design sketches, make written notes, tell a story, act it out, or do anything else that will bring your life mission design together.
What would the design of your heart bring to this assignment?

64. From page 194:
What intention would create the context for your life design? What would a day, a week, a month, and a year look like?

65. From page 194:
What would a year of living dangerously be for you? This would be a year of living full out, holding nothing back, living fully alive and awake, and taking the risks the voice in your heart calls you to. What would a year of living "unafraid" create? What does this tell you about your life mission?

66. From page 195:
Ideally, what would you choose for your life if money and life force in general were not a challenge?

67. From page 196:
If you were to stand before the One that sent you, how would you account for what you did with the design given you for your life?

68. From page 197:
What if the Angel of Death were with me, here, now? What if I were

writing my last thoughts on this life? How would I have to have lived, to feel I had nothing to fear in this moment about what comes next? Who would I have to have become, to walk calmly toward what is next?

What legacy would you like your life to create?

A character in a movie I saw (The Replacements) *talked about the effect of being part of something great. He said all it takes is a moment of being part of something great, and nothing in your world will ever be the same.*

What is the "something great" you would choose to part of?

69. From page 198:

Even your compensatory self, shadow, ego attractions, have a connection to your unique self. What you are drawn to create will have both sides of your nature. It will reflect your nature. It will have useful information if you treat it lightly.

You have many selves with intentions for your legacy. Allow them their voice without identifying with their story. They are not who you are, and still, there will be something there for you.

Write about what has fascinated you in your life and why. How has this fascination motivated you? What are some of your passions and interests?

70. From page 199:

Your impulses, wherever they come from, for the design of your life, are worth noticing. Your idea to allow your imagination to create from unlimited possibility is helpful to consider for the horizontal world. Go with that for now. Design your life, your ideal, from wherever it comes for now. You can go to deeper levels after you see where that takes you.

What do your impulses tell you about your life mission? What is your ideal life? What can you imagine for your life and life mission from unlimited possibility?

71. From pages 199-200:

Use your inner vision to create your ideal life, unrestricted by time, no limits on time, or outside of time.

72. From pages 201-202:

Think of lucid dreaming. You wake up in your dreams and realize you are not what you were dreaming in that moment. You recognize you were lost in a dream. You recognize that within the dream everything seemed real to you and you were a part of it. You thought you were a part of it. Then you woke up, only you were still in the dream, watching the dream, while you were still sleeping.

From this vantage point you quickly discover you can decide what will happen, what to dream. You can choose within this subtle world landscape. You can direct the subtle landscape, the cast and crew, and the direction of the action.

Lucid dream now, if that is a helpful way to think of it. Choose or design your lives now. Try as many variations as your creativity can imagine. You can be in any number of possible lives; experience each of them, and be touched by each of them. You can link the tapestry and weave and move simultaneously through each, conscious of all that happens. Everything is possible in this subtle world.

Create as many lives as you can imagine in this way, knowing you don't have to choose one over the other. Create lives you would actually love to live, that speak to your heart. You can experience them all. What clues for your life mission can you find in these lives?

73. From pages 202-203:

If something in each of the many lucid dream lives was important to your heart, how could you include what is important from each in the creation of your life mission life? Create a lucid dream life that includes the important qualities, activities, and people from the previous exercise that you consciously hold within the context container called your life mission embodied life.

Describe how this life develops the embodiment of both your inner and outer life mission.

74. From page 204:

There is a particular version of you required for the life mission you said yes to. Which "you" are you the one for?

What did the One and you create for you to be the one for? It was created for you to play the leading role. Within your dream only you can play that part. There are moments in life where "you are the one." You are the only one. What life mission are you set up to be that "one" for? Who would you have to be to say *yes* in that moment? What are you the "one" for?

There are long moments or nexus points in the horizontal world where eternity enters. Eternity pauses in the breath of a moment. In that moment you are the "one" for that moment of choice, and All That Is waits for you to take your place, to say *yes*. What is your place?

Chapter 11: Moving into the World

75. From page 214:
When preparing a meal in the horizontal world, you gather the ingredients you need before you begin the alchemy. Gather your ingredients with intention.

What ingredients will you need for the alchemy of living your life mission? What are the key ingredients? What qualities will you need? What are the steps in preparing the meal of your life mission? What people would be ingredients?

76. From page 216:
It was time for Caravan to move in the horizontal world as well. It was time to check my bags for what to carry. What would my camel be in this pilgrimage? What would "my ship of the desert" be in the horizontal world? What should I pack?

What did you pack for your life mission pilgrimage in the horizontal world?

77. From page 217:
In the movie *Shakespeare in Love*, Voila says she would spend her whole life dreaming if she could spend it in the company of players. She meant fellow actors. Who would be in your "Company of Players"? What is the domain of your company of players?

78. From page 220:
What is "home" to you?

79. From page 228:
Use this tradition of making resolutions. Bring what you do remember of your assignment to create a resolution for the year coming, for the life that is coming, for the resolve needed for each and every day you have in the horizontal world.

Like a New Year's resolution, create a life mission life resolution. From what you have identified about your life mission to this point, what resolution would you create?

Chapter 12: The Way of the Heart and What's Next

80. From page 234:
I did each of the biographies you suggested and a few I thought of. I created several versions of my story and possibly my ancestors. I sifted each through the filter of what the story prepared me for, and why I might choose all that if my soul were wise. I looked for the clue to life mission and put the tendency toward therapy aside. I asked myself what in those terms kept me from finding why and what it served.

I thought about the campfires I shared with Savitri and the others. I could hear them still telling their stories, over and over. Each time they told their story, something dropped away that was not part of the high story of their life mission. Sometimes something would be added. That would be the first stages of their life mission stories.

I didn't know how many times they told and retold their stories before I arrived at their campfire, and I didn't really remember how many times they told their story. It was only important they get to the life mission story that empowered them, the high story life mission story that ran deep in their bones, in the truth they felt.

When their story found resonance, when it felt just right, we could begin to add other clues and the story would have a foundation. As far as I could remember, the work of Caravan started there. Our story was the foundation.

Use the Caravan process of telling the story of your life over and over until you feel it's the version that is most empowering, holds the truth of the purpose of having the life you lived, and begins to inform you about your reason for being here. Remember that this isn't therapy. For this process, you aren't looking for the source of wounds or dysfunctions (unless you can see how such wounds prepared you for your calling in some way). The filters and context for this exercise are to ask, "If your soul is infinitely wise and knows what it's doing, why would it set your life up in the way it did? What was it preparing your for?"

Additional clues might be found in writing the story of your family, and even your culture. Also, it may be helpful to do specific biographies, such as the story of your relationship to money, career, romance, or your body.

81. From page 237:

Then, as the sense of the possible "what" begins to emerge, one question would be, "In service to what?" That would be the reason "why" behind the "what." This thing we think might be what we come to do and be . . . what is the purpose of it? What is it in service to? Why would we do it? Why would we make that agreement with the One that sent us?"

In service to what?

As you try on ideas about what your life mission is, ask yourself each time, "In service to what?" Why would I do it? Why would I make that agreement with the One?

The Way of the Heart

The Way of the Heart was born to serve the fulfillment of both our personal and collective destinies, that we may truly live the way of our hearts. In the process, we recast our "history" into our "highest story."

Through the integration of spirit, science and art (the good, the true, and the beautiful, respectively), *The Way of the Heart* offers a path that works with the fields of all life, and which provides the blueprint that informs, and creates the life we live. This path is designed to transform self-identity, patterns and difficulties, while it deepens both divine self-awareness and the power to act from the freedom of real choice.

thewayoftheheart.com
thecaravanofremembering.com